SING GLORY

SING **GLORY**

**HYMNS, PSALMS AND SONGS
FOR A NEW CENTURY**

JUBILATE HYMNS

Kevin
Mayhew

We hope you enjoy the music in this book. Further copies are available from your local music shop or Christian bookshop.

In case of difficulty, please contact the publisher direct by writing to:

The Sales Department
KEVIN MAYHEW LTD
Buxhall
Stowmarket
Suffolk IP14 3BW

Phone 01449 737978
Fax 01449 737834
E-mail info@kevinmayhewltd.com

Please ask for our complete catalogue of outstanding Church Music.

First published in Great Britain in 1999 by Kevin Mayhew Ltd.

Compilation © 1999 Jubilate Hymns Ltd.

The right of Jubilate Hymns Ltd to be identified as the compiler of this work has been asserted by them in acordance with the Copyright, Designs and Patents Act 1988.

Full Music   ISBN 1 84003 419 X
ISMN M 57004 584 6
Catalogue No: 1413124

Words only   ISBN 1 84003 450 5
Catalogue No: 1413121

0 1 2 3 4 5 6 7 8 9

Cover design by Jonathan Stroulger

Music Setter: Chris Hinkins

Text Setter: Fiona Connell Finch

Printed and bound in Great Britain

PREFACE

The opening of a new millennium is an appropriate time to publish a book of words and music for Christian congregations and *Sing Glory* is offered to the churches with the prayer that God in Trinity may be glorified through its use. It builds on the experience of a group of writers and editors which goes back for more than thirty years and has seen the publication of a series of many books from the hugely successful *Youth Praise* of the 1960s to *World Praise* in 1995.

Through all this period the Jubilate group has been an expanding team of men and women, lay and clerical, representing both Anglican and Free Church traditions. The great majority of Jubilate members stand in the Evangelical tradition but their work includes material from across the historic Christian denominations and covers translations and paraphrases of the words and music of Christian worship from the earliest times, together with the psalms of the Hebrew people.

From the very earliest days the Christian Faith has been a singing Faith. St. Paul in his letter to the Ephesians mentions three kinds of works which were part of the singing tradition. He calls them "psalms, hymns, and spiritual songs" and those three categories offer a very useful distinction in our own century. The disciples of Jesus, on the same night that he was betrayed, sang the *Passover hymn* (Matthew 26 v 30 REB) and they inherited a large collection of psalms from their Jewish background. Pliny, the Roman governor of Bithynia, writing to the Emperor Trajan early in the 2nd century, refers to Christians "singing a hymn to Christ as a god". Even today we sing modern translations of the *Phos Hilaron*, a very ancient hymn. Songs, both spontaneous and structured, reflecting the popular culture of the day, have also always been associated with the worship of God's people.

An unhelpful polarisation still exists between some guardians of traditional church music and some advocates of informal music. Both groups have their share of extremists but both also have those with a more balanced outlook, avoiding the worst excesses. *Sing Glory* stands in the moderate position, building on the conviction that St. Paul was wise to recognise those three distinct kinds of material. One of the criteria by which this book may fairly be judged is not therefore whether any tradition is the "right" one. In *Sing Glory* we have attempted to bring some of the best of each category together under one cover.

Jubilate writers and editors are themselves not of one mind on what is "good". Not all those named in the different teams who put this book together would endorse everything contained within it. Where they do agree is in recognising that all three kinds of material are in common and widespread use within the churches today and are likely to remain so in the foreseeable future, and a book which seeks to serve these churches must be generous in its contents, not rejecting work simply because it is uncongenial to this or that person or group. *Sing*

Glory is for churches committed to a breadth of musical vocabulary, who value using hymns, especially those from recent writers, as well as contemporary worship songs ranging across a wide variety of sources, traditions and spirituality.

Nevertheless the different editorial teams have aimed, within their own tradition, to accept or discard psalms, hymns or songs on their merit and not merely on longevity of use on the one hand or transient popularity on the other.

One unusual feature of *Sing Glory* is its special category of psalms. Many famous hymns, especially from the 18th century were written as metrical psalms and we have distinguished them as such. That in no way diminishes their standing in the churches nor does it imply that they ought not to be sung as hymns in services. What it does seek to do is to help the Christian church to value the different strands in its heritage.

In common with virtually all hymnbooks, *Sing Glory* has been prepared by editors willing to take responsibility for the form in which the traditional texts are included. Many hymnbooks have claimed to offer the original text of hymns, sometimes concealing the actual editing that has gone on since that text was first published. Jubilate editors have always tried to be honest in facing the need to provide texts that are not full of archaisms for the sake of historical accuracy. Sometimes, for the sake of lucidity, texts have been altered to avoid the worst features of past and present fashions in words. We have tried to learn the lessons of a few mistakes in our earlier work and in doing so we have done no more than recognise the risks that many editors have taken in past decades. A wooden literalism is, in itself, no mark of virtue or praiseworthy editing.

One other distinctive feature of *Sing Glory* is the inclusion of a small number of items from other countries, continents and cultures, some of which are included in both English versions and their original language. We hope that in a small way this will remind Christians in the English tradition that they are not only a part of a world-wide Church, but also a minority part of it in the present era.

A second important feature, as regards the words, is the large number of contemporary or recent authors whose work has been included in the hymn and psalm sections. Nearly 70 hymn writers from the second half of the 20th century have gained acceptance (not counting the song writers who, inevitably, are almost all from this period). Older authors of hymns, pre-1950, number about 135 in all.

Many of Jubilate's books have applied a strict code of anonymity to the choice of accepted hymn texts. Texts have been assessed, accepted, or rejected with no indication of the authors' names in the judging process. This is as true of the work of Jubilate's own writers as of those who have no direct connection with the editors. Some past critics have complained at the number of hymns by Jubilate's members, assuming that some nepotistic motive had affected the editors' judgement. Editors of earlier hymnbooks very often included a disproportionate number of their own hymns and we can only say that no such decision has been allowed to influence the inclusion (or exclusion) of hymn texts in *Sing Glory*. The exceptions to this rule, are a mere handful where a few gaps were evident and needed filling at a very late stage in the process. Jubilate writers have produced over 1,000 hymn texts and around 100 are in this book.

The ordering of material in *Sing Glory* is unique in design and is aimed to assist the planning of worship services, following the pattern found in many traditions of approach to worship, praise, confession, assurance of forgiveness, adoration, scripture reading, intercession, offering, the Peace, affirmation of faith, with special sections for Holy Communion, Christian initiation and healing, and followed by response to the word preached and indeed to the whole service. The pattern of the church's year is indexed at the back of the book, as are various aspects of Christian worship and living.

The breadth of the book's contents and the origin of the texts should help would-be purchasers to recognise that *Sing Glory* is aimed at a very wide market of contemporary Christian churches. We offer them this book, confident that it will provide them with hymns, psalms and worship songs for the new era, incorporating the best of old and new for a wide range of occasions and needs when the churches want to *Sing Glory* to God.

Michael Baughen	General Editor
David Iliff	Hymn Music Editor
David Peacock	Editorial Co-ordinator and Songs Editor
Michael Saward	Hymn Words Editor

Legal Information and Acknowledgements

Reprinting

Those seeking to reprint material in this book, which is the property of Jubilate Hymns or associated authors and composers (attributed '/Jubilate Hymns') may write to the Copyright Manager, Jubilate Hymns, 4 Thorne Park, Road, Chelston, Torquay TQ2 6RX. In the United States of America these are administered by Hope Publishing Company, Carol Stream , Illinois 60188.

Texts by authors and composers held by some major copyright holders (Thankyou Music, CopyCare, Kevin Mayhew etc), together with those administered by Jubilate, are covered by the Church Copyright Licence which allows local churches reproduction on overhead projector acetates, in service bulletins and other formats. Music books intended for congregational use published by Kevin Mayhew Ltd are now covered by the new Music Reproduction Licence also issued by CCL (Europe) Ltd as an extension to the basic Church Copyright Licence. Full details of the licences should be acquired from: Christian Copyright Licensing Ltd, P O Box 1339, Eastbourne, East Sussex BN21 4YF.

Every effort has been made to trace copyright owners, and apologies are extended to anyone whose rights have inadvertently not been acknowledged. Any omissions or inaccuracies of copyright details will be corrected in future editions.

Acknowledgements

In a book of this size, we are dependent on a wide team of people with experience and expertise. We are grateful to the following for their help in compiling the material:

General Editor: Michael Baughen

Hymn texts
Michael Saward [Chair], Annette Farrer, Brian Hoare, Christopher Idle, David Mowbray, Noël Tredinnick

Hymn music
David Iliff [Chair], John Barnard, Paul Lavender, Noël Tredinnick, Norman Warren, Geoff Weaver, David Wilson

Songs
David Peacock [Chair], Christopher Hayward, Stephen James, Roger Mayor, Andrew Maries, John Marsh, Mike Stanley

For the major task of copyright clearance and assistance in preparing the work we are deeply grateful to Merrilyn Williams of Jubilate Hymns.

We also thank Louise Mawson, John Barnard, Amanda Greenslade, Bunty Grundy, Lynn Lewis, Paul de Lusignan and Rebecca Peacock for their help in getting the material ready for publication. We thank Kevin Mayhew and Jonathan Bugden for their support, encouragement and assistance.

My personal thanks to Michael Baughen, David Iliff and Michael Saward for their major contribution in the preparation of this book.

David Peacock
Editorial co-ordinator

CONTENTS

1
© Michael Saward/Jubilate Hymns

1. Sing glory to God the Father,
   the King of the universe,
       changelessly the same.
   Sing praise to the world's creator
   and magnify his holy name.

       He made all that is round us
           and all that is beyond,
       his hands uphold the planets,
           to him they all respond.

2. Sing glory to God the Saviour,
   the Lord of the galaxies,
       bearer of our shame.
   Sing praise to the world's redeemer
   and magnify his holy name.

       He suffered grief and torment,
           for sin he paid the price,
       he rose in glorious triumph,
           both priest and sacrifice.

3. Sing glory to God the Spirit,
   the power of the elements,
       setting hearts aflame.
   Sing praise to the world's life-giver
   and magnify his holy name.

       His gifts to all are given,
           his fruit transforms our hearts,
       his fellowship enriches,
           a grace which he imparts.

4. Sing glory, the whole creation!
   Give thanks to the Trinity,
       heaven's love proclaim.
   Sing praise to our God, almighty,
   and magnify his holy name.

GATHERING FOR WORSHIP

HYMNS

2 © David Mowbray/Jubilate Hymns

1. First of the week and finest day,
   when God commanded light to shine:
   cast darkness and its works away
   to celebrate with bread and wine!

2. First of the week was Easter morn
   when Christ the Lord
       from death was raised;
   new life, fresh hope that day was born
   and God in heaven
       and earth was praised.

3. First of the week the Spirit came
   to fill the church with grace and power;
   the rushing wind and tongues of flame
   were heralds of that promised hour.

4. First of the week we set aside
   to meet, to learn, to give, to pray;
   to spread Christ's gospel far and wide –
   in truth, this is the Lord's own day.

3 © 1995 Stephen Dean. Published by OCP Publications

1. Thanks be to God
       whose love has gathered us this day:
   thanks be to God
       who helps and guides us on our way.
   Thanks be to God
       who gives us voice
       that we may thank him;
   Deo gratias, Deo gratias,
   thanks be to God most high.

2. Thanks be to God
       for all the gifts of life and light:
   thanks be to God
       whose care protects us day and night.

Thanks be to God
    who keeps in mind us who forget him:
Deo gratias, Deo gratias,
thanks be to God most high.

3. Thanks be to God
       who knows our secret joys and fears:
   thanks be to God
       who when we call him always hears.
   Thanks be to God
       our rock and strength ever sustaining:
   Deo gratias, Deo gratias,
   thanks be to God most high.

4. Thanks be to God
       who never turns his face away:
   thanks be to God
       who heals and pardons all who stray.
   Thanks be to God
       who welcomes us into the kingdom:
   Deo gratias, Deo gratias,
   thanks be to God most high.

5. Thanks be to God
       who made our world and all we see:
   thanks be to God
       who gave his Son to set us free.
   Thanks be to God
       whose Spirit brings warmth
       and rejoicing:
   Deo gratias, Deo gratias,
   thanks be to God most high.

4 Marty Haugen
© 1982 GIA Publications Inc.

1. Here in this place
       the new light is streaming,
   now is the darkness vanished away:
   see in this space
       our fears and our dreamings
       brought here to you
       in the light of this day.
   Gather us in, the lost and forsaken,
       gather us in, the blind and the lame:
   call to us now and we shall awaken,
       we shall arise
       at the sound of our name.

2. We are the young,
    our lives are a mystery,
  we are the old who yearn for your face;
  we have been sung
    throughout all of history,
    called to be light
    to the whole human race.
  Gather us in, the rich and the haughty,
    gather us in, the proud
    and the strong:
  give us a heart so meek and so lowly,
    give us the courage to enter the song.

*3. Here we will take the wine and the water,
    here we will take
    the bread of new birth:
  here you shall call your sons
    and your daughters,
    call us anew to be salt for the earth.
  Give us to drink
    the wine of compassion,
    give us to eat the bread that is you:
  nourish us well and teach us to fashion
    lives that are holy
    and hearts that are true.

4. Not in the dark of buildings confining,
    not in some heaven light-years away,
  here in this place
    the new light is shining,
    now is the kingdom,
    and now is the day.
  Gather us in and hold us for ever,
    gather us in and make us your own,
  gather us in, all peoples together –
    fire of your love
    in our flesh and our bone.

* optional verse 3

PSALMS

5 From *Deus Misereatur* Psalm 67, Henry Lyte

1. God of mercy, God of grace,
  show the brightness of your face:
  shine upon us, Saviour, shine,
  fill your church with light divine,
  and your saving health extend
  to the earth's remotest end.

2. Let the people praise you, Lord!
  be by all who live adored:
  let the nations shout and sing
  glory to their Saviour King,
  at your feet their tribute pay,
  and your holy will obey.

3. Let the people crown you King!
  Then shall earth her harvest bring,
  God to us his blessing give,
  we to God devoted live;
  all below and all above,
  one in joy and light and love.

6 From Psalm 122
© Basil Bridge

1. I rejoiced to hear them say,
    'Come and worship God today!
  Come, with heart and mind and soul,
    seek the peace that makes us whole;
  see disordered lives restored
    in the presence of the Lord:
  from your burdens find release;
    in his presence there is peace.'

2. Here in gratitude we bring
    all we are to serve our King;
  his forgiveness we entreat
    in whom love and justice meet:
  bring our needs to him in prayer,
    ask his help, and trust his care;
  join with all, in every place,
    who have sought
    and known his grace.

3. God, the Lord of peace, is near –
     come in faith, and meet him here;
   let each restless soul be still,
     glad to know and do his will:
   as a city's walls and towers
     offered safety – God is ours!
   Therefore we rejoice, and say,
     'Come and worship God today!'

8 Alexander Gondo © 1995 WGRG, Iona Community, from
     Come all you people (Wild Goose Publications, 1995)

Come all you people,
come and praise your Maker.
Come all you people,
come and praise your Maker.
Come all you people,
come and praise your Maker.
Come now and worship the Lord.

SONGS

7 David Evans
     © 1986 Kingsway's Thankyou Music

1. Be still,
     for the presence of the Lord,
       the holy One, is here;
   come bow before him now
   with reverence and fear:
   in him no sin is found –
   we stand on holy ground.
   Be still,
     for the presence of the Lord,
       the holy One, is here.

2. Be still,
     for the glory of the Lord
       is shining all around;
   he burns with holy fire,
   with splendour he is crowned:
   how awesome is the sight –
   our radiant King of light!
   Be still,
     for the glory of the Lord
       is shining all around.

3. Be still,
     for the power of the Lord
       is moving in this place:
   he comes to cleanse and heal,
   to minister his grace –
   no work too hard for him.
   In faith receive from him.
   Be still,
     for the power of the Lord
       is moving in this place.

9 Mike Stanley
     © 1995 CJM Music

     Come let us go,
     up to the mountain of the Lord,
     to the temple of his Holy Spirit.
     Come let us go,
     up to the mountain of the Lord
     and glorify his holy name.

1. Through noise and confusion,
   our witness shall be heard;
   we raise our voices,
   to proclaim your holy word.
     Come let us go . . .

2. Heavenly Father
   receive my brokenness;
   change me, re-arrange me,
   restore my worthiness.
     Come let us go . . .

3. With banners lifted
   we approach his glorious throne;
   by graces gifted
   his power shall be known.
     Come let us go . . .

4. Zion, holy mountain
   we turn our eyes to you;
   lead us ever closer
   in spirit and in truth.
     Come let us go . . .

10 Brian Doerksen
© 1998 Vineyard Songs (UK/Eire)

Come, now is the time to worship,
come, now is the time to give your heart;
come, just as you are to worship,
come, just as you are before your God.
Come.

One day every tongue
will confess you are God,
one day every knee will bow.
Still, the greatest treasure remains
for those who gladly choose you now.

Come, now is the time to worship . . .

11 From Malawi, Tom Colvin
© 1969 Hope Publishing Co. Administered by CopyCare.

1. Humbly in your sight
    we come together, Lord:
   grant us now the blessing
    of your presence here.

2. These our hearts are yours –
    we give them to you, Lord:
   purify our love to make it
    like your own.

3. These our ears are yours,
    we give them to you, Lord:
   open them to hear the gospel
    straight from you.

4. These our eyes are yours,
    we give them to you, Lord:
   may we always see this world
    as with your sight.

5. These our hands are yours,
    we give them to you, Lord:
   give them strength and skill to work
    and build for you.

6. These our tongues are yours,
    we give them to you, Lord:
   may we speak your healing words
    of light and truth.

7. These our feet are yours,
    we give them to you, Lord:
   may we always walk the path of light
    with you.

8. Our whole selves are yours,
    we give them to you, Lord:
   take us now and keep us safe
    for evermore.

12 © Roger Mayor/Jubilate Hymns

1. We have come as the family of God
   to offer our worship to him;
   for we've gathered together
    in our Father's house
   to exalt the name
    of Jesus Christ, his Son;
   For we believe in Jesus Christ,
    God's only Son,
   and we believe he died
    and rose again;
   and we believe he is
    the King of glory,
   we believe he's coming back again!

2. We have come as the family of God
   to hear and receive his holy word;
   and we've gathered together
    all with one accord
   to proclaim to the world
    that he is Lord!
   For we believe . . .

13 From Zimbabwe
© Patrick Matsikenyiri/ Copyright Control

Jesus, we are here;
Jesus, we are here;
Jesus, we are here;
we are here for you.

Jesu tawa pano;
Jesu tawa pano;
Jesu tawa pano;
tawa pano mu zita renyu.

For other items on this theme, see

HYMNS
28 Born in song
14 Christ is our corner-stone
48 Let hymns of joyful praise abound
49 Let us love and sing and wonder
293 Today I awake
483 Welcome to another day!

PSALM
85 Let everything that has breath

SONGS
19 Come Holy Spirit
109 Glory and gratitude and praise
124 Let everything that, everything that has breath
135 Sanna
523 To be in your presence

INVOCATION

HYMNS

14 From the Latin, John Chandler

1. Christ is our corner-stone,
   on him alone we build;
   with his true saints alone
   the courts of heaven are filled;
   on his great love
   our hope we place
   of present grace
   and joys above.

2. With psalms and hymns of praise
   this holy place shall ring;
   our voices we will raise,
   the Three-in-One to sing;
   and thus proclaim
   in joyful song
   both loud and long,
   that glorious name.

3. Here, gracious God, draw near
   as in your name we bow;
   each true petition hear,
   accept each faithful vow;
   and more and more
   on all who pray
   each holy day
   your blessings pour.

4. Here may we gain from heaven
   the grace which we implore;
   and may that grace, once given,
   be with us evermore,
   until that day
   when all the blessed
   to endless rest
   are called away.

15 © Jocelyn Marshall

1. Come with the sound of trumpet,
   come with the beat of drum,
   come with the church bells ringing.
   Oh come, Lord Jesus, come.
   Come in the new dawn's silence,
   come in the heat of noon,
   come in the evening splendour,
   but come, Lord Jesus, soon.

2. Come to our world expectant,
   come to our homes and hearts,
   come to our towns and cities,
   Lord, come, and loving starts.
   Come as your Church awaits you,
   come as your people pray,
   come as your children listen,
   so come to us today.

16 William Cowper

1. Jesus, where'er thy people meet,
   there they behold thy mercy-seat;
   where'er they seek thee,
      thou art found,
   and every place is hallowed ground.

2. For thou, within no walls confined,
   inhabitest the humble mind;
   such ever bring thee where they come,
   and going, take thee to their home.

3. Dear Shepherd of thy chosen few,
   thy former mercies here renew;
   here to our waiting hearts proclaim
   the sweetness of thy saving name.

4. Here may we prove
      the power of prayer,
   to strengthen faith and sweeten care;
   to teach our faint desires to rise,
   and bring all heaven before our eyes.

5. Lord, we are few, but thou art near;
    nor short thine arm, nor deaf thine ear;
    O rend the heavens,
        come quickly down,
    and make a thousand hearts thine own!

17 Carl P. Daw Jnr.
© 1982 Hope Publishing Co. Administered by CopyCare

1. Like the murmur of the dove's song,
    like the challenge of her flight,
    like the vigour of the wind's rush,
    like the new flame's eager might:
        come, Holy Spirit, come.

2. To the members of Christ's Body,
    to the branches of the Vine,
    to the Church in faith assembled,
    to her midst as gift and sign:
        come, Holy Spirit, come.

3. With the healing of division,
    with the ceaseless voice of prayer,
    with the power to love and witness,
    with the peace beyond compare:
        come, Holy Spirit, come.

SONGS

18 From Psalm 46. © 1989 WGRG, Iona Community from
Love from below (Wild Goose Publications, 1988)

Be still and know that I am God.
Be still and know that I am God.

19 John L. Bell © 1992,1995 WGRG, Iona Community from
Come all you people (Wild Goose Publications 1995)

ALL   Come, Holy Spirit,
        descend on us,
        descend on us;
        we gather here in Jesus' name.

LEADER (Come, Holy Spirit . . .)
        (Come, breath of heaven . . .)
        (Come, word of mercy . . .)

20 From NIGERIA, unknown
© Nigerian and English Copyright Control

Come, O Holy Spirit, come.
Come, Almighty Spirit, come.
Come, come, come.

Wa wa wa Emimimo.
Wa, wa, wa Alagbara.
Wao, wao, wao.

21 © 1990 Paul Inwood/World Library Publications

1. Come, light of the world,
    light up our lives, Lord;
    come, light of the world,
    light up our hearts.
    Dispel all our darkness,
    remove all our blindness;
    come, light of the world,
    be light for our eyes.

2. Come, strength of our days,
    strengthen our lives, Lord;
    come, strength of our days,
    strengthen our hearts.
    Come, fill us with courage
    to follow you always;
    come, strength of our days,
    be strength for our minds.

3. Come, joy for the world,
    fill us with gladness;
    come, joy for the world,
    gladden our hearts.
    Come, bring us together
    with singing and laughter;
    come, joy for the world,
    bring warmth to our lives.

4. Come, hope of the world,
    comfort your people;
    come, hope of the world,
    comfort our hearts.
    Come, heal all our sorrow
    with love and compassion;
    come, hope of the world,
    bring peace to us all.

5. Come, Spirit of God,
    be with us now, Lord;
    come, Spirit of God,
    fill us with truth.
    Enlighten our lives, Lord,
    with radiance and power;
    come, Spirit of God,
    inspire all we do.

22 From SOUTH AFRICA, unknown
© East African and English Copyright Control

Spirit of Jesus –
  Holy Spirit, come to us.
Grace of the Father –
  Holy Spirit, come to us.

Neema, neema,
neema ime funelwa.

For other items on this theme, see

HYMNS
447 Gift of Christ from God our Father
304 It is God who holds the nations

SONGS
242 Be still
  7 Be still, for the presence of the Lord
564 Here I stand at the door
333 I believe in Jesus
523 To be in your presence
249 Word of justice

PRAISE AND THANKSGIVING

23 After Francis of Assisi, William Draper
© in this version Jubilate Hymns

1. All creatures of our God and King,
   lift up your voice and with us sing.
     Alleluia, alleluia!
   Bright burning sun with golden beam,
   soft shining moon with silver gleam,
     O praise him, O praise him.
     Alleluia, alleluia, alleluia!

2. Swift rushing wind so wild and strong,
   white clouds that sail in heaven along.
     O praise him, alleluia!
   New rising dawn in praise rejoice,
   you lights of evening find a voice;
     O praise him, O praise him.
     Alleluia, alleluia, alleluia!

3. Cool flowing water, pure and clear,
   make music for your Lord to hear,
     Alleluia, alleluia!
   Fierce fire so masterful and bright
   giving to us both warmth and light,
     O praise him, O praise him.
     Alleluia, alleluia, alleluia!

4. Earth ever fertile, day by day
   bring forth your blessings on our way.
     O praise him, alleluia!
   All fruit and crops that richly grow,
   all trees and flowers God's glory show;
     O praise him, O praise him.
     Alleluia, alleluia, alleluia!

5. People and nations, take your part,
   love and forgive with all your heart;
     Alleluia, alleluia!
   All who long pain and sorrow bear,
   trust God and cast on him your care;
     O praise him, O praise him.
     Alleluia, alleluia, alleluia!

6. Death, once the ancient enemy,
   hear now our Easter melody,
     O praise him, alleluia!

You are the pathway home to God,
our door to life through Christ our Lord;
  O praise him, O praise him.
  Alleluia, alleluia, alleluia!

7. Let all things their creator bless
   and worship him in lowliness,
     Alleluia, alleluia!
   Praise, praise the Father, praise the Son,
   and praise the Spirit, Three-in-One.
     O praise him, O praise him.
     Alleluia, alleluia, alleluia!

24 After Edward Perronet and John Rippon
© in this version Jubilate Hymns

1. All hail the power of Jesus' name!
   Let angels prostrate fall,
   bring forth the royal diadem
   and crown him Lord of all.

2. Crown him, you martyrs of our God,
   who witnessed to his call;
   exalt the One whose path you trod,
   and crown him Lord of all.

3. Descendants of his chosen race,
   you ransomed from the Fall,
   hail him who saves you by his grace,
   and crown him Lord of all.

4. Sinners, whose love cannot forget
   the wormwood and the gall,
   go, spread your offering at his feet
   and crown him Lord of all.

5. Let every people, nation, tribe,
   on this terrestrial ball,
   to him all majesty ascribe
   and crown him Lord of all.

6. O that in heaven with that great throng,
   we at his feet may fall,
   join in the everlasting song
   and crown him Lord of all.

25 Job Hupton and John Neale
© in this version Jubilate Hymns

1. Alleluia! raise the anthem,
   let the skies resound with praise;
   sing to Christ who paid our ransom,
   Ancient of eternal days,
   God eternal, Word incarnate,
   whom the heaven of heaven obeys.

2. Long before he formed the mountains,
   spread the seas or made the sky,
   love eternal free and boundless,
   moved the Lord of life to die;
   foreordained the Prince of princes
   for the throne of Calvary.

3. There for us and our redemption
   see him all his life-blood pour:
   there he wins our full salvation,
   dies that we may die no more –
   then arising lives for ever,
   King of kings whom we adore.

4. Now above the vast creation,
   high in God's all-holy light,
   there he lives and reigns in triumph,
   bears the marks of mortal fight;
   there his own, redeemed for ever,
   sing in wonder day and night.

5. Praise and honour to the Father,
   praise and honour to the Son,
   praise and honour to the Spirit,
   ever Three and ever One:
   one in grace and one in glory
   while eternal ages run!

26 John Newton
© in this version Jubilate Hymns

1. Amazing grace – how sweet the sound –
   that saved a wretch like me!
   I once was lost, but now am found;
   was blind, but now I see.

2. God's grace first taught my heart to fear,
   his grace my fears relieved;
   how precious did that grace appear
   the hour I first believed!

3. Through every danger, trial and snare
   I have already come;
   his grace has brought me safe thus far,
   and grace will lead me home.

4. The Lord has promised good to me,
   his word my hope secures;
   my shield and stronghold he shall be
   as long as life endures.

5. And when this earthly life is past,
   and mortal cares shall cease,
   I shall possess with Christ at last
   eternal joy and peace.

27A Francis Pott
Traditional version

1. Angel-voices ever singing
   round thy throne of light –
   angel harps for ever ringing,
   rest not day nor night:
   Thousands only live to bless thee,
   and confess thee,
   Lord of might.

2. Thou, who art beyond the farthest
   mortal eye can scan.
   Can it be that thou regardest
   songs of sinful man?
   Can we know that thou art near us
   and wilt hear us?
   Yes, we can.

3. Lord, we know that thou rejoicest
   o'er each work of thine;
   thou didst ears and hands and voices
   for thy praise design;
   Craftsman's art and music's measure
   for thy pleasure
   all combine.

4. In thy house, great God, we offer
   of thine own to thee;
   and for thine acceptance proffer,
   all unworthily.
   Hearts and minds,
      and hands and voices,
   in our choicest
   psalmody.

5. Honour, glory, might and merit,
   thine shall ever be,
   Father, Son and Holy Spirit,
   blèssed Trinity:
   Of the best that thou hast given
   earth and heaven
   render thee.

27B Francis Pott
© in this version Jubilate Hymns

1. Angel-voices ever singing
      round your throne of light,
   angels' music ever ringing
      rests not day nor night:
   thousands only live to bless you
      and confess you Lord of might.

2. Lord beyond our mortal sight,
      in glory far away,
   can it be that you delight
      in sinners' songs today;
   may we know that you are near us
      and will hear us? Yes, we may!

3. Yes, we know your heart rejoices
      in each work divine,
   using minds and hands and voices
      in your great design;
   craftsman's art and music's measure
      for your pleasure all combine.

4. Here to you, great God, we offer
      praise in harmony,
   and for your acceptance proffer
      all unworthily,
   hearts and minds and hands and voices
      in our choicest psalmody.

5. Honour, glory, might and merit,
      for your works and ways,
   Father, Son and Holy Spirit,
      God through endless days:
   with the best that you have given
      earth and heaven render praise.

28 © 1983 Brian Hoare/Jubilate Hymns

1. Born in song!
   God's people have always been singing.
   Born in song!
   Hearts and voices raised.
   So today we worship together;
   God alone is worthy to be praised.

2. Praise to God!
   For he is the one who has made us.
   Praise to God!
   We his image bear.
   Heaven and earth are full of his glory;
   let creation praise him everywhere.

3. Christ is King!
   He left all the glory of heaven.
   Christ is King!
   Born to share in our pain;
   crucified, for sinners atoning,
   risen, exalted, soon to come again.

4. Sing the song!
   God's Spirit is poured out among us.
   Sing the song!
   He has made us anew.
   Every member part of the Body;
   given his power, his will to seek and do.

5. Tell the world!
   all power to Jesus is given.
   tell the world!
   he is with us always.
   Spread the word,
      that all may receive him;
   every tongue confess
      and sing his praise.

6. Then the end!
   Christ Jesus shall reign in his glory.
   Then the end
   of all earthly days.
   Yet above the song will continue;
   all his people still shall sing his praise.

29 Richard Mant
© in this version Jubilate Hymns

1. Bright the vision that delighted
   once the sight of Judah's seer;
   sweet the countless tongues united
   to entrance the prophet's ear.

2. Round the Lord in glory seated
   cherubim and seraphim
   filled his temple, and repeated
   each to each the alternate hymn:

3. 'Lord, your glory fills the heaven;
   earth is with its fullness stored;
   unto you be glory given,
   holy, holy, holy, Lord.'

4. Heaven is still with glory ringing,
   earth takes up the angels' cry,
   'Holy, holy, holy,' singing,
   'Lord of hosts, the Lord most high.'

5. With his seraphim before him,
   with his holy Church below,
   thus united we adore him,
   let our glorious anthem flow:

6. 'Lord, your glory fills the heaven;
   earth is with its fullness stored;
   unto you be glory given,
   Holy, holy, holy, Lord.'

30 Hereford B. George

1. By every nation, race and tongue,
   worship and praise be ever sung;
     praise the Father; Alleluia!
   For pardoned sin, death overcome,
   and hopes that live beyond the tomb:
     Alleluia, alleluia;
     alleluia, alleluia, alleluia!

2. Saints who on earth have suffered long,
   for Jesus' sake enduring wrong,
     ever-faithful: Alleluia!
   Where faith is lost in sight, rejoice
   and sing with never-wearied voice:
     Alleluia, alleluia;
     alleluia, alleluia, alleluia!

3. Let earth and air and sea unite
   to celebrate his glorious might,
     their creator: Alleluia!
   Sun, moon and stars in endless space
   echo the song of every race:
     Alleluia, alleluia;
     alleluia, alleluia, alleluia!

31 George Bell
By permission of Oxford University Press

1. Christ is the King! O friends rejoice;
   brothers and sisters, with one voice
   let the world know he is your choice.
     Alleluia, alleluia, alleluia!

2. O magnify the Lord, and raise
   anthems of joy and holy praise
   for Christ's brave saints of ancient days.
     Alleluia, alleluia, alleluia!

3. They with a faith for ever new
   followed the King, and round him drew
   thousands of servants brave and true.
     Alleluia, alleluia, alleluia!

4. O Christian women, Christian men,
   all the world over, seek again
   the way disciples followed then.
     Alleluia, alleluia, alleluia!

5. Christ through all ages is the same:
   place the same hope in his great name;
   with the same faith his word proclaim.
     Alleluia, alleluia, alleluia!

6. Let Love's unconquerable might
   your scattered companies unite
   in service to the Lord of light.
     Alleluia, alleluia, alleluia!

7. So shall God's will on earth be done,
   new lamps be lit, new tasks begun,
   and the whole church at last be one.
     Alleluia, alleluia, alleluia!

32 Brian Wren
© 1969, 1995 Stainer & Bell

1. Christ is alive! Let Christians sing.
   The cross stands empty to the sky.
   Let streets and homes with praises ring.
   Love, drowned in death, shall never die.

2. Christ is alive! No longer bound
   to distant years in Palestine,
   but saving, healing, here and now,
   and touching every place and time.

3. In every insult, rift and war,
   where colour, scorn or wealth divide,
   Christ suffers still, yet loves the more,
   and lives, where even hope has died.

4. Women and men, in age and youth,
   can feel the Spirit, hear the call,
   and find the way, the life, the truth,
   revealed in Jesus, freed for all.

5. Christ is alive, and comes to bring
   good news to this and every age,
   till earth and sky and ocean ring
   with joy, with justice, love and praise.

33 Isaac Watts

1. Come let us join our cheerful songs
   with angels round the throne;
   ten thousand thousand
      are their tongues,
   but all their joys are one.

2. Worthy the Lamb who died, they cry,
   to be exalted thus!
   Worthy the Lamb, our lips reply,
   for he was slain for us!

3. Jesus is worthy to receive
   all praise and power divine;
   and all the blessings we can give
   with songs of heaven combine.

4. Let all who live beyond the sky,
   the air and earth and seas
   unite to lift his glory high
   and sing his endless praise!

5. Let all creation join in one
   to bless the sacred name
   of him who reigns upon the throne,
   and to adore the Lamb!

34 Henry Alford
© in this version Jubilate Hymns

1. Come, you thankful people, come,
   raise the song of harvest home!
   all is safely gathered in
   now before the storms begin:
   God our maker will provide
   for our needs to be supplied;
   come, with all his people, come,
   raise the song of harvest home!

2. All the world is God's own field,
   harvests for his praise to yield;
   wheat and weeds together sown
   here for joy or sorrow grown:
   first the blade and then the ear,
   then the full corn shall appear –
   Lord of harvest, grant that we
   wholesome grain and pure may be.

3. For the Lord our God shall come
   and shall bring his harvest home;
   he himself on that great day,
   worthless things shall take away,
   give his angels charge at last
   in the fire the weeds to cast,
   but the fruitful ears to store
   in his care for evermore.

4. Even so, Lord, quickly come –
   bring your final harvest home!
   gather all your people in
   free from sorrow, free from sin,
   there together purified,
   ever thankful at your side –
   come, with all your angels, come,
   bring that glorious harvest home!

35 John Newton

1. Glorious things of you are spoken,
   Zion, city of our God;
   he whose word cannot be broken
   formed you for his own abode;
   on the rock of ages founded,
   what can shake your sure repose?
   with salvation's walls surrounded
   you may smile at all your foes.

2. See, the streams of living waters
   springing from eternal love!
   well supply your sons and daughters
   and all fear of want remove;
   who can faint while such a river
   ever flows their thirst to assuage?
   grace, which like the Lord the giver
   never fails from age to age.

3. Round each habitation hovering
   see the cloud and fire appear
   for a glory and a covering,
   showing that the Lord is near:
   thus they march, the pillar leading,
   light by night and shade by day;
   daily on the manna feeding
   which he gives them as they pray.

4. Saviour, since of Zion's city
   I through grace a member am,
   let the world deride or pity,
   I will glory in your name:
   fading are the world's best pleasures,
   all its boasted pomp and show;
   solid joys and lasting treasures
   none but Zion's children know.

36 Shirley Erena Murray
© 1992 Hope Publishing Co. Administered by CopyCare

1. For the music of creation,
   for the song your Spirit sings,
   for your sound's divine expression,
   burst of joy in living things:
   God, our God, the world's composer,
   hear us, echoes of your voice:
   music is your art, your glory,
   let the human heart rejoice!

2. Psalms and symphonies exalt you,
   drum and trumpet, string and reed,
   simple melodies acclaim you,
   tunes that rise from deepest need,
   hymns of longing and belonging,
   carols from a cheerful throat,
   lilt of lullaby and lovesong
   catching heaven in a note.

3. All the voices of the ages
   in transcendent chorus meet,
   worship lifting up the senses,
   hands that praise and dancing feet;
   over discord and division
   music speaks your joy and peace,
   harmony of earth and heaven,
   song of God that cannot cease!

37 From *Gloria in excelsis*
© Christopher Idle/Jubilate Hymns

1. Glory in the highest
      to the God of heaven!
   Peace to all your people
      through the earth be given!
   Mighty God and Father,
      thanks and praise we bring,
   singing Alleluia
      to our heavenly king;
   singing Alleluia
      to our heavenly king.

2. Jesus Christ is risen,
      God the Father's Son!
   With the Holy Spirit,
      you are Lord alone!
   Lamb once killed for sinners,
      all our guilt to bear,
   show us now your mercy,
      now receive our prayer;
   show us now your mercy,
      now receive our prayer.

3. Christ the world's true Saviour,
      high and holy One,
   seated now and reigning
      from your Father's throne:
   Lord and God, we praise you!
      Highest heaven adores:
   in the Father's glory,
      all the praise be yours;
   in the Father's glory,
      all the praise be yours!

38 From *Te Deum*
© Christopher Idle/Jubilate Hymns

1. God, we praise you! God, we bless you!
   God, we name you sovereign Lord!
   Mighty King whom angels worship,
   Father, by your church adored:
   all creation shows your glory,
   heaven and earth draw near your throne
   singing 'Holy, holy, holy,'
   Lord of hosts, and God alone!

2. True apostles, faithful prophets,
   saints who set their world ablaze,
   martyrs, once unknown, unheeded,
   join one growing song of praise,
   while your church on earth confesses
   one majestic Trinity;
   Father, Son, and Holy Spirit,
   God, our hope eternally.

3. Jesus Christ, the King of glory,
   everlasting Son of God,
   humble was your virgin mother,
   hard the lonely path you trod;
   by your cross is sin defeated,
   hell confronted face to face,
   heaven opened to believers
   sinners justified by grace.

4. Christ, at God's right hand victorious,
   you will judge the world you made;
   Lord, in mercy help your servants
   for whose freedom you have paid;
   raise us up from dust to glory,
   guard us from all sin today;
   King enthroned above all praises,
   save your people, God, we pray!

39 Thomas Chisholm and in this version Jubilate Hymns
© 1923, renewal 1951 Hope Publishing Co.
Administered by CopyCare

1. Great is your faithfulness,
     O God my Father,
   you have fulfilled all your promise to me;
   you never fail
     and your love is unchanging –
   all you have been you for ever will be.
     Great is your faithfulness,
     great is your faithfulness,

morning by morning
     new mercies I see;
all I have needed
     your hand has provided –
great is your faithfulness,
     Father, to me.

2. Summer and winter,
     and springtime and harvest,
   sun, moon and stars
     in their courses above
   join with all nature in eloquent witness
   to your great faithfulness,
     mercy and love.
     Great is your faithfulness . . .

3. Pardon for sin, and a peace everlasting,
   your living presence
     to cheer and to guide;
   strength for today,
     and bright hope for tomorrow –
   these are the blessings
     your love will provide.
     Great is your faithfulness . . .

40 From *Glory and Honour* Revelation 4-5
© Timothy Dudley-Smith

1. Heavenly hosts in ceaseless worship
   'Holy, holy, holy!' cry;
   'He who is, who was and will be,
   God almighty, Lord most high.'
   Praise and honour, power and glory,
   be to him who reigns alone!
   We, with all his hands have fashioned,
   fall before the Father's throne.

2. All creation, all redemption,
   join to sing the Saviour's worth;
   Lamb of God
     whose blood has bought us,
   kings and priests, to reign on earth.
   Wealth and wisdom, power and glory,
   honour, might, dominion, praise,
   now be his from all his creatures
   and to everlasting days!

41 Joseph Hart

1. How good is the God we adore!
   our faithful, unchangeable friend:
   his love is as great as his power
   and knows neither measure nor end.

2. For Christ is the first and the last;
   his Spirit will guide us safe home;
   we'll praise him for all that is past
   and trust him for all that's to come.

42 John Newton

1. How sweet the name of Jesus sounds
   in a believer's ear!
   it soothes our sorrows,
      heals our wounds
   and drives away our fear.

2. It makes the wounded spirit whole,
   and calms the troubled breast;
   it satisfies the hungry soul,
   and gives the weary rest.

3. Dear name, the rock on which I build,
   my shield and hiding-place;
   my never-failing treasury, filled
   with boundless stores of grace!

4. Jesus, my shepherd, brother, friend,
   my prophet, priest and king;
   my Lord, my life, my way, my end –
   accept the praise I bring.

5. Weak is the effort of my heart,
   and cold my warmest thought;
   but when I see you as you are,
   I'll praise you as I ought.

6. Till then I would your love proclaim
   with every fleeting breath;
   and may the music of your name
   refresh my soul in death.

43 Francis Rowley. From *The Australian Hymn Book* 1977 HarperCollins. Administered by CopyCare

1. I will sing the wondrous story
   of the Christ who died for me;
   how he left the realms of glory
   for the cross of Calvary:
      Yes, I'll sing the wondrous story
      of the Christ who died for me,
      sing it with his saints in glory
      gathered by the crystal sea.

2. I was lost, but Jesus found me,
   found the sheep that went astray;
   raised me up and gently led me
   back into the narrow way:
      Yes, I'll sing . . .

3. I was faint and fears possessed me,
   I was bruised from many a fall;
   hope was gone,
      and shame distressed me,
   but his love has pardoned all:
      Yes, I'll sing . . .

4. Days of darkness still may meet me,
   sorrow's path I often tread;
   but his presence still is with me,
   by his guiding hand I'm led:
      Yes, I'll sing . . .

5. He will keep me till the river
   rolls its waters at my feet;
   then at last he'll bring me over
   saved by grace and made complete.
      Yes, I'll sing . . .

44 Walter Smith © in this version Jubilate Hymns

1. Immortal, invisible, God only wise,
   in light inacessible hid from our eyes;
   most holy, most glorious,
      the ancient of days,
   almighty, victorious,
      your great name we praise.

2. Unresting, unhasting, and silent as light,
   nor wanting nor wasting,
      you rule us in might;
   your justice like mountains
      high soaring above,
   your clouds which are fountains
      of goodness and love.

3. To all you are giving,
   to both great and small,
   in all you are living,
   the true life of all;
   we blossom and flourish,
   uncertain and frail;
   we wither and perish, but you never fail.

4. We worship before you,
   great Father of light,
   while angels adore you,
   all veiling their sight;
   our praises we render,
   O Father, to you
   whom only the splendour of light
   hides from view.

45 Isaac Watts
© in this version Jubilate Hymns

1. Jesus shall reign where'er the sun
   does his successive journeys run;
   his kingdom stretch from shore to shore
   till moons shall rise and set no more.

2. People and realms of every tongue
   declare his love in sweetest song,
   and infant voices shall proclaim
   their early blessings on his name.

3. Blessings abound where Jesus reigns –
   the prisoner leaps to lose his chains,
   the weary find eternal rest,
   and all who suffer want are blessed.

4. To him shall endless prayer be made,
   and princes throng to crown his head;
   his name like incense shall arise
   with every morning sacrifice.

5. Let all creation rise and bring
   distinctive honours to our King;
   angels descend with songs again
   and earth repeat the loud 'Amen!'

46 Isaac Watts

1. Join all the glorious names
   of wisdom, love and power,
   that ever mortals knew,
   that angels ever bore;
   all are too poor to speak his worth,
   too poor to set my Saviour forth!

2. Great Prophet of my God,
   my tongue shall bless your name;
   by you the joyful news
   of our salvation came;
   the joyful news of sins forgiven,
   of hell subdued and peace with heaven.

3. Jesus, my great High Priest,
   the Lamb of God who died!
   my guilty conscience seeks
   no sacrifice beside;
   the power of your atoning blood
   has won acceptance with my God.

4. Divine almighty Lord,
   my Conqueror and my King;
   your sceptre and your sword,
   your reigning grace I sing;
   yours is the power – and so I sit
   in willing service at your feet.

5. Now let my soul arise,
   and tread the tempter down;
   my Captain leads me on
   to conquest and a crown;
   the child of God shall win the day,
   though death and hell obstruct the way.

47 George Herbert

1. Let all the world in every corner sing,
    'My God and King!'
   The heavens are not too high,
   his praise may thither fly;
   the earth is not too low,
   his praises there may grow;
   let all the world in every corner sing,
    'My God and King!'

2. Let all the world in every corner sing,
    'My God and King!'
   The church with psalms must shout –
   no door can keep them out;
   but above all, the heart
   must bear the longest part;
   let all the world in every corner sing,
    'My God and King!'

48 Martin E. Leckebusch
© Kevin Mayhew

1. Let hymns of joyful praise abound
   and countless human voices sound;
   let songs of worship echo round,
   proclaiming that the King is crowned!

2. Bring skilful words and melody,
   bring rhythm, too, and harmony
   to celebrate in rhapsody
   the Lord of endless majesty.

3. The Lamb who once was crucified
   is seated at his Father's side;
   his name is honoured far and wide –
   our voices join the swelling tide.

4. Our worship we delight to bring,
   for he has given everything –
   and evermore the cry shall ring
   that Jesus Christ is Lord and King!

49 John Newton

1. Let us love and sing and wonder;
   let us praise the saviour's name!
   he has hushed the law's loud thunder;
   he has quenched Mount Sinai's flame;
   he has freed us by his blood;
   he has brought us near to God.

2. Let us love the Lord who bought us,
   dying for our rebel race;
   called us by his word and taught us
   by the Spirit of his grace;
   he has freed us by his blood;
   he presents our souls to God.

3. Let us sing, though fierce temptation
   threatens hard to drag us down;
   for the Lord, our strong salvation,
   holds in view the conqueror's crown;
   he who freed us by his blood,
   soon will bring us home to God.

4. Let us wonder; he has suffered –
   see what God in Christ has done!
   Debts are paid and mercy offered;
   love and justice meet as one;
   he who freed us by his blood
   has secured our peace with God!

5. Let us praise, and join the chorus
   of the saints enthroned on high;
   here they trusted him before us –
   now their praises fill the sky:
   'You have freed us by your blood,
   you are worthy, Lamb of God!'

50 From *Phos Hilaron*
© Christopher Idle/Jubilate Hymns

1. Light of gladness, Lord of glory,
   Jesus Christ our King most holy,
   shine among us in your mercy;
       earth and heaven join their hymn.

2. Let us sing at sun's descending
   as we see the lights of evening,
   Father, Son, and Spirit praising
       with the holy seraphim.

3. Son of God, through all the ages
   worthy of our holiest praises,
   yours the life that never ceases,
       light which never shall grow dim.

51 Michael Perry
© Mrs B. Perry/Jubilate Hymns

1. Like a mighty river flowing,
   like a flower in beauty growing,
   far beyond all human knowing
       is the perfect peace of God.

2. Like the hills serene and even,
   like the coursing clouds of heaven,
   like the heart that's been forgiven
       is the perfect peace of God.

3. Like the summer breezes playing,
   like the tall trees softly swaying,
   like the lips of silent praying
       is the perfect peace of God.

4. Like the morning sun ascended,
   like the scents of evening blended,
   like a friendship never ended
       is the perfect peace of God.

5. Like the azure ocean swelling,
   like the jewel all-excelling,
   far beyond our human telling
       is the perfect peace of God.

52 George Bourne

1. Lord, enthroned in heavenly splendour,
   glorious first-born from the dead,
   you alone our strong defender
   lifting up your people's head:
     Alleluia, alleluia,
   Jesus, true and living bread!

2. Prince of life, for us now living,
   by your body souls are healed;
   Prince of peace, your pardon giving,
   by your blood our peace is sealed:
     Alleluia, alleluia,
   Word of God in flesh revealed.

3. Paschal Lamb! your offering finished,
   once for all, when you were slain;
   in its fullness undiminished
   shall for evermore remain:
     Alleluia, alleluia,
   cleansing souls from every stain.

4. Great High Priest of our profession,
   through the veil you entered in,
   by your mighty intercession
   grace and mercy there to win:
     Alleluia, alleluia,
   only sacrifice for sin.

5. Life-imparting heavenly Manna,
   stricken rock, with streaming side;
   heaven and earth, with loud hosanna,
   worship you, the Lamb who died:
     Alleluia, alleluia,
   risen, ascended, glorified!

53 Michael Perry
© Mrs B. Perry/Jubilate Hymns

1. O God beyond all praising,
     we worship you today
   and sing the love amazing
     that songs cannot repay;
   for we can only wonder
     at every gift you send,
   at blessings without number
     and mercies without end;
   we lift our hearts before you
     and wait upon your word,
   we honour and adore you,
     our great and mighty Lord.

2. Then hear, O gracious Saviour,
     accept the love we bring,
   that we who know your favour
     may serve you as our King;
   and whether our tomorrows
     be filled with good or ill,
   we'll triumph through our sorrows
     and rise to bless you still;
   to marvel at your beauty
     and glory in your ways,
   and make a joyful duty
     our sacrifice of praise.

54 After Martin Rinkart, Catherine Winkworth

1. Now thank we all our God
     with hearts and hands and voices;
   such wonders he has done!
   In him the world rejoices.
   He, from our mothers' arms,
   has blessed us on our way
   with countless gifts of love,
   and still is ours today.

2. So may this generous God
     through all our life be near us;
   to fill our hearts with joy,
   and with his peace to cheer us;
   to keep us in his grace,
   and guide us when perplexed;
   to free us from all ills
   in this world and the next.

3. All praise and thanks to God
   who reigns in highest heaven,
   to Father and to Son
   and Spirit now be given,
   the one eternal God
   whom heaven and earth adore;
   for so it was, is now,
   and shall be evermore.

55 Charles Wesley

1. O for a thousand tongues to sing
     my great redeemer's praise,
   the glories of my God and King,
   the triumphs of his grace!

2. Jesus, the name that charms our fears
   and bids our sorrows cease;
   this music in the sinner's ears
   is life and health and peace.

3. He breaks the power of cancelled sin,
   he sets the prisoner free;
   his blood can make the foulest clean,
   his blood availed for me.

4. He speaks – and, listening to his voice,
   new life the dead receive,
   the mournful broken hearts rejoice,
   the humble poor believe.

5. Hear him, you deaf!
      his praise, you dumb,
   your loosened tongues employ;
   you blind, now see your Saviour come,
   and leap, you lame, for joy!

6. My gracious Master and my God,
   assist me to proclaim
   and spread through all the earth abroad
   the honours of your name.

56

1. O Lord my God,
      when I in awesome wonder
   consider all the works
      thy hand hath made;
   I see the stars,
      I hear the mighty thunder,
   thy power throughout
      the universe displayed;
         then sings my soul,
            my Saviour God, to thee,
         'How great thou art,
            how great thou art!'
         Then sings my soul,
            my Saviour God, to thee,
         'How great thou art,
            how great thou art!'

2. When through the woods
      and forest glades I wander
   and hear the birds
      sing sweetly in the trees;
   when I look down
      from lofty mountain grandeur,
   and hear the brook,
      and feel the gentle breeze;
         then sings my soul . . .

3. And when I think that God
      his Son not sparing,
   sent him to die – I scarce can take it in.
   That on the cross
      my burden gladly bearing,
   he bled and died to take away my sin;
         then sings my soul . . .

4. When Christ shall come
      with shout of acclamation
   and take me home –
      what joy shall fill my heart!
   Then I shall bow in humble adoration
   and there proclaim,
      'My God, how great thou art!'
         then sings my soul . . .

57 Thomas Ken

Praise God from whom all blessings flow:
praise him, all creatures here below,
praise him above, ye heavenly host –
praise Father, Son, and Holy Ghost.

58 John Newman

1. Praise to the Holiest in the height,
   and in the depth be praise;
   in all his words most wonderful,
   most sure in all his ways!

2. O loving wisdom of our God!
   when all was sin and shame,
   a second Adam to the fight
   and to the rescue came.

3. O wisest love! that flesh and blood,
   which did in Adam fail,
   should strive afresh against the foe,
   should strive and should prevail.

4. And that the highest gift of grace
   should flesh and blood refine;
   God's presence and his very self,
   and essence all-divine.

5. O generous love! that he, who smote
   in Man for man the foe.
   The double agony in Man
   for man should undergo.

6. And in the garden secretly,
   and on the cross on high,
   should teach his brethren, and inspire
   to suffer and to die.

7. Praise to the Holiest in the height,
   and in the depth be praise;
   in all his words most wonderful,
   most sure in all his ways!

59 After Joachim Neander, Catherine Winkworth and others

1. Praise to the Lord,
   the almighty, the King of creation!
   O my soul, praise him,
   for he is your health and salvation!
   Come, all who hear;
   brothers and sisters, draw near,
   praise him in glad adoration!

2. Praise to the Lord,
   above all things so mightily reigning;
   keeping us safe at his side,
   and so gently sustaining.
   Have you not seen
   all you have needed has been
   met by his gracious ordaining?

3. Praise to the Lord,
   who when darkness
   and sin are abounding,
   who when the godless are rampant,
   all goodness confounding,
   shines with his light,
   scatters the terrors of night,
   safely his people surrounding.

4. Praise to the Lord,
   who shall prosper our work
   and defend us;
   surely his goodness and mercy
   shall daily attend us.
   Ponder anew
   what the almighty can do,
   who with his love will befriend us.

5. Praise to the Lord –
   O let all that is in me adore him!
   All that has life and breath,
   come now with praises before him!
   Let the 'Amen!'
   sound from his people again –
   gladly with praise we adore him!

60 © Timothy Dudley-Smith

1. Rejoice in God! let trumpets sound
   in witness to the world around,
   his faithfulness proclaim;
   who led his people by the hand
   and brought them
   to their promised land
   that all the earth should understand
   the greatness of his Name.

2. Rejoice in God, the God of grace,
   and come with thanks before his face
   for all his tender care;
   whose mercy meets us in our need,
   whose word of life is life indeed,
   on whom, in Christ, our spirits feed,
   who loves to answer prayer.

3. Rejoice in God whose only Son
   a fallen world's salvation won
   and broke the sinner's chain.
   He came in love to seek and save
   when for us all his life he gave,
   and then from cross
   and death and grave
   triumphant rose again.

4. Rejoice in God and for him build
   a living temple, Spirit-filled,
   of everlasting worth;
   a church united, true and strong,
   where all who love the Lord belong,
   and find in him their strength and song,
   the joy of all the earth.

5. Rejoice in God! your voices raise
   in honour, blessing, love and praise
       to his eternal throne;
   that every heart, with one accord,
   and every tongue may tell abroad
   the loving-kindness of the Lord,
       and make his glory known.

61 © 1981 Ernest Sands. Published by OCP Publications

1. Sing of the Lord's goodness,
   Father of all wisdom,
   come to him and bless his name.
   Mercy he has shown us,
   his love is for ever,
   faithful to the end of days.
       Come then all you nations,
       sing of your Lord's goodness,
       melodies of praise and thanks to God;
       ring out the Lord's glory,
       praise him with your music,
       worship him and bless his name.

2. Power he has wielded,
   honour is his garment,
   risen from the snares of death.
   His word he has spoken,
   one bread he has broken,
   new life he now gives to all.
       Come then . . .

3. Courage in our darkness,
   comfort in our sorrow –
   Spirit of our God most high!
   Solace for the weary,
   pardon for the sinner,
   splendour of the living God!
       Come then . . .

4. Praise him with your singing,
   praise him with the trumpet,
   praise God with the lute and harp.
   Praise him with the cymbals,
   praise him with your dancing,
   praise God till the end of days.
       Come then . . .

62 From *Magnificat* (Luke 1)
© Timothy Dudley-Smith

1. Tell out, my soul,
       the greatness of the Lord!
   Unnumbered blessings,
       give my spirit voice;
   tender to me the promise of his word;
   in God my Saviour
       shall my heart rejoice.

2. Tell out, my soul,
       the greatness of his name!
   Make known his might,
       the deeds his arm has done;
   his mercy sure,
       from age to age the same;
   his holy name; the Lord, the mighty one.

3. Tell out, my soul,
       the greatness of his might!
   Powers and dominions lay their glory by.
   Proud hearts and stubborns wills
       are put to flight,
   the hungry fed, the humble lifted high.

4. Tell out, my soul,
       the glories of his word!
   Firm is his promise, and his mercy sure.
   Tell out, my soul,
       the greatness of the Lord
   to children's children and for evermore!

63 James Montgomery

1. Stand up and bless the Lord,
   you people of his choice;
   stand up and praise the Lord your God
   with heart and soul and voice.

2. Though high above all praise,
   above all blessing high,
   who would not fear his holy name,
   give thanks and glorify?

3. O for the living flame
   from his own altar brought,
   to touch our lips, our minds inspire,
   and wing to heaven our thought!

4. God is our strength and song,
   and his salvation ours;
   then be his love in Christ proclaimed
   with all our ransomed powers.

5. Stand up and bless the Lord,
   the Lord your God adore;
   stand up and praise his glorious name,
   both now and evermore.

64 © Timothy Dudley-Smith

1. Thanks be to God for his saints
     of each past generation,
   one with us still in one body,
     one great congregation;
   with them proclaim
     Jesus for ever the same,
   Author of life and salvation.

2. Thanks be to God for his blessings
     which daily surround us;
   glory to Christ, the Redeemer
     who sought us and found us,
   who from the grave
     rose, the almighty to save,
   breaking the fetters that bound us.

3. Thanks be to God for the years
     that are yet in his keeping,
   trusting each day to the care
     of a Father unsleeping,
   on to the end,
     Christ our companion and friend,
   joy at the last for our weeping.

4. Thanks be to God who has called us
     and daily defends us,
   who with the Son and the Spirit
     unchanging befriends us;
   now in that name,
     Jesus for ever the same,
   forth to his service he sends us.

65 John Ellerton
   © in this version Jubilate Hymns

1. The day you gave us, Lord is ended,
   the darkness falls at your behest;
   to you our morning hymns ascended,
   your praise shall sanctify our rest.

2. We thank you
     that your church unsleeping,
   while earth rolls onward into light,
   through all the world
     her watch is keeping,
   and rests not now by day or night.

3. As to each continent and island
   the dawn leads on another day,
   the voice of prayer is never silent,
   nor dies the strain of praise away.

4. The sun that bids us rest is waking
   your church beneath the western sky,
   and hour by hour fresh lips are making
   your wondrous doings heard on high.

5. So be it, Lord; your throne shall never,
   like earth's proud empires, pass away;
   your kingdom stands,
     and grows for ever,
   till all your creatures own your sway.

66 From a Hebrew doxology, Thomas Olivers
   © in this version Jubilate Hymns

1. The God of Abraham praise
   who reigns enthroned above;
   the ancient of eternal days
   and God of love!
   The Lord, the great I AM,
   by earth and heaven confessed –
   we bow before his holy name
   for ever blessed.

2. To him we lift our voice
   at whose supreme command
   from death we rise to gain the joys
   at his right hand:
   we all on earth forsake –
   its wisdom, fame, and power;
   the God of Israel we shall make
   our shield and tower.

3. Though nature's strength decay,
   and earth and hell withstand,
   at his command we fight our way
   to Canaan's land:
   the water's deep we pass
   with Jesus in our view,
   and through the howling wilderness
   our path pursue.

4. He by his name has sworn –
   on this we shall depend,
   and as on eagles' wings upborne
   to heaven ascend:
   there we shall see his face,
   his power we shall adore,
   and sing the wonders of his grace
   for evermore.

5. There rules the Lord our King,
   the Lord our righteousness,
   victorious over death and sin,
   the Prince of peace:
   on Zion's sacred height
   his kingdom he maintains,
   and glorious with his saints in light
   for ever reigns.

6. Triumphant hosts on high
   give thanks eternally
   and 'Holy, holy, holy' cry,
   'great Trinity!'
   Hail Abraham's God and ours!
   one mighty hymn we raise,
   all power and majesty be yours
   and endless praise!

67 © Brian Hoare/Jubilate Hymns

1. The Lord is King!
   He set the stars in space,
   and fashioned all our varied human race.
   Creator God,
   whose hand sustains us still,
   your kingdom stands,
   and all things serve your will.

2. The Lord is King!
   He sent his Son to earth,
   his glory laid aside in human birth.
   O Saviour Christ,
   who died and rose again,
   your kingdom comes
   where in our lives you reign.

3. The Lord is King!
   He sent his Spirit here
   to heal and save,
   to banish doubt and fear.

Spirit of truth, exalt the Living Word,
whose kingdom grows
   till all shall own him Lord.

4. The Lord is King!
   From all in earth and heaven
   be blessing, honour,
   praise and glory given.
   While earthly kingdoms fade
   and cease to be,
   God's kingdom lasts for all eternity.

68 © Christopher Idle/Jubilate Hymns

1. The victory of our God is won
   and all creation sings!
   Four living creatures round the throne
   acclaim the King of kings;
   the elders bring their crowns to him
   in worship day and night
   while cherubim and seraphim
   sing praise in burning light.

2. Then all believers in the Lord
   combine in perfect praise:
   the patriarchs who know their God,
   with saints of ancient days;
   the twelve apostles of the Lamb,
   the prophets in their place,
   the white-robed martyrs praise his name
   and glory in his grace.

3. The Christians of these latter years
   shall not be missing there:
   the pastors and the pioneers
   who wrestled with despair;
   the churches where ten thousand pray,
   the groups of two or three –
   the angels hear them sing that day
   how Jesus set them free.

4. All glory to the Lamb who died
   and rescued us by blood,
   the Saviour who was crucified
   to bring the world to God!
   Let all who witness to his word
   from every tribe and tongue
   sing 'Holy, holy, holy, Lord'
   in everlasting song.

69
Brian Wren
© 1969, 1995 Stainer & Bell

1. There's a spirit in the air,
   telling Christians everywhere;
   praise the love that Christ revealed,
   living, working, in our world.

2. Lose your shyness, find your tongue,
   tell the world what God has done:
   God in Christ has come to stay.
   Live tomorrow's life today!

3. When believers break the bread,
   when a hungry child is fed,
   praise the love that Christ revealed,
   living, working, in our world.

4. Still the Spirit gives us light,
   seeing wrong and setting right:
   God in Christ has come to stay.
   Live tomorrow's life today!

5. When a stranger's not alone,
   where the homeless find a home,
   praise the love that Christ revealed,
   living, working, in our world.

6. May the Spirit fill our praise,
   guide our thoughts
      and change our ways:
   God in Christ has come to stay.
   Live tomorrow's life today!

7. There's a Spirit in the air,
   calling people everywhere;
   praise the love that Christ revealed,
   living, working, in our world.

70 Isaac Watts

1. This is the day the Lord has made,
   he calls the hours his own;
   let heaven rejoice, let earth be glad,
   and praise surround the throne.

2. Today he rose and left the dead,
   and Satan's empire fell;
   today the saints his triumphs spread,
   and all his wonders tell.

3. Hosanna to the anointed king,
   to David's holy Son!
   help us, O Lord; descend and bring
   salvation from your throne.

4. Blessed be the Lord, who freely came
   to save our sinful race;
   he comes, in God his Father's name,
   with words of truth and grace.

5. Hosanna in the highest strains
   the church on earth can raise!
   the highest heaven in which he reigns
   shall give him nobler praise.

71 Frances van Alstyne

1. To God be the glory!
      great things he has done;
   so loved he the world
      that he gave us his Son
   who yielded his life
      an atonement for sin,
   and opened the life-gate
      that all may go in.
         Praise the Lord, praise the Lord!
         let the earth hear his voice;
         praise the Lord, praise the Lord!
         let the people rejoice:
         O come to the Father
         through Jesus the Son
         and give him the glory;
         great things he has done.

2. O perfect redemption,
      the purchase of blood!
   To every believer the promise of God:
   the vilest offender who truly believes,
   that moment from Jesus
      a pardon receives.
         Praise the Lord . . .

3. Great things he has taught us,
      great things he has done,
   and great our rejoicing
      through Jesus the Son:
   but purer and higher and greater will be
   our joy and our wonder
      when Jesus we see!
         Praise the Lord . . .

72 From the Latin, John Neale
© in this version Jubilate Hymns

1. To the name of our salvation
   honour, worship, let us pay;
   which for many a generation
   deep in God's foreknowledge lay:
   saints of every race and nation
   sing aloud that name today.

2. Jesus is the name we treasure
   more than words can ever tell;
   name of grace beyond all measure,
   ear and heart delighting well:
   this our refuge and our treasure
   conquering sin and death and hell.

3. Highest name for adoration,
   strongest name of victory,
   sweetest name for meditation
   in our pain and misery:
   name for greatest veneration
   by the citizens on high.

4. Name of love, whoever preaches
   speaks like music to the ear;
   who in prayer this name beseeches
   finds its comfort ever near:
   who its perfect wisdom reaches
   heavenly joy possesses here.

5. Jesus! – name of all our praising
   in this world to which you came;
   here we sing of love amazing,
   and your saving power proclaim;
   hearts and voices heavenward raising,
   all our hope is in your name!

73 Joseph Addison
© in this version Jubilate Hymns

1. When all your mercies, O my God,
   my thankful soul surveys,
   uplifted by the view, I'm lost
   in wonder, love and praise.

2. Unnumbered blessings on my soul
   your tender care bestowed
   before my infant heart perceived
   from whom these blessings flowed.

3. Ten thousand thousand precious gifts
   my daily thanks employ;
   nor is the least a cheerful heart
   that takes those gifts with joy.

4. In health and sickness, joy and pain,
   your goodness I'll pursue;
   and after death, in distant worlds,
   the glorious theme renew.

5. Throughout eternity, O Lord,
   a joyful song I'll raise;
   but all eternity's too short
   to utter all your praise!

74 From the German 19th Century, Edward Caswall
© in this version Jubilate Hymns

1. When morning gilds the skies,
   my heart awakening cries:
       may Jesus Christ be praised!
   Alike at work and prayer
   I find my Lord is there;
       may Jesus Christ be praised!

2. To God, the Word, on high
   the hosts of angels cry:
       may Jesus Christ be praised!
   Let mortals too, upraise
   their voice in hymns of praise:
       may Jesus Christ be praised!

3. Let earth's wide circle round
   in joyful notes resound:
       may Jesus Christ be praised!
   Let air and sea and sky
   from depth to height reply:
       may Jesus Christ be praised!

4. The night becomes as day
   when from the heart we say:
       may Jesus Christ be praised!
   The powers of darkness fear
   when this glad song they hear,
       may Jesus Christ be praised!

5. Does sadness fill my mind?
   My strength in him I find;
       may Jesus Christ be praised!
   When earthly hopes grow dim
   my comfort is in him:
       may Jesus Christ be praised!

6. Be this, while life is mine,
   my canticle divine:
      may Jesus Christ be praised!
   Be this the eternal song
   through all the ages long:
      may Jesus Christ be praised!

75 Charles Wesley

1. You servants of God,
      your master proclaim,
   and publish abroad his wonderful name;
   the name all-victorious of Jesus extol,
   his kingdom is glorious,
      and rules over all.

2. God rules in the height,
      almighty to save –
   though hid from our sight,
      his presence we have;
   the great congregation
      his triumph shall sing,
   ascribing salvation to Jesus our King.

3. 'Salvation to God
      who sits on the throne!'
   let all cry aloud, and honour the Son;
   the praises of Jesus the angels proclaim,
   fall down on their faces
      and worship the Lamb.

4. Then let us adore and give him his right:
   all glory and power,
      all wisdom and might,
   all honour and blessing –
      with angels above –
   and thanks never ceasing,
      and infinite love.

76 Richard Baxter
© in this version Jubilate Hymns

1. You holy angels bright
   who wait at God's right hand,
   or through the realms of light
   fly at your Lord's command:
      assist our song,
      or else the theme
      too high will seem
      for mortal tongue.

2. You faithful souls at rest,
   who ran this earthly race,
   and now from sin released
   behold the Saviour's face:
      his praises sound
      and all unite
      in sweet delight
      to see him crowned.

3. You saints who serve below,
   adore your heavenly king,
   and as you onward go
   your joyful anthems sing:
      take what he gives
      and praise him still
      through good and ill,
      who ever lives.

4. So take, my soul, your part;
   triumph in God above,
   and with a well-tuned heart
   sing out your songs of love:
      with joy proclaim
      through all your days
      in ceaseless praise
      his glorious name!

PSALMS

77 From *Jubilate Deo* Psalm 100, William Kethe
© in this version Jubilate Hymns

1. All people that on earth do dwell,
   sing to the Lord with cheerful voice:
   serve him with joy, his praises tell,
   come now before him and rejoice!

2. Know that the Lord is God indeed,
   he formed us all without our aid;
   we are the flock he loves to feed,
   the sheep who by his hand are made.

3. O enter then his gates with praise,
   and in his courts his love proclaim;
   give thanks and bless him all your days:
   let every tongue confess his name.

4. For God, our mighty Lord, is good,
   his mercy is for ever sure;
   his truth at all times firmly stood,
   and shall from age to age endure.

5. Praise God the Father, God the Son,
and God the Spirit evermore;
all praise to God the Three-in-One,
let heaven rejoice and earth adore!

78 From Psalms 149 and 150, Michael Perry
© Mrs B Perry/Jubilate Hymns

1. Bring to the Lord a glad new song,
children of grace extol your king:
your love and praise to God belong –
to instruments of music, sing!
Let those be warned
   who spurn God's name,
let rulers all obey God's word,
for justice shall bring tyrants shame –
let every creature praise the Lord!

2. Sing praise within these hallowed walls,
worship beneath the dome of heaven;
by cymbals' sounds and trumpets' calls
let praises fit for God be given:
with strings and brass
   and wind rejoice –
then, join our song in full accord
all living things with breath and voice;
let every creature praise the Lord!

79 From Psalm 47, John L Bell © 1993 WGRG, Iona
Community from *Psalms of patience, protest and praise*
(Wild Goose Publications 1993)

1. Clap your hands all you nations,
Amen. Hallelujah!
shout for joy all you people;
Amen. Hallelujah!
Holy is the most high;
Amen. Hallelujah!
mighty over the earth.
Amen. Hallelujah!

2. God subdues every nation,
Amen. Hallelujah!
God is king of all creatures;
Amen. Hallelujah!
God has given this land,
Amen. Hallelujah!
to the people he loves.
Amen. Hallelujah!

3. To the shouting in triumph,
Amen. Hallelujah!
to the blasting of trumpets,
Amen. Hallelujah!
God has gone up,
Amen. Hallelujah!
God ascends over all.
Amen. Hallelujah!

4. Praise the Lord with your singing,
Amen. Hallelujah!
sing God psalms for ever
Amen. Hallelujah!
God is monarch of all,
Amen. Hallelujah!
sovereign over the earth.
Amen. Hallelujah!

5. Those on earth who are mighty
Amen. Hallelujah!
still belong to our Maker,
Amen. Hallelujah!
God exalted on high
Amen. Hallelujah!
God for ever our Lord.
Amen. Hallelujah!

80 From Psalm 147
© Timothy Dudley-Smith

1. Fill your hearts with joy and gladness,
sing and praise your God and mine!
Great the Lord in love and wisdom,
might and majesty divine!
He who framed the starry heavens
knows and names them as they shine.

2. Praise the Lord, his people, praise him!
wounded souls his comfort know;
those who fear him find his mercies,
peace for pain and joy for woe;
humble hearts are high exalted,
human pride and power laid low.

3. Praise the Lord for times and seasons,
cloud and sunshine, wind and rain;
spring to melt the snows of winter
till the waters flow again;
grass upon the mountain pastures,
golden valleys thick with grain.

4. Fill your hearts with joy and gladness,
   peace and plenty crown your days;
   love his laws, declare his judgements,
   walk in all his words and ways;
   he the Lord and we his children:
   praise the Lord, all people, praise!

81 From *Jubilate Deo* Psalm 100
© Michael Baughen/Jubilate Hymns

1. Come, rejoice before your maker
   all you peoples of the earth;
   serve the Lord your God with gladness,
   come before him with a song!

2. Know for certain that Jehovah
   is the true and only God:
   we are his, for he has made us;
   we are sheep within his fold.

3. Come with grateful hearts before him,
   enter now his courts with praise;
   show your thankfulness towards him,
   give due honour to his name.

4. For the Lord our God is gracious –
   everlasting in his love;
   and to every generation
   his great faithfulness endures.

82 From Psalm 118, Isaac Watts

1. From all who live beneath the skies
   let the Creator's praise arise!
   let the Redeemer's name be sung
   through every land, by every tongue!

2. Eternal are your mercies, Lord,
   eternal truth attends your word;
   your praise shall sound
      from shore to shore
   till suns shall rise and set no more.

83 From Psalm 136, Isaac Watts
© in this version Jubilate Hymns

1. Give to our God immortal praise,
   mercy and truth are all his ways;
   wonders of grace to God belong:
   repeat his mercies in your song.

2. Give to the Lord of lords renown,
   the King of kings with glory crown:
   his mercies ever shall endure
   when lords and kings
      are known no more.

3. He built the earth, he spread the sky,
   and fixed the starry lights on high;
   wonders of grace to God belong:
   repeat his mercies in your song.

4. He fills the sun with morning light,
   he bids the moon direct the night;
   his mercies ever shall endure
   when suns and moons
      shall shine no more.

5. He sent his Son with power to save
   from guilt and darkness and the grave;
   wonders of grace to God belong:
   repeat his mercies in your song.

6. All through this world
      he guides our feet
   and leads us to his heavenly seat;
   his mercies ever shall endure
   when this vain world shall be no more.

84 From Psalm 146, Isaac Watts
© in this version Jubilate Hymns

1. I'll praise my maker while I've breath,
   and when my voice is lost in death,
   praise shall possess my noblest powers;
   my days of praise are never past
   while life and thought and being last
   or immortality endures.

2. Happy are those whose hopes rely
   on God the Lord, who made the sky,
   the earth, the sea, the night and day;
   his truth for ever stands secure,
   he keeps his promise to the poor,
   and none who seeks is turned away.

3. The Lord gives eyesight to the blind,
   he calms and heals the troubled mind,
   he sends the wounded
      conscience peace;
   he helps the stranger in distress,
   the widow and the fatherless,
   and grants the prisoner glad release.

4. I'll praise him while he lends me breath,
   and when my voice is lost in death
   praise shall employ my noblest powers;
   my days of praise are never past
   while life and thought and being last
   or immortality endures.

85

CHOIR: Let everything that has breath
        praise the Lord:
ALL: Let everything that has breath
        praise the Lord!

CHOIR: O praise God in his sanctuary,
        praise him in the firmament of his
        power; praise him for his mighty
        acts, praise him according to his
        abundant goodness:
ALL: Let everything that has breath
        praise the Lord!

CHOIR: Praise him in the blast of the ram's
        horn, praise him on the lute and
        harp, praise him with the timbrels
        and dances, praise him on the
        strings and pipe:
ALL: Let everything that has breath
        praise the Lord!

CHOIR: Praise him on the high-sounding
        cymbals, praise him on the loud
        cymbals; let everything that has
        breath praise the Lord:
ALL: Let everything that has breath
        praise the Lord!

CHOIR: Praise the Lord!

86 From Psalm 95 (*Venite*)
        © Richard Bewes/Jubilate Hymns

1. Let us sing to the God of salvation,
   let us sing to the Lord our rock;
   let us come to his house
      with thanksgiving,
   let us come before the Lord and sing!
      Praise our maker,
      praise our Saviour,

   praise the Lord
   our everlasting King:
   every throne
   must bow before him –
   God is Lord of everything!

2. In his hand are the earth's
      deepest places,
   and the strength of the hills is his;
   all the sea is the Lord's,
      for he made it –
   by his hand the solid rock
      was formed.
         Praise our maker . . .

3. Let us worship the Lord our Maker,
   let us kneel to the Lord our God;
   for we all are the sheep
      of his pasture –
   he will guide us
      by his powerful hand.
         Praise our maker . . .

4. Let today be the time
      when you hear him!
   May our hearts not be hard or cold,
   lest we stray from the Lord
      in rebellion
   as his people did in time of old.
         Praise our maker . . .

87 From *Cantate Domino* Psalm 98, Erik Routley
        © 1974 Hope Publishing Co. Administered by CopyCare

1. New songs of celebration render
   to him who has great wonders done:
   Love sits enthroned
      in ageless splendour –
   come and adore the mighty one!
   He has made known his great salvation
   which all his friends with joy confess;
   he has revealed to every nation
   his everlasting righteousness.

2. Joyfully, heartily resounding,
   let every instrument and voice
   peal out the praise of grace abounding,
   calling the whole world to rejoice.
   Trumpets and organs, set in motion
   such sounds as make the heavens ring;
   all things that live in earth and ocean,
   make music for your mighty king.

3. Rivers and seas and torrents roaring,
   honour the Lord with wild acclaim;
   mountains and stones look up adoring
   and find a voice to praise his name
   Righteous, commanding, ever-glorious,
   praises be his that never cease:
   just is our God, whose truth victorious
   establishes the world in peace.

88 From Psalm 115
© Timothy Dudley-Smith

1. Not to us be glory given
   but to him who reigns above:
   glory to the God of heaven
   for his faithfulness and love!
   What though unbelieving voices
   hear no word and see no sign,
   still in God my heart rejoices,
   working out his will divine.

2. Not what human fingers fashion,
   gold and silver, deaf and blind,
   dead to knowledge and compassion,
   having neither heart nor mind,
   lifeless gods, yet some adore them,
   nerveless hands and feet of clay;
   all become, who bow before them,
   lost indeed, and dead as they.

3. Not in them is hope of blessing,
   hope is in the living Lord:
   high and low, his name confessing,
   find in him their shield and sword.
   Hope of all whose hearts revere him,
   God of Israel, still the same!
   God of Aaron! Those who fear him,
   he remembers them by name.

4. Not the dead, but we the living
   praise the Lord with all our powers;
   of his goodness freely giving,
   his is heaven; earth is ours.
   Not to us be glory given
   but to him who reigns above:
   glory to the God of heaven
   for his faithfulness and love!

89 From Psalm 96
© David Preston/Jubilate Hymns

1. O sing a new song,
   O sing to the Lord;
   O sing, all the earth:
   his name be adored!
   Tell forth his salvation
   as day follows day;
   among all the peoples
   his wonders display.

2. For great is the Lord,
   most worthily praised,
   more awesome than gods
   the heathen have raised;
   the Lord made the heavens,
   so great is his might,
   and dwells amid majesty,
   beauty and light.

3. Ascribe to the Lord,
   all nations on earth,
   due glory and strength,
   due honour and worth;
   let all the earth seek him,
   with offerings draw near,
   in holiness worship
   and bow down with fear.

4. Proclaim to all lands:
   'The Lord reigns today!
   this earth shall be freed
   from change and decay:
   his justice is coming' –
   O heavens, rejoice,
   and oceans re-echo
   with thunderous voice!

5. Then forest and field
   for gladness shall sing
   to welcome the Lord
   their Maker and King;
   for by his true judgement
   at last shall be weighed
   all lands and all peoples,
   the world that he made.

90 From Psalm 104, after William Kethe, Robert Grant

1. O worship the King
       all glorious above,
   and gratefully sing
       his power
       and his love,
   our shield and defender,
       the Ancient of Days,
   pavilioned in splendour
       and girded with praise.

2. O tell of his might
       and sing of his grace,
   whose robe is the light,
       whose canopy space;
   his chariots of wrath
       the deep thunder-clouds form,
   and dark is his path
       on the wings of the storm.

3. The earth with its store
       of wonders untold,
   Almighty, your power has
       founded of old,
   established it fast by a
       changeless decree,
   and round it has cast
       like a mantle the sea.

4. Your bountiful care
       what tongue can recite?
   it breathes in the air,
       it shines in the light;
   it streams from the hills,
       it descends to the plain,
   and sweetly distils in the dew
       and the rain.

5. We children of dust
       are feeble and frail –
   in you we will trust,
       for you never fail;
   your mercies how tender,
       how firm to the end!
   our maker, defender,
       redeemer and friend.

6. O measureless Might,
       unchangeable Love,
   whom angels delight
       to worship above!
   your ransomed creation
       with glory ablaze,
   in true adoration shall
       sing to your praise!

91 From Psalm 148, Michael Perry
© Mrs B. Perry/Jubilate Hymns

1. Praise him, praise him, praise him,
       powers and dominations!
   praise his name in glorious light
       you creatures of the day!
   Moon and stars, ring praises
       through the constellations:
   Lord God, whose word
       shall never pass away!

2. Praise him, praise him, praise him,
       ocean depths and waters,
   elements of earth and heaven
       your several praises blend!
   birds and beasts and cattle,
       Adam's sons and daughters,
   worship the king
       whose reign shall never end!

3. Praise him, praise him, praise him,
       saints of God who fear him!
   to the highest name of all,
       concerted anthems raise,
   all you seed of Israel,
       holy people near him
   whom he exalts and crowns
       with endless praise!

92 From Psalm 148, Anonymous
Foundling Hospital Collection

1. Praise the Lord, you heavens, adore him;
   praise him, angels in the height;
   sun and moon, rejoice before him;
   praise him, all you stars and light.
   praise the Lord, for he has spoken,
   worlds his mighty voice obeyed;
   laws which never shall be broken
   for their guidance he has made.

2. Praise the Lord, for he is glorious,
   never shall his promise fail;
   God has made his saints victorious,
   sin and death shall not prevail.
   praise the God of our salvation!
   hosts on high, his power proclaim;
   heaven and earth and all creation
   praise and glorify his name!

93 From Psalm 103, Henry Lyte

1. Praise, my soul, the king of heaven!
   to his feet your tribute bring:
   ransomed, healed, restored, forgiven,
   who like me his praise should sing?
     Alleluia, alleluia!
   praise the everlasting king!

2. Praise him for his grace and favour
   to our fathers in distress;
   praise him still the same as ever,
   slow to blame and swift to bless:
     Alleluia, alleluia!
   glorious in his faithfulness!

3. Father-like, he tends and spares us;
   all our hopes and fears he knows,
   in his hands he gently bears us,
   rescues us from all our foes,
     Alleluia, alleluia!
   widely as his mercy flows.

4. Angels, help us to adore him –
   you behold him face to face;
   sun and moon, bow down before him,
   praise him, all in time and space:
     Alleluia, alleluia!
   praise with us the God of grace!

94 From Psalm 96
© Stephen Horsfall/Jubilate Hymns

1. Sing a new song
     of glory and salvation,
   through all the earth
     let voices now be raised;
   speak of God's mighty power
     in every nation –
   great is the Lord,
     and greatly to be praised!

2. Sing and adore,
     shout loud with jubilation,
   tell of the truth and splendour
     of that Name;
   come with thanksgiving,
     worship, all creation –
   praise be to God
     for evermore the same.

3. Say to the earth:
     God's rule is never-ending,
   soon Christ shall come
     to judge our human race –
   anthems of joy
     from earth and heaven blending
   as all creation joins
     to sing God's grace!

95 From *Cantate Domino* Psalm 98
© Michael Baughen/Jubilate Hymns

1. Sing to God new songs of worship –
   all his deeds are marvellous;
   he has brought salvation to us
   with his hand and holy arm:
   he has shown to all the nations
   righteousness and saving power;
   he recalled his truth and mercy
   to his people Israel.

2. Sing to God new songs of worship –
   earth has seen his victory;
   let the lands of earth be joyful
   praising him with thankfulness:
   sound upon the harp his praises,
   play to him with melody;
   let the trumpets sound his triumph,
   show your joy to God the King!

3. Sing to God new songs of worship –
   let the sea now make a noise;
   all on earth and in the waters
   sound your praises to the Lord:
   let the hills rejoice together,
   let the rivers clap their hands,
   for with righteousness and justice
   he will come to judge the earth.

96 From Psalm 150, Henry Baker
© in this version Jubilate Hymns

1. Sing praise to the Lord!
   praise him in the height;
   rejoice in his word
   you angels of light:
   you heavens, adore him
   by whom you were made,
   and worship before him
   in brightness arrayed.

2. Sing praise to the Lord!
   praise him upon earth
   in tuneful accord,
   you saints of new birth:
   praise him who has brought you
   his grace from above;
   praise him who has taught you
   to sing of his love.

3. Sing praise to the Lord!
   all things that give sound,
   each jubilant chord
   re-echo around:
   loud organs, his glory
   proclaim in deep tone,
   and sweet harp, the story
   of what he has done.

4. Sing praise to the Lord!
   thanksgiving and song
   to him be outpoured
   all ages along:
   for love in creation,
   for heaven restored,
   for grace of salvation,
   sing praise to the Lord!

   Amen, amen.

97 From Psalm 98, Isaac Watts

1. Sweet is the work, my God, my King,
   to praise your name,
     give thanks and sing;
   to show your love by morning light,
   and talk of all your truth at night.

2. Sweet is the day, the first and best,
   on which I share your sacred rest;
   so let my heart in tune be found,
   like David's harp of joyful sound.

3. My heart shall triumph in the Lord
   and bless his works, and bless his word:
   God's works of grace,
     how bright they shine –
   how deep his counsels, how divine!

4. Soon I shall see and hear and know
   all I desired on earth below,
   and all my powers for God employ
   in that eternal world of joy.

98 From Psalm 97, Josiah Conder
© in this version Jubilate Hymns

1. The Lord is King! Lift up your voice,
   O earth, and all you heavens, rejoice;
   from world to world the song shall ring:
   'The Lord omnipotent is King!'

2. The Lord is King! Who then shall dare
   resist his will, distrust his care
   or quarrel with his wise decrees,
   or doubt his royal promises?

3. He reigns! You saints, his praises sing:
   your Father reigns, your God is King!
   holy and true are all his ways –
   let every creature sing his praise!

4. God reigns!
     He reigns with glory crowned:
   let Christians make a joyful sound
   And Christ is seated at his side:
   the man of love, the crucified.

5. Come, make your needs,
     your burdens known:
   he will present them at the throne;
   and angel hosts are waiting there
   his messages of love to bear.

6. One Lord one kingdom all secures;
   he reigns, and life and death are yours;
   through earth and heaven
     one song shall ring:
   'The Lord omnipotent is King!'

99 From Psalm 24
© Christopher Idle/Jubilate Hymns

1. This earth belongs to God,
the world, its wealth, and all its people;
he formed the waters wide
and fashioned every sea and shore.
  A Who may go up the hill of the Lord
  and stand in the place of holiness?
  B Only the one whose heart is pure,
  whose hands and lips are clean.

2. Lift high your heads, you gates;
rise up, you everlasting doors, as
here now the King of glory
enters into full command.
  A Who is the King, this King of glory,
  where is the throne
  he comes to claim?
  B Christ is the King, the Lord of glory,
  fresh from his victory.

3. Lift high your heads, you gates,
and fling wide open the ancient doors,
for here comes the King of glory
taking universal power.
  A Who is the King, this King of glory,
  what is the power by which he reigns?
  B Christ is the King, his cross his glory,
  and by love he rules.

4. All glory be to God
the Father, Son and Holy Spirit;
from ages past it was,
is now and evermore shall be.

The congregation may divide at A and B.

100 From Psalm 89
© Timothy Dudley-Smith

1. Timeless love! We sing the story,
praise his wonders, tell his worth;
love more fair than heaven's glory,
love more firm than ancient earth!
Tell his faithfulness abroad:
who is like him? Praise the Lord!

2. By his faithfulness surrounded,
north and south his hand proclaim;
earth and heaven formed and founded,
skies and seas, declare his name!
Wind and storm obey his word:
who is like him? Praise the Lord!

3. Truth and righteousness enthrone him,
just and equal are his ways;
more than happy, those who own him,
more than joy, their songs of praise!
Sun and shield and great reward:
who is like him? Praise the Lord!

SONGS

101 © 1985 Fintan O'Carroll and Christopher Walker
Published by OCP Publications

Alleluia, alleluia!
Alleluia, alleluia!

1. Father we praise you as Lord,
all of the earth gives you worship,
for your majesty fills the heavens,
fills the earth.
  Alleluia, alleluia . . .

2. Blessèd apostles sing praise;
prophets and martyrs give glory:
'for your majesty praise the Spirit,
praise the Son!'
  Alleluia, alleluia . . .

3. You are the Christ everlasting
born for us all of a virgin,
you have conquered death,
opened heaven to all believers.
  Alleluia, alleluia . . .

4. Help those you saved by your blood,
raise them to life with your martyrs.
Save your people, Lord,
as their ruler raise them up.
  Alleluia, alleluia . . .

102 © 1997 Darlene Zschech/Hillsongs, Australia/
Kingsway's Thankyou Music

Almighty God, my Redeemer,
my hiding place, my safe refuge;
no other name like Jesus,
no power can stand against you.

My feet are planted on this Rock,
and I will not be shaken:
my hope it comes from you alone,
my Lord and my salvation.

    Your praise is always on my lips,
    your word is living in my heart,
    and I will praise you with a new song:
    my soul will bless you, Lord.
    You fill my life with greater joy;
    yes, I delight myself in you,
    and I will praise you with a new song:
    my soul will bless you, Lord.

When I am weak, you make me strong:
when I'm poor, I know I'm rich,
for in the power of your name
all things are possible,
all things are possible,
all things are possible,
all things are possible.
    Your praise is always . . .

103 From SOUTH AFRICA. Xhosa text as in *Bongan 'iNkosi*
© South African and English Copyright Control

Amen, we praise your name, O God!
Amen, we praise your name, O God!
Amen, amen.
Amen, amen.
Amen, we praise your name, O God!

Amen, siyakudumisa!
Amen, siyakudumisa!
Amen, Bawo.
Amen, Bawo.
Amen, siyakudumisa!

104 From KENYA, unknown
© Copyright Control

ALL   Bless the Lord, bless the Lord,
      Bless the Lord;
      there is no other God.

LEADER My sisters . . .

      My brothers . . .

      You children . . .

      You elders . . .

      Together . . .

105 From Psalm 103
© Ateliers et Presses de Taizé

Bless the Lord, my soul,
and bless God's holy name.
Bless the Lord, my soul,
who leads me into life.

106 Gary Sadler and Jamie Harvill © 1992 Integrity's
Praise Music./Kingsway's Thankyou Music. For UK only.

Blessing and honour, glory and power
be unto the Ancient of Days;
from every nation, all of creation
bow before the Ancient of Days.
    Every tongue in heaven and earth
    shall declare your glory,
    every knee shall bow
      at your throne in worship;
    you will be exalted, O God,
    and your kingdom shall not pass away,
    O Ancient of Days.

Blessing and honour . . .
Your kingdom shall reign over all the earth:
sing unto the Ancient of Days;
    for none can compare
      to your matchless worth:
sing unto the Ancient of Days.

Every tongue in heaven and earth
shall declare your glory,
every knee shall bow
  at your throne in worship;
you will be exalted, O God,
and your kingdom shall not pass away,
O Ancient of Days.

107 Ian Smale
© 1984 Kingsway's Thankyou Music

Father God, I wonder
how I managed to exist
without the knowledge
of your parenthood
and your loving care.
But now I am your child,
I am adopted in your family,
and I can never be alone
because, Father God,
you're there beside me.
  I will sing your praises,
  I will sing your praises,
  I will sing your praises, for evermore;
  I will sing your praises,
  I will sing your praises,
  I will sing your praises, for evermore.

108 Henry Smith © 1978 Integrity's Hosanna! Music/
Kingsway's Thankyou Music. For UK only

  Give thanks with a grateful heart,
  give thanks to the Holy One;
  give thanks because he's given
  Jesus Christ, his Son.
  Give thanks . . .
And now let the weak say, 'I am strong',
let the poor say 'I am rich',
because of what the Lord has done for us;
and now let the weak say, 'I am strong',
let the poor say 'I am rich',
because of what the Lord has done for us.
  Give thanks . . .

109 John L. Bell © 1995 WGRG, Iona Community, from
Come all you people (Wild Goose Publications 1995)

Glory and gratitude and praise,
now let earth to heaven raise;
glory and gratitude and praise –
these we offer to God.

110 © Ateliers et Presses de Taizé

Glory to God, glory to God,
glory in the highest!
Glory to God, glory to God,
alleluia, alleluia!

   Gloria, gloria,
   in excelsis Deo!
   Gloria, gloria,
   alleluia, alleluia!

111 From Peru, unknown
© Copyright Control

LEADER	Glory to God, glory to God, glory in the highest!
ALL	Glory to God, glory to God, glory in the highest!
LEADER	To God be glory for ever!
ALL	To God be glory for ever!
LEADER	Alleluia! Amen!
GROUP 1	Alleluia! Amen!
LEADER	Alleluia! Amen!
GROUPS 1 & 2	Alleluia! Amen!
LEADER	Alleluia! Amen!
GROUPS 1, 2, 3	Alleluia! Amen!
ALL	Alleluia! Amen! Alleluia! Amen!

Alternative verses:

LEADER	Glory to God, glory to God glory to Christ Jesus . . .
LEADER	Glory to God, glory to God glory to the Spirit . . .

112
From *Gloria in Excelsis,* Chris Rolinson
© 1996 CJM Music

Glory, glory, glory in the highest,
glory, glory, glory in the highest,
peace to all on earth.

Lord God heavenly King,
Almighty God and Father;
we worship you,
we give you thanks
we praise you for your glory
    Glory, glory . . .

O Lord Jesus Christ,
Son of the Father;
Lord God, Lamb of God,
you take away the sin of the world,
    Glory, glory . . .

Have mercy on us,
have mercy on us –
for you are seated
    at the right hand of the Father,
receive our prayer.
    Glory, glory . . .

You alone are the One,
you alone are Lord,
you alone are most High
    Jesus Christ,
with the Holy Spirit
in the glory, glory, glory of the Father,
glory, glory, glory of the Father,
glory of his name!

113
From Psalm 48, Steve McEwan
© 1985 Bodysongs. Administered by CopyCare

Great is the Lord
    and most worthy of praise,
in the city of our God, the holy place,
the joy of the whole earth.
Great is the Lord,
    in whom we have the victory –
he aids us against the enemy,
we bow down on our knees.

And Lord, we want to lift
    your name on high;
and Lord, we want to thank you
for the works you've done in our lives;
and Lord, we trust in your unfailing love;
for you alone are God eternal,
throughout earth and heaven above.

114
From THE CARIBBEAN, traditional

Halle, halle, hallelujah!
Halle, halle, hallelujah!
Halle, halle, hallelujah!
Hallelujah, hallelujah!

115
© Steve James/Jubilate Hymns

Have you not known
    there's an everlasting God?
O give thanks, O give thanks to the Lord!
Have you not heard,
    he is Lord of all the earth?
O give thanks to the Lord!
The waters and the land
    are in the hollow of his hand.
O give thanks, O give thanks to the Lord!
For he is the One
who makes the weary strong –
let our joy in the Lord be our song!
    We will run and not grow
        weary in the race,
    we will rise up on eagle's wings
        and soar before his face;
    he is God,
        and he has saved us by his grace.
    Hallelujah, he is God!

Lift your eyes and see his vast eternity –
O give thanks, O give thanks to the Lord!
Like the stars he knows our name,
by his power we remain.
O give thanks to the Lord!
For all that he has done,
our salvation he has won.
O give thanks, O give thanks to the Lord!
For he is the One
who makes the weary strong –
let our joy in the Lord be our song!

We will run and not grow
weary in the race,
we will rise up on eagle's wings
and soar before his face;
he is God,
and he has saved us by his grace.
Hallelujah, he is God!

116 From CAMEROON, unknown
© Copyright Control

He came down that we may have love;
he came down that we may have love;
he came down that we may have love;
  hallelujah for evermore.

He came down that we may have peace . . .

He came down that we may have joy . . .

He came down that we may have power . . .

He came down that we may have hope . . .

117 From Psalm 99, Twila Paris
© 1985 Straightway/Mountain Spring/EMI Christian
Music Publishing. Administered by CopyCare.

He is exalted, the King is exalted on high –
I will praise him;
he is exalted, for ever exalted –
and I will praise his name!

  He is the Lord;
  for ever his truth shall reign;
  heaven and earth
  rejoice in his holy name.
  He is exalted,
  the King is exalted on high.

118 Kevin Prosch © 1991 Mercy/Vineyard Publishing
Administered by CopyCare

He is the Lord, and he reigns on high –
he is the Lord;
spoke into the darkness, created the light –
he is the Lord;
who is like unto him, never ending in days?
he is the Lord;
and he comes in power when
we call on his name –
he is the Lord!

  Show your power, O Lord our God;
  show your power, O Lord our God,
  our God!

Your gospel, O Lord,
  is the hope for our nation –
you are the Lord;
it's the power of God for our salvation –
you are the Lord;
we ask not for riches, but look to the cross;
you are the Lord;
and for our inheritance give us the lost –
you are the Lord!
  Send your power, O Lord our God;
  send your power, O Lord our God,
  our God!

119 Carl Tuttle. © 1985 Mercy/Vineyard Publishing
Administered by CopyCare

1. Hosanna, hosanna,
    hosanna in the highest.
  Hosanna, hosanna,
    hosanna in the highest.
  Lord, we lift up your name,
  with hearts full of praise.
  Be exalted, O Lord my God –
  hosanna in the highest.

2. Glory, glory, glory to the King of kings;
  glory, glory, glory to the King of kings;
  Lord, we lift up your name
  with hearts full of praise.
  Be exalted, O Lord my God –
  glory to the King of kings.

120 From Isaiah 61:3, David Hadden
© 1994 Restoration Music/Sovereign Music UK

  He's given me a garment of praise
  instead of a spirit of despair;
  he's given me a garment of praise
  instead of a spirit of despair.
  He's given me . . .

A crown of beauty instead of ashes,
the oil of gladness instead of mourning.
My soul rejoices as I delight myself in God –
he's given me a garment of praise
instead of a spirit of despair.
  He's given me . . .

121 Nathan Fellingham
© 1995 Kingsway's Thankyou Music

Holy, holy, holy is the Lord God Almighty.
Holy, holy, holy is the Lord God Almighty.
Who was and is and is to come,
who was and is and is to come.
  Lift up his name
  with the sound of singing,
  lift up his name in all the earth,
  lift up your voice and give him glory –
  for he is worthy to be praised.

122 Phil Lawson Johnston
© 1991 Kingsway's Thankyou Music

1. Jesus is the name we honour,
   Jesus is the name we praise.
   Majestic name above all other names;
   the highest heaven and earth proclaim
   that Jesus is our God.
     We will glorify, we will lift him high,
     we will give him honour and praise.
     We will glorify, we will lift him high,
     we will give him honour and praise.

2. Jesus is the name we worship,
   Jesus is the name we trust.
   He is the King above all other kings;
   let all creation stand and sing
   that Jesus is our God.
     We will glorify . . .

3. Jesus is the Father's splendour,
   Jesus is the Father's joy.
   He will return to reign in majesty,
   and every eye at last shall see
   that Jesus is our God.
     We will glorify . . .

123 Chris Bowater
© 1988 Sovereign Lifestyle Music

Jesus shall take the highest honour,
Jesus shall take the highest praise:
let all earth join heaven in exalting
the Name which is above all other names!
Let's bow the knee in humble adoration,
for at his name every knee must bow;
let every tongue confess he is Christ,
  God's only Son –

Sovereign Lord, we give you glory now:
  for all honour and blessing and power,
  belongs to you, belongs to you;
  all honour and blessing and power,
  belongs to you, belongs to you,
  Lord Jesus Christ, Son of the living God.

124 Matt Redman
© 1997 Kingsway's Thankyou Music

  Let everything that,
  everything that,
  everything that has breath
    praise the Lord.
  Let everything that . . .

Praise you in the morning,
praise you in the evening,
praise you when I'm young
  and when I'm old;
praise you when I'm laughing,
praise you when I'm grieving,
praise you
  every season of the soul.
If we could see
  how much you're worth –
your power, your might,
  your endless love –
then surely we would never cease to praise:
  Let everything that . . .

Praise you in the heavens,
joining with the angels,
praising you for ever and a day;
praise you on the earth now,
  joining with creation,
calling all the nations,
  to your praise.
If we could see
  how much you're worth –
your power, your might,
  your endless love –
then surely we would never cease to praise:
  Let everything that . . .

125 Robert & Dawn Critchley
© 1989 Kingsway's Thankyou Music

1. Lord, I come before
   your throne of grace;
   I find rest in your presence
   and fullness of joy.
   In worship and wonder
   I behold your face,
   singing, 'what a faithful God have I'.
       What a faithful God have I,
       what a faithful God;
       what a faithful God have I,
       faithful in every way.

2. Lord of mercy,
   you have heard my cry;
   through the storm
   you're the beacon,
   my song in the night.
   In the shelter of your wings,
   hear my heart's reply,
   singing, 'what a faithful God have I'.
   What a faithful God . . .

3. Lord all sovereign,
   granting peace from heaven,
   let me comfort those who suffer
   with the comfort you have given.
   I will tell of your great love
       for as long as I live,
   singing, 'what a faithful God have I'.
   What a faithful God . . .

126 Rick Founds. © 1989 Maranatha! Music
Administered by CopyCare

Lord, I lift your name on high,
Lord, I love to sing your praises;
I'm so glad you're in my life,
I'm so glad you came to save us.

You came from heaven to earth
  to show the way,
from the earth to the cross, my debt to pay;
from the cross to the grave,
from the grave to the sky,
Lord, I lift your name on high.

127 Jessy Dixon, Randy Scruggs & John W. Thompson
© 1983 Windswept Pacific Music

1. Lord of lords, King of kings,
   maker of heaven and earth
       and all good things,
   we give you glory;
   Lord Jehovah, Son of Man,
   precious Prince of peace
       and the great I AM,
   we give you glory:
       Glory to God, glory to God,
       glory to God almighty in the highest!

2. Lord, you're righteous in all your ways,
   we bless your holy name
       and we give you praise,
   we give you glory;
   you reign for ever in majesty –
   we praise you and lift you up
       for eternity,
   we give you glory:
       Glory to God . . .

128 From Psalm 45, Graham Kendrick
© 1991 Make Way Music

1. My heart is full of admiration
   for you, my Lord, my God and King;
   your excellence, my inspiration,
   your words of grace
   have made my spirit sing.

2. You love what's right
   and hate all evil;
   therefore your God sets you on high;
   and on your head pours oil of gladness,
   while fragrance fills your royal palaces.
       All the glory, honour and power
       belong to you, belong to you;
       Jesus, Saviour, anointed One,
       I worship you, I worship you,
       I worship you, I worship you.

3. Your throne, O God, will last for ever;
   justice will be your royal decree;
   in majesty, ride out victorious
   for righteousness, truth and humility.
       All the glory, . . .

129 © 1993 Darlene Zschech/Hillsongs Australia/ Kingsway's Thankyou Music

1. My Jesus, my Saviour.
   Lord, there is none like you;
   all of my days I want to praise
   the wonders of your mighty love.

2. My comfort, my shelter,
   tower of refuge and strength,
   let every breath, all that I am,
   never cease to worship you.

   Shout to the Lord all the earth,
   let us sing power and majesty,
   praise to the King:
   mountains bow down
      and the seas will roar
   at the sound of your name.
   I sing for joy
      at the work of your hands,
   for ever I'll love you, for ever I'll stand;
   nothing compares
      to the promise I have in you.

130 Noel and Tricia Richards © 1991 Kingsway's Thankyou Music

   My lips shall praise you,
   my great Redeemer;
   my heart will worship,
   almighty Saviour.

1. You take all my guilt away,
   turn the darkest night to brightest day:
   you are the restorer of my soul.
      My lips . . .

2. Love that conquers every fear!
   in the midst of trouble you draw near,
   you are the restorer of my soul.
      My lips . . .

3. You're the source of happiness,
   bringing peace when I am in distress;
   you are the restorer of my soul.
      My lips . . .

131 Alan Rose © 1997 Kingsway's Thankyou Music

   Oh, our Lord and King,
   our praise to you we bring,
   there is no other rock but you.
   Seated high above –
   you are the one we love –
   this is our song
      of praise to you.

1. King for ever!
   you are the first and you're the last.
   You are sovereign;
   all your commands will always
   come to pass, to give you glory!
      Oh, our Lord and King . . .

2. Who is like you,
   who else is worthy of our praise?
   we exalt you; you reign in majesty
   and awesome splendour – King for ever!
      Oh, our Lord and King . . .

3. Abba Father,
   your steadfast love will never fail;
   you are faithful, you are God
   and I will worship
      in your courts for ever.
   Oh, our Lord and King . . .

132 Dave Bilbrough © 1996 Kingsway's Thankyou Music

   Our God is great, our God is great,
   our God is great, our God is great.
   Our God is great, our God is great,
   our God is great, our God is great.

1. He gave us the wind,
      the sun and the snow,
   the sand on the seashore,
      the flowers that grow,
   morning and evening,
      winter and spring;
   come join all creation and sing.
      Our God is great . . .

2. The gifts that he brings
   are new every day,
   from glorious sunset to soft falling rain,
   the mist on the hills,
   the light and the shade;
   come join all creation in praise.
   Our God is great, our God is great,
   our God is great, our God is great.
   Our God is great, our God is great,
   our God is great, our God is great.

   For music and dancing, the sounds
   that we hear;
   for colours and words,
   the life that we share, we say:
   Our God is great . . .

133 After Thomas Ken. Andy Piercy and Dave Clifton
© 1993 IQ Music

Praise God from whom all blessings flow,
praise him all creatures here below.
Praise him above you heavenly host,
praise Father, Son and Holy Ghost.

Give glory to the Father,
give glory to the Son,
give glory to the Spirit
   while endless ages run.

'Worthy the Lamb,' all heaven cries,
'to be exalted thus;'
'Worthy the Lamb,' our hearts reply,
'for he was slain for us.'
   Praise God from whom . . .

134 Twila Paris. © 1996 Ariose Music/EMI Christian
Music Publishing. Administered by CopyCare.

1. Righteous and holy in all of your ways,
   we come before you
      with honour and praise.
   Here to adore you for all of our days,
   we come before you
      with honour and praise.
   Lord of the heavens,
      how faithful you are,
   shine down upon us,
      O bright morning star.
   Righteous and holy in all of your ways,
   we come before you
      with honour and praise.

2. Filling the temple,
   the work of your grace,
   we come before you
      with honour and praise.
   Here to adore you for all of our days,
   we come before you
      with honour and praise.
   Lord of the heavens,
      how faithful you are,
   rise in our spirits, O bright morning star.
      Righteous and holy . . .

   Here to adore you for all of our days,
   we come before you
      with honour and praise,
   honour and praise, honour and praise.
   Righteous and holy,
      we come before you,
   righteous and holy,
      honour and praise,
      honour and praise.

135 From SOUTH AFRICA, traditional

Sanna, sanna-nina,
sanna, sanna, sanna.
Sanna, sanna-nina,
sanna, sanna, sanna.

   Sanna, sanna, sanna
   sanna-nina,
   sanna, sanna, sanna.
   Sanna, sanna, sanna
   sanna-nina,
   sanna, sanna, sanna.

(*sanna* is a shortened form of *Hosanna*)

136 Louise Hunt and Nathan Fellingham
© 1997 Kingsway's Thankyou Music

1. The name of the Lord is a strong tower;
   the name of the Lord
      brings refuge and strength;
   the name of the Lord
      gives hope to the hopeless,
   the name of the Lord
      breathes life to the dead.

2. The name of the Lord
   give strength to the weary,
the name of the Lord
   brings freedom from fear:
the name of the Lord
   gives peace to the restless,
the name of the Lord
   will heal the oppressed.

   O Lord, you never change,
   holy God, you remain the same,
   for your love – it never fades,
   your faithfulness surrounds me.
      For you alone are God,
         and I bow before you,
      you alone are God,
         I worship, adore you.
      You alone are God,
         none other before you,
         and I offer up my life again.

3. The name of the Lord
   covers me with mercy,
the name of the Lord
   brings everlasting joy;
the name of the Lord
   will lift all my burdens,
the name of the Lord –
   it makes me complete.

   I call, and you answer me,
   for you know my every need,
   in your love I put my trust,
   your faithfulness surrounds me.
      For you alone are God . . .

   O taste and see that the Lord is good,
   how blessèd is the man
   who hides himself in him.
   O Lord, you never change . . .
      For you alone are God . . .

137 Martin J. Smith. © 1993 Curious? Music UK. Administered by Kingsway's Thankyou Music Worldwide (excluding USA)

1. Thank you for saving me –
      what can I say?
   you are my everything,
      I will sing your praise.
   You shed your blood for me –
      what can I say?

   you took my sin and shame,
   a sinner called by name.
      Great is the Lord,
      great is the Lord!
      For we know your truth
      has set us free –
      you've set your hope in me.

2. Mercy and grace are mine,
      forgiven is my sin –
   Jesus my only hope,
      the Saviour of the world.
   'Great is the Lord,' we cry,
      'God, let your kingdom come!'
   your word has let me see,
   thank you for saving me.
      Great is the Lord...

      . . . Thank you for saving me –
         what can I say?

138 From SOUTH AFRICA, unknown
© South African and English Copyright Control

1. We are on the Lord's road,
      we are on the Lord's road,
   we are on the Lord's road,
      we are on the Lord's road,
   on our way to heaven –
   we are on the Lord's road,
   on our way to heaven –
   we are on the Lord's road.

2. We shall sing the Lord's praise,
      we shall sing the Lord's praise,
   we shall sing the Lord's praise,
      we shall sing the Lord's praise,
   on our way to heaven –
   we shall sing the Lord's praise,
   on our way to heaven –
   we shall sing the Lord's praise.

3. We shall live the Lord's word,
      we shall live the Lord's word,
   we shall live the Lord's word,
      we shall live the Lord's word,
   on our way to heaven –
   we shall live the Lord's word,
   on our way to heaven –
   we shall live the Lord's word.

4. Hallelujah, amen,
     hallelujah, amen,
   hallelujah, amen,
     hallelujah, amen,
   on our way to heaven –
   hallelujah, amen,
   on our way to heaven –
   hallelujah, amen.

1. *Sizohamba naye (wo) sizohamba naye*
   Sizohamba naye . . .
   ngomhla wenjabula
   sizohamba naye
   ngomhla wenjabula
   sizohamba naye.

2. *Sizohalalisa (wo) sizohalalisa*
   sizohalalisa . . .
   ngomhla wenjabula
   sizohalalisa naye
   ngomhla wenjabula
   sizohalalisa naye.

3. *Sizohlabelela (wo) sizohlabelela*
   sizohlabelela . . .
   ngomhla wenjabula
   sizohlabelela naye
   ngomhla wenjabula
   sizohlabelela naye.

139 Mark Altrogge
© 1997 PDI Praise. Administered by CopyCare

We sing your mercies,
we sing your endless praises,
we sing your everlasting love.
We sing your mercies,
we sing your endless praises,
Sovereign One who died,
Sovereign One who died for us.

1. Should he who made the stars
   be hung upon a tree?
   and should the hands that healed
   be driven through for me?
   Should he who gave us bread
   be made to swallow gall?
   should he who gave us breath and life
   be slaughtered for us all?
     We sing your mercies . . .

2. Should he who is the Light
   be cast into the dark?
   and should the Lord of love
   be pierced through his own heart?
   Should he who called us friends
   be deserted by us all?
   should he who lived a sinless life
   be punished for our fall?
     We sing your mercies . . .

140 Tommy Walker. © 1992 Integrity's Hosanna!
Music/Kingsway's Thankyou Music. For UK only

Where there once was only hurt,
he gave his healing hand;
here there once was only pain,
he brought comfort like a friend –
I feel the sweetness of his love
piercing my darkness;
I see the bright and morning sun
as it ushers in his joyful gladness.
     He's turned my mourning
       into dancing again,
     he's lifted my sorrow;
     I can't stay silent, I must sing
     for his joy has come.

Where there once was only hurt . . .
     He's turned my mourning . . .

His anger lasts for a moment in time;
but his favour is here,
and will be on me for all my lifetime.
     He's turned my mourning . . .

141 Paul Oakley
© 1995 Kingsway's Thankyou Music

Who is there like you,
and who else would give their life for me,
even suffering in my place?
And who could repay you?
All of creation looks to you,
and you provide for all you have made.

     So I'm lifting up my hands,
       lifting up my voice,
     lifting up your name,
       and in your grace I rest,
     for your love has come to me
       and set me free.

And I'm trusting in your word,
   trusting in your cross,
trusting in your blood
   and all your faithfulness,
for your power at work in me
   is changing me.

142 Stuart Townend
© 1995 Kingsway's Thankyou Music

Who paints the skies into glorious day?
Only the splendour of Jesus.
Who breathes his life into fists of clay?
Only the splendour of Jesus.
Who shapes the valleys and brings the rain?
Only the splendour of Jesus.
Who makes the desert to live again?
Only the splendour of Jesus.

Teach every nation his marvellous ways;
each generation shall sing his praise.
   He is wonderful, he is glorious,
   clothed in righteousness,
   full of tenderness;
   come and worship him –
   he's the Prince of life –
   he will cleanse our hearts
   in his river of fire.

Who hears the cry of the barren one?
Only the splendour of Jesus.
Who breaks the curse of the heart of stone?
Only the splendour of Jesus.
Who storms the prison and sets men free,
Only the splendour of Jesus.
Purchasing souls for eternity?
Only the splendour of Jesus.

Teach every nation his marvellous ways;
each generation shall sing his praise.
   He is wonderful . . .

143 Chris Rolinson, Joanne Boyce, Mike Stanley
©1995 CJM Music

   You are the fountain of holiness,
   Father of righteousness,
   great is your faithfulness,
   you are worthy, worthy, Lord.

1. Praise him!
    All nations, all peoples bless his name,
    Yahweh, faithful and just;
    mighty, Lord above all,
    from age to age proclaim:
       You are the fountain . . .

2. Praise him!
    Marvellous things he has done –
    creation, work of his hands,
    heaven, sun, moon and stars,
    from age to age proclaim:
       You are the fountain . . .

3. Praise him!
    For us the Word became flesh –
    Jesus, his gift of love
    given once for all,
    from age to age proclaim:
       You are the fountain . . .

For other items on this theme, see

HYMNS

380 All glory, praise and honour
398 Alleluia, alleluia! hearts to heaven
458 Alleluia, sing to Jesus
168 And can it be that I should gain
317 At the name of Jesus
618 Awake, my soul, and with the sun
571 By the sacrifice of Jesus
591 Christ is the world's Light, he and none other
400 Christ the Lord is risen again
319 Christ triumphant, ever reigning
454 Come and see the shining hope
433 Come see the Lord in his breathtaking
    splendour
320 Come sing the praise of Jesus
321 Crown him with many crowns
403 Exult, creation round God's throne!
665 Fill now my life, O Lord my God
298 For the beauty of the earth
299 For the fruits of his creation
405 Glory to Jesus! risen, conquering Son
337 God of God, the uncreated
504 God of gods, we sound his praises
667 Happy are those
382 Hark! the voice of love and mercy
455 Here from all nations, all tongues
290 Holy, holy, holy, Lord God almighty!
406 I know that my redeemer lives
304 It is God who holds the nations
408 Jesus Christ is risen today
409 Jesus lives! Your terrors now
323 Jesus! the name high over all
177 Jesus, your blood and righteousness
178 King of glory, king of peace
472 Let all mortal flesh keep silence
578 Let saints on earth together sing
536 Lord of our growing years
412 Love's redeeming work is done
411 Low in the grave he lay
383 Man of sorrows!
324 Name of all majesty
413 Now lives the Lamb of God
306 O Lord of heaven and earth and sea
308 Praise God for the harvest
327 Praise to Christ, the Lord incarnate
440 Rejoice, the Lord is king!
  1 Sing glory to God the Father
415 The day of resurrection!
416 The strife is past, the battle done
311 We plough the fields, and scatter
390 We sing the praise of him who died
584 What shall our greeting be?

PSALMS

  5 God of mercy, God of grace
340 Joy to the world – the Lord has come!
312 Let us gladly with one mind
543 O Lord, you are the centre of my life

SONGS

421 Alleluia, alleluia, Jesus, risen Lord of life!
423 Christ is risen
272 Christ your glory
  8 Come all you people
609 Come see a vision
  9 Come, let us go
610 Far and Near
192 Here I am
443 Here is the risen Son
656 In the Lord I'll be ever thankful
394 Jesus Christ, I think upon your sacrifice
615 Men of faith
568 My first love
426 No more weeping
197 Over the mountains and the seas
693 Send forth your light and your truth
278 Skills and abilities
396 There is a redeemer
551 We are marching
428 You are mighty

CONFESSING OUR SINS TO GOD

HYMNS

144 Edward Cooper

1. Father of heaven, whose love profound
   a ransom for our souls has found:
   before your throne we sinners bend –
   to us your pardoning love extend.

2. Almighty Son, incarnate Word,
   our prophet, priest, redeemer, Lord:
   before your throne we sinners bend –
   to us your saving grace extend.

3. Eternal Spirit, by whose breath
   the soul is raised from sin and death:
   before your throne we sinners bend –
   to us your living power extend.

4. Transcendent – Father, Spirit, Son –
   mysterious Godhead, Three-in-One:
   before your throne we sinners bend –
   grace, pardon, life to us extend.

145 Rosamond Herklots
By permission of Oxford University Press

1. 'Forgive our sins as we forgive,'
   you taught us, Lord, to pray;
   but you alone can grant us grace
   to live the words we say.

2. How can your pardon reach and bless
   the unforgiving heart
   that broods on wrongs, and will not let
   old bitterness depart?

3. In blazing light your cross reveals
   the truth we dimly knew:
   what trivial debts are owed to us,
   how great our debt to you!

4. Lord, cleanse the depths
   within our souls
   and bid resentment cease;
   then, bound to all in bonds of love,
   our lives will spread your peace.

146 From the Italian c.1815, Edward Caswall

1. Glory be to Jesus,
   who, in bitter pains,
   poured for me the life-blood
   from his sacred veins.

2. Grace and life eternal
   in that blood I find:
   blessed be his compassion
   wonderfully kind!

3. Abel's blood for vengeance
   pleaded to the skies,
   but the blood of Jesus
   for our pardon cries.

4. When that blood is sprinkled
   on our guilty hearts,
   Satan in confusion
   terror-struck departs.

5. When this earth exulting
   lifts its praise on high,
   angel hosts rejoicing
   make their glad reply.

6. Raise your thankful voices,
   swell the mighty flood;
   louder still and louder
   praise the Lamb of God!

147 Brian Foley
© Faber Music

1. How can we sing with joy to God,
   how can we pray to him,
   when we are far away from God
   in selfishness and sin?

2. How can we claim to do God's will
   when we have turned away
   from things of God to things of earth,
   and willed to disobey?

3. How can we praise the love of God
which all his works make known,
when all our works turn from his love
to choices of our own?

4. God knows the sinful things we do,
the Godless life we live,
yet in his love he calls to us,
so ready to forgive.

5. So we will turn again to God –
his ways will be our ways,
his will our will, his love our love,
and he himself our praise!

148 Gregory the Great. Translation © James Quinn S. J.
reprinted by permission of Cassell & Co.

1. Now let us all with one accord,
in company with ages past,
keep vigil with our heavenly Lord
in his temptation and his fast.

2. The covenant, so long revealed
to those of faith in former time,
Christ by his own example sealed,
the Lord of love, in love sublime.

3. Your love, O Lord, our sinful race
has not returned, but falsified;
author of mercy, turn your face
and grant repentance for our pride.

4. Remember, Lord, though frail we be,
in your own image were we made,
help us, lest in anxiety,
we cause your name to be betrayed.

5. Therefore we pray you, Lord, forgive;
so when our wanderings
here shall cease,
we may with you for ever live,
in love and unity and peace.

149 Charles Wesley

1. O for a heart to praise my God –
a heart from sin set free,
a heart that's sprinkled with the blood
so freely shed for me.

2. A heart resigned, submissive, meek,
my great redeemer's throne;
where only Christ is heard to speak,
where Jesus reigns alone.

3. A humble, lowly, contrite heart,
believing, true, and clean,
which neither life nor death can part
from him who dwells within.

4. A heart in every thought renewed,
and full of love divine;
perfect and right and pure and good –
your life revealed in mine.

5. Your nature, gracious Lord, impart –
come quickly from above,
write your new name upon my heart,
your new best name of love!

150 Augustus Toplady
© in this version Jubilate Hymns

1. Rock of ages, cleft for me,
hide me now, my refuge be;
let the water and the blood
from your wounded side which flowed,
be for sin the double cure,
cleanse me from its guilt and power.

2. Not the labours of my hands
can fulfil your law's demands;
could my zeal no respite know,
could my tears for ever flow,
all for sin could not atone:
you must save and you alone.

3. Nothing in my hand I bring,
simply to your cross I cling;
naked, come to you for dress,
helpless, look to you for grace;
stained by sin, to you I cry:
'Wash me, Saviour, or I die!'

4. While I draw this fleeting breath,
when my eyelids close in death,
when I soar through realms unknown,
bow before the judgement throne:
hide me then, my refuge be,
Rock of ages, cleft for me.

151
Alan Gaunt
© 1991 Stainer & Bell

1. Teach us how grave a thing it is
   to break love's laws deliberately,
   to flout your holiness, great God,
   or flaunt our shame presumptuously.

2. Have pity on our weakness, Lord,
   and deal with us forgivingly;
   but make us sterner with ourselves,
   exacting strict integrity.

3. Restrain us from excessive zeal
   in judging other people's sins,
   for in our verdict passed on them,
   your judgement of ourselves begins.

4. Prevent us throwing any stones,
   aware of our unworthiness;
   but, even more, remembering Christ,
   who loves us in our sinfulness.

5. He routed those who came to vent
   their fury in self-righteousness,
   but bore their malice to the end
   to perish on their bitterness.

6. God, give us his hard-centred love
   to deal with human wickedness;
   but make us hard on self alone,
   contending for your gentleness.

152
Isaac Watts
© in this version Jubilate Hymns

1. What offering shall we give
   or what atonement bring
   to God by whom alone we live,
   high heaven's eternal king?

2. For all the blood of beasts
   on Jewish altars slain
   could never give the conscience peace
   or wash away its stain:

3. But Christ, the heavenly Lamb,
   takes all our sins away –
   a sacrifice of nobler name
   and richer blood than they.

4. In faith I lay my hand
   upon his head divine
   while as a penitent I stand
   and there confess my sin.

5. So I look back to see
   the weight he chose to bear
   when hanging on the cross for me –
   because my guilt was there.

5. Believing, we rejoice
   to know our sins forgiven;
   we bless the Lamb with heart and voice
   and join the praise of heaven.

PSALMS

153
From Psalm 51 adapted from *The Psalter* 1912
© in this version Word & Music/Jubilate Hymns

1. God, be merciful to me,
   let your love my refuge be;
   my offences wash away,
   cleanse me from my sin today.
   My transgressions I confess,
   grief and guilt my soul oppress;
   I have sinned against your grace
   and provoked you to your face.

2. Wash me, wash me pure within,
   cleanse, O cleanse me from my sin:
   in your righteousness I trust,
   in your judgements you are just.
   Come, salvation to impart,
   teach your wisdom to my heart;
   make me pure, your grace bestow,
   that your mercy I may know.

3. Gracious God, my heart renew,
   make my spirit right and true;
   from my sins O hide your face,
   blot them out in boundless grace.
   Cast your servant not away,
   let your Spirit with me stay;
   make me joyful, willing, strong,
   teach me your salvation's song!

154 From Psalm 25 Verses: © The Grail/A. P. Watt
Chorus: © Paul Inwood. Published by OCP Publications

ALL Remember, remember your mercy, Lord;
  remember, remember your mercy, Lord:
  hear your people's prayer
    as they call to you;
  remember, remember your mercy, Lord.

1. SOLO
  Lord, make me know your ways,
  Lord, teach me your paths;
  make me walk in your truth,
    and teach me,
  for you are God my Saviour.
ALL Remember, remember your mercy . . .

2. SOLO
  Remember your mercy, Lord,
  and the love
    you have shown from of old;
  do not remember the sins of my youth.
    In your love remember me,
    in your love remember me
  because of your goodness, O Lord.
ALL Remember, remember your mercy . . .

3. SOLO
  The Lord is good and upright,
  he shows the path to all who stray;
  he guides the humble in the right path,
  he teaches his way to the poor.
ALL Remember, remember your mercy . . .

SONGS

155 From *The Alternative Service Book* © 1980 Central
Board of Finance of the Church of England;
1999 The Archbishop's Council

Almighty God, our heavenly Father,
we have sinned against you,
and against our fellow neighbours,

in thought and word and deed,
through negligence, through weakness,
through our own deliberate fault.

We are truly sorry
and repent of all our sins.
For the sake of your Son, Jesus Christ,

who died for us,
who died for us,
who died for us,
forgive us all that is past;
and grant that we may serve you
in newness of life
MEN   to the glory of your name,
WOMEN to the glory of your name,
MEN   to the glory of your name,
WOMEN to the glory of your name,
ALL   to the glory of your name.
    Amen, amen.

156 From INDIA, traditional

SOLO Father in heaven, have mercy upon us;
ALL Father in heaven, have mercy upon us.

SOLO Jesus Christ, have mercy upon us;
ALL Jesus Christ, have mercy upon us.

SOLO Father in heaven, have mercy upon us;
ALL Father in heaven, have mercy upon us.

SOLO *Ishworo, Ishworo daya koro;*
ALL *Ishworo, Ishworo daya koro.*

SOLO *Ishworo daya koro;*
ALL *Ishworo daya koro.*

SOLO *Ishworo, Ishworo daya koro;*
ALL *Ishworo, Ishworo daya koro.*

157 Andy Piercy
© 1995 I.Q. Music

Father, hear our prayer
that our lives may be
consecrated only unto you;
cleanse us with your fire,
fill us with your power
that the world may glorify your name.
  Lord, have mercy on us.
  Christ, have mercy on us.
  Lord, have mercy on us.

158
From Luke 15, Geoff Twigg
© 1993 Geoff Twigg/Jubilate Hymns

Father, we have sinned against you,
failed to do what's right;
we have walked alone in darkness
hiding from the light.
Father, we have run away
from what we know is true;
now we turn around and we are
coming home to you.
> We have sinned,
> > we have broken your law,
> we're returning once more, home to you;
> we have sinned,
> > we are seeking your face,
> we return by your grace, home to you.

159
From Psalm 123, Jacques Berthier
© Ateliers et Presses de Taizé

CONTINUOUS RESPONSE
> Holy Lord, have mercy on us all,
> Lord have mercy on us;
> Holy Lord . . .

OR
> *Miserere nobis Domine,*
> *miserere nobis;*
> *miserere nobis Domine,*
> *miserere nobis.*

1. SOLO
   Behold, as the eyes of servants
   are on the hands of their masters:

2. SOLO
   Our eyes are fixed on the Lord our God
   until he shows us his mercy.

160
Traditional liturgical text

Lamb of God,
you take away the sin of the world,
have mercy on us, Lord

Lamb of God,
you take away the sin of the world,
have mercy on us, Lord.

Lamb of God,
you take away the sin of all the world,
grant us peace.

161
From GHANA, traditional

Lord, have mercy.
Lord, have mercy.
Lord, have mercy.
Lord, have mercy on us.

Kyrie eleison.
Kyrie eleison.
Kyrie eleison.
Kyrie eleison.

162
From RUSSIA, traditional

Lord, have mercy.
Lord, have mercy.
Lord, have mercy.

Kyrie eleison.
Kyrie eleison.
Kyrie eleison.

163
Brian Doerkson. © 1990 Mercy/Vineyard Publishing
Administered by CopyCare

Purify my heart,
let me be as gold and precious silver;
purify my heart,
let me be as gold, pure gold.
> Refiner's fire, my heart's one desire
> is to be holy,
> set apart for you, Lord;
> I choose to be holy,
> set apart for you, my master,
> ready to do your will.

Purify my heart,
cleanse me from within and make me holy;
purify my heart,
cleanse me from my sin, deep within.
> Refiner's fire . . .

164 Joanne Boyce
© 1995 CJM Music

1. Show mercy to us, loving Father,
   we have sinned against you,
   please make us anew;
   in your love and your grace
     you forgive us;
   Lord, have mercy,
   Lord, have mercy.

2. Look not on our failings, Lord Jesus,
   we have sinned against you,
   please make us anew;
   by your life and your death
     you redeem us;
   Christ have mercy.
   Christ have mercy.

3. Come fill our hearts Holy Spirit,
   we have sinned against you,
   please make us anew;
   forgive us, and heal us, and save us;
   Lord, have mercy,
   Lord, have mercy.

165 Graham Kendrick
© 1997 Make Way Music

1. Who sees it all, before whose gaze
   is darkest night bright as the day;
   watching as in the secret place
   his likeness forms upon a face?

2. Who sees it all, the debt that's owed
   of lives unlived, of love unknown?
   Who weighs the loss of innocence,
   or feels the pain of our offence?
     God sees, God knows.
     God loves the broken heart;
     and holds, and binds, and heals
     the broken heart.

3. Who knows the fears that drive a choice,
   unburies pain and gives it voice?
   And who can wash a memory,
   or take the sting of death away?
     God sees, God knows . . .

4. Whose anger burns at what we've done,
   then bears our sin as if his own?
   Who will receive us as we are,
   whose arms are wide and waiting now?
     God sees, God knows . . .

5. Whose broken heart upon a cross
   Won freedom, joy and peace for us?
   Whose blood redeems, who ever lives
   and all because of love forgives?
     God sees, God knows . . .

166 Ian White. © Kingsway's Thankyou Music Worldwide
excluding Australasia

   You are merciful to me,
   you are merciful to me,
   you are merciful to me, my Lord.
   You are merciful to me . . .

Every day my disobedience
grieves your loving heart;
but then redeeming love breaks through
and causes me to worship you.

(MEN – WOMEN ECHO)
   Redeemer (Redeemer)
   Saviour (Saviour)
   Healer (Healer)
   and Friend (and Friend).
   Every day (every day)
   renew my ways (renew my ways),
   fill me with love (fill me with love)
   that never ends (that never ends).

   You are merciful to me . . .

167 Chris Rolinson
© 1995 CJM Music

You came to heal the broken hearted,
Lord, have mercy.
You came to call the lost and weary,
Christ, have mercy.
You plead for us at Father's right hand,
O Lord, our Lord,
have mercy, have mercy on us.
   Lord have mercy,
   Lord, have mercy,
   have mercy, have mercy on us.

For other items on this theme, see

HYMNS
463 Before I take the body of my Lord
296 Creator of the earth and skies
497 Dear Lord and Father of mankind
502 Glory to you, my God, this night
488 Heal me, hands of Jesus
577 Lord of the church
559 My God, accept my heart this day
385 O sacred head surround
310 To you, O Lord, our hearts we raise
681 Wind of God, dynamic Spirit

PSALMS
682 Create in us clean hearts
545 To you, O Lord, I lift up my soul

SONGS
191 God of grace, I turn my face
333 I believe in Jesus
567 Let me tell you how I need you
614 Lord the light of your love
274 Restore O Lord

ASSURANCE OF GOD'S LOVE
AND MERCY FOR US

HYMNS

168 Charles Wesley
© in this version Jubilate Hymns

1. And can it be that I should gain
   an interest in the Saviour's blood?
   Died he for me, who caused his pain;
   for me, who him to death pursued?
   Amazing love! – how can it be
   that you, my God, should die for me?

2. What mystery here! – the Immortal dies;
   who can explore his strange design?
   In vain the first-born seraph tries
   to sound the depths of love divine.
   What mercy this! – let earth adore;
   let angel minds enquire no more.

3. He left his Father's throne above –
   so free, so infinite his grace –
   emptied himself in all his love
   and bled for Adam's helpless race.
   What mercy this, immense and free,
   for, O my God, it found out me!

4. Long my imprisoned spirit lay,
   fast bound in sin and nature's night;
   your sunrise turned that night to day;
   I woke – the dungeon flamed with light.
   My chains fell off, my heart was new
   I rose, went out and followed you!

5. No condemnation now I dread;
   Jesus, and all in him, is mine!
   Alive in him, my living head,
   and clothed in righteousness divine,
   bold I approach the eternal throne
   and claim the crown
     through Christ my own.

169 Charitie Lees Bancroft

1. Before the throne of God above
   I have a strong, a perfect plea:
   a great high priest, whose name is Love,
   who ever lives and pleads for me.

2. My name is written on his hands,
   my name is hidden in his heart;
   I know that while in heaven he stands
   no power can force me to depart.

3. When Satan tempts me to despair
   and tells me of the guilt within,
   upward I look, and see him there
   who made an end of all my sin.

4. Because the sinless Saviour died,
   my sinful soul is counted free;
   for God, the just, is satisfied
   to look on him and pardon me.

5. Behold him there! the risen Lamb,
   my perfect, sinless Righteousness,
   the great unchangeable I AM,
   the King of glory and of grace!

6. One with my Lord, I cannot die:
   my soul is purchased by his blood,
   my life is safe with Christ on high,
   with Christ, my Saviour and my God.

170 Charles Wesley

1. Christ whose glory fills the skies,
   Christ the true, the only light;
   Sun of righteousness, arise,
   triumph over shades of night:
     Dayspring from on high, be near;
     Daystar, in my heart appear!

2. Dark and cheerless is the dawn
   till your mercy's beams I see;
   joyless is the day's return
   till your glories shine on me:
   as they inward light impart,
   cheer my eyes and warm my heart.

3. Visit then this soul of mine,
   pierce the gloom of sin and grief;
   fill me, radiancy divine,
   scatter all my unbelief:
   more and more yourself display,
   shining to the perfect day!

171 © Christopher Idle/Jubilate Hymns

1. Freedom and life are ours
   for Christ has set us free!
   never again submit to powers
   that lead to slavery:
   Christ is the Lord who breaks
   our chains, our bondage ends,
   Christ is the Rescuer who makes
   the helpless slaves his friends.

2. Called by the Lord to use
   our freedom and be strong,
   not letting liberty excuse
   a life of blatant wrong:
   freed from the law's stern hand
   God's gift of grace to prove,
   know that the law's entire demand
   is gladly met by love.

3. Spirit of God, come, fill,
   emancipate us all!
   speak to us, Word of truth, until
   before your feet we fall:
   glory and liberty
   our Father has decreed,
   and if the Son shall make us free
   we shall be free indeed!

172 From Psalm 32 © Timothy Dudley-Smith

1. Happy are those,
   beyond all measure blessed,
   who know their guilt is gone,
   their faults forgiven;
   who taste the joys
   that come from sin confessed,
   whose hearts are blameless
   in the sight of heaven.
   Blessings are ours
   beneath a Father's hand;
   by love made welcome,
   uncondemned we stand.

2. God is our strength
   when troubles flood the heart;
   from his high throne
   he stoops to hear our prayer.
   When trials come,
   the Lord shall take our part,
   our Rock of refuge
   from the storms of care.
   safely enfolded
   in his keeping strong,
   his sure salvation is our triumph-song.

3. God is our guide
   who watches all our way;
   gently he teaches us our path to find.
   Be not self-willed,
   like beasts that go astray,
   God will direct our feet
   and form our mind:
   mercy embraces us on every side
   with God our joy, our saviour,
   strength and guide.

173 From Romans 8, Michael Perry © Mrs B. Perry/Jubilate Hymns

1. He lives in us, the Christ of God,
   his Spirit joins with ours;
   he brings to us the Father's grace
   with powers beyond our powers.
   so when enticing sin grows strong,
   and human nature fails,
   God's Spirit in our inner self
   fights for us, and prevails.

2. Our pangs of guilt and fears of death
   are Satan's stratagems –
   by Jesus Christ who died for us
   God pardons; who condemns?
   And when we cannot feel our faith,
   nor bring ourselves to pray,
   the Spirit pleads with God for us
   in words we could not say.

3. God gave the Son to save us all –
   no greater love is known!
   and shall that love abandon us
   who have become Christ's own?
   For God has raised him from the grave,
   in this we stand assured;
   so none can tear us from God's love
   in Jesus Christ our Lord.

174 William Edwards and Richard Bewes
Verses 3 and 4 © Richard Bewes/Jubilate Hymns

1. Here is love vast as the ocean,
   loving kindness as the flood,
   when the Prince of life, our ransom,
   shed for us his precious blood.
   Who his love will not remember?
   Who can cease to sing his praise?
   He can never be forgotten
   throughout heaven's eternal days.

2. On the mount of crucifixion
   fountains opened deep and wide;
   through the floodgates of God's mercy
   flowed a vast and gracious tide.
   Grace and love, like mighty rivers,
   poured incessant from above;
   and heaven's peace and perfect justice
   kissed a guilty world in love.

3. Through the years of human darkness,
   shone the lamp the prophets trimmed,
   making known redemption's story,
   of the love of God undimmed.
   Christ for every tongue and nation!
   All must come beneath his sway;
   his the everlasting kingdom
   that shall never pass away.

4. When the stars shall fall from heaven,
   and the sun turn black as night,
   when the skies recede and vanish,
   and the elements ignite.
   Then the Son of Man in glory,
   coming as the Morning Star,
   shall return to claim his loved ones,
   gathered in from near and far.

175 Horatius Bonar
© in this version Jubilate Hymns

1. I bless the Christ of God,
   I rest on love divine,
   and with unfaltering voice and heart
   I call this Saviour mine.

2. For nothing I have done
   can save my guilty soul;
   no burden that my flesh has borne
   can make my spirit whole.

3. Not what I feel or do –
   no toil, nor pain nor blood,
   not all my prayers and sighs and tears
   can give me peace with God.

4. Your work alone, O Christ,
   can ease this weight of sin;
   your blood alone, O Lamb of God,
   can give me peace within.

5. Not love for you, O Lord,
   but your great love for me
   can rid me of this dark unrest
   and set my spirit free.

6. Your voice alone, O God,
   can speak the word of grace
   to calm the tempests in my heart
   and make its raging cease.

7. And so I bless your name,
   I trust your love divine;
   by grace, for all eternity,
   I dare to call you mine.

176 John G. Whittier
© in this version Jubilate Hymns

1. Immortal love for ever full,
   for ever flowing free,
   for ever shared, for ever whole,
   a never-ebbing sea!

2. Upon our lips we bear the name
   all other names above;
   yet love alone knows whence it came,
   that all-embracing love.

3. We may not climb the heavenly steeps
   to bring the Lord Christ down;
   in vain we search the lowest deeps,
   for him no depths can drown.

4. But warm, sweet, tender, even yet
   a present help is he;
   and faith has still its Olivet,
   and love its Galilee.

5. The margin of his robe we feel
   through sorrow and through pain;
   we touch the Lord whose love can heal,
   and we are whole again.

6. Through him the earliest
         prayers are said
   that children's lips can frame;
   the last low whispers of our dead
   are burdened with his name.

7. Alone, O Love no words can tell,
   your saving name is given;
   to turn aside from you is hell,
   to walk with you is heaven!

177 After Niklaus von Zinzendorf, John Wesley
© in this version Jubilate Hymns

1. Jesus, your blood and righteousness
   my beauty are, my glorious dress!
   mid flaming worlds, in these arrayed
   with joy shall I lift up my head.

2. This stainless robe its beauty wears
   when all else fades with passing years;
   no age can change its glorious hue –
   the robe of Christ is ever new.

3. When from dust of death I rise
   to claim my home beyond the skies,
   then this shall be my only plea –
   that Jesus died and lives for me!

4. Bold shall I stand in that great day,
   and none condemn me, try who may:
   fully absolved through Christ I am
   from sin and fear, from guilt and shame.

5. O let the dead now hear your voice,
   let those once lost in sin rejoice!
   their beauty this, their glorious dress:
   Jesus, your blood and righteousness.

178A George Herbert
© in this version Word & Music/Jubilate Hymns

1. King of glory, King of peace
      I will love you;
   since your mercies never cease,
      faith shall prove you!
   You have granted my request,
      you have heard me;
   though my sinful soul transgressed,
      you have spared me.

2. Praises with my utmost art
      I will bring you;
   songs of triumph from my heart
      I will sing you.
   Though my sins against me cried,
      this shall cheer me:
   God in Christ has justified
      and will clear me.

3. Seven whole days – not one in seven –
      I will praise you;
   worship lifts the heart to heaven,
      love obeys you!
   Once you died, when no-one sought
      to console you;
   now eternity's too short
      to extol you!

178B George Herbert
Traditional version

1. King of glory, King of peace
   I will love thee;
   and that love may never cease,
   I will move thee
   Thou hast granted my request,
   thou hast heard me;
   thou didst note my working breast,
   thou hast spared me.

2. Wherefore with my utmost art
   I will sing thee,
   and the cream of all my heart
   I will bring thee.
   Though my sins against me cried,
   thou didst clear me,
   and alone, when they replied,
   thou didst hear me.

3. Seven whole days, not one in seven,
   I will praise thee;
   in my heart, though not in heaven,
   I can raise thee.
   Small it is, in this poor sort
   to enrol thee;
   e'en eternity's too short
   to extol thee.

179 Charles Wesley

1. Love divine, all loves excelling,
   joy of heaven, to earth come down:
   fix in us your humble dwelling,
   all your faithful mercies crown.

2. Jesus, you are all compassion,
   boundless love that makes us whole:
   visit us with your salvation,
   enter every trembling soul.

3. Come, almighty to deliver,
   let us all your grace receive;
   suddenly return, and never,
   never more your temple leave.

4. You we would be always blessing,
   serve you as your hosts above,
   pray, and praise you without ceasing,
   glory in your perfect love.

5. Finish then your new creation;
   pure and sinless let us be;
   let us see your great salvation,
   perfect in eternity:

6. Changed from glory into glory
   till in heaven we take our place,
   there to cast our crowns before you,
   lost in wonder, love and praise!

180 Luke Connaughton
© McCrimmon Publishing Co.

1. Love is his word, love is his way,
   feasting with all, fasting alone,
   living and dying, rising again,
   love, only love, is his way:
   Richer than gold
   is the love of my Lord,
   better than splendour and wealth.

2. Love is his way, love is his mark,
   sharing his last Passover feast,
   Christ at his table, host to the twelve,
   love, only love, is his mark:
   Richer than gold . . .

3. Love is his mark, love is his sign,
   bread for our strength, wine for our joy,
   'This is my body, this is my blood' –
   love, only love, is his sign:
   Richer than gold . . .

4. Love is his sign, love is his news,
   'Do this,' he said, 'lest you forget
   all my deep sorrow, all my dear blood' –
   love, only love, is his news:
   Richer than gold . . .

5. Love is his news, love is his name,
   we are his own, chosen and called,
   family, brethren, cousins and kin,
   love, only love, is his name:
   Richer than gold . . .

6. Love is his name, love is his law,
   hear his command, all who are his:
   'Love one another, I have loved you' –
   love, only love, is his law.
   Richer than gold . . .

7. Love is his law, love is his word:
   love of the Lord, Father and Word,
   love of the Spirit, God ever one,
   love, only love, is his word:
       Richer than gold . . .

181 © Timothy Dudley-Smith

1. No weight of gold or silver
   can measure human worth;
   no soul secures its ransom
   with all the wealth of earth:
   no sinners find their freedom
   but by the gift unpriced,
   the Lamb of God unblemished,
   the precious blood of Christ.

2. Our sins, our griefs and troubles
   he bore and made his own;
   we hid our faces from him,
   rejected and alone.
   His wounds are for our healing,
   our peace is by his pain:
   behold, the Man of sorrows,
   the Lamb for sinners slain!

3. In Christ the past is over,
   a new world now begins;
   with him we rise to freedom
   who saves us from our sins.
   We live by faith in Jesus
   to make his glory known:
   behold, the Man of sorrows,
   the Lamb upon his throne!

182 Michael Perry./Jubilate Hymns
© Mrs B. Perry/Jubilate Hymns

1. Not the grandeur of the mountains,
   nor the splendour of the sea,
   can excel the ceaseless wonder
   of my Saviour's love to me:
       for his love to me is faithful,
       and his mercy is divine;
       and his truth is everlasting,
       and his perfect peace is mine.

2. Not the streams that fill the valleys,
   nor the clouds that drift along,
   can delight me more than Jesus
   or replace my grateful song:
       for his love . . .

3. Yet these all convey his beauty
   and proclaim his power and grace –
   for they are among the tokens
   of the love upon his face:
       for his love . . .

183 Samuel T. Francis
© in this version Jubilate Hymns

1. Oh, the deep, deep love of Jesus!
   Vast, unmeasured, boundless, free,
   rolling as a mighty ocean
   in its fullness over me:
   underneath me, all around me,
   is the current of his love,
   leading onward, leading homeward,
   to my glorious rest above.

2. Oh, the deep, deep love of Jesus!
   Spread his love from shore to shore:
   how he loves us, ever loves us,
   changes never, nevermore,
   watches over all his loved ones,
   whom he died to call his own,
   ever for them interceding,
   at his heavenly Father's throne.

3. Oh, the deep, deep love of Jesus!
   Love of every love the best:
   vast the ocean of his blessing,
   sweet the haven of his rest!
   Oh, the deep, deep love of Jesus,
   very heaven of heavens to me,
   and it lifts me up to glory,
   evermore his face to see.

184 Bryn Rees
© Alexander Scott

1. The kingdom of God
       is justice and joy;
   for Jesus restores
       what sin would destroy.
   God's power and glory
       in Jesus we know;
   and here and hereafter
       the kingdom shall grow.

2. The kingdom of God
   is mercy and grace;
   the captives are freed,
   the sinners find place,
   the outcast are welcomed
   God's banquet to share;
   and hope is awakened
   in place of despair.

3. The kingdom of God
   is challenge and choice:
   believe the good news,
   repent and rejoice!
   His love for us sinners
   brought Christ to his cross:
   our crisis of judgement
   for gain or for loss.

4. God's kingdom is come,
   the gift and the goal;
   in Jesus begun,
   in heaven made whole.
   The heirs of the kingdom
   shall answer his call;
   and all things cry 'Glory!'
   to God all in all.

185 Brian Foley. © 1971 Faber Music
Reprinted from the *New Catholic Hymnal* by
permission of the publishers

1. There is no moment of my life,
   no place where I may go,
   no action which God does not see,
   no thought he does not know.

2. Before I speak, my words are known,
   and all that I decide,
   to come or go: God knows my choice,
   and makes himself my guide.

3. If I should close my eyes to him,
   he comes to give me sight;
   if I should go where all is dark,
   he makes my darkness light.

4. He knew my days before all days,
   before I came to be;
   he keeps me, loves me, in my ways –
   no lover such as he.

186 John L. Bell and Graham Maule
© 1988 WGRG, Iona Community, from *Enemy of Apathy* (Wild Goose Publications 1988)

1. The love of God comes close
   where stands an open door
   to let the stranger in,
   to mingle rich and poor.
   The love of God is here to stay,
   embracing those who walk his way.

2. The peace of God comes close
   to those caught in the storm,
   forgoing lives of ease
   to ease the lives forlorn.
   The peace of God is here to stay,
   embracing those who walk his way.

3. The joy of God comes close
   where faith encounters fears,
   where heights and depths of life
   are found through smiles and tears.
   The joy of God is here to stay,
   embracing those who walk his way.

4. The grace of God comes close
   to those whose grace is spent,
   when hearts are tired or sore
   and hope is bruised and bent.
   The grace of God is here to stay,
   embracing those who walk his way.

5. The Son of God comes close
   where people praise his name,
   where bread and wine are blest
   and shared as when he came.
   The Son of God is here to stay,
   embracing those who walk his way.

187 © Randle Manwaring

1. With loving hands,
   at work among the suffering
   and broken hearts, he ministers,
   who is their king.

2. With wounded hands,
   outstretched upon a cruel tree,
   he lies and then is lifted up
   in agony.

3. With pleading hands,
   towards the world he longs to bless,
   he waits, with heaven's life to fill
   our emptiness.

188 Frederick W. Faber
© in this version Jubilate Hymns

1. There's a wideness in God's mercy
   like the wideness of the sea;
   there's a kindness in his justice
   which is more than liberty.

2. There is no place where earth's sorrows
   are more keenly felt than heaven;
   there is no place where earth's failings
   have such gracious judgement given.

3. There is plentiful redemption
   through the blood that Christ has shed;
   there is joy for all the members
   in the sorrows of the head.

4. For the love of God is broader
   than the measure of our mind,
   and the heart of the eternal
   is most wonderfully kind.

5. If our love were but more simple
   we should take him at his word,
   and our lives would be illumined
   by the glory of the Lord.

SONGS

189 From Lamentations 3
© D. A. Carson

Because of the Lord's great love.
because of the Lord's great love,
because of the Lord's great love,
we are not consumed.
His mercies never fail,
his mercies never fail,
his mercies never fail,
we are not consumed.

For him I therefore will wait –
his faithfulness is great,
and his mercies are fresh
   as the morning's dawn.
For him I therefore will wait –
his faithfulness is great,
and I say to myself the Lord is your song!

190 From John 1:29.
© 1995 WGRG, Iona Community, from *Come all you people* (Wild Goose Publications 1995)

Behold the Lamb of God,
behold the Lamb of God.
He takes away the sin,
the sin of the world.

191 Chris Bowater
© 1990 Sovereign Lifestyle Music

1. God of grace, I turn my face
   to you – I cannot hide;
   my nakedness, my shame, my guilt,
   are all before your eyes.

2. Strivings and all anguished dreams
   in rags lie at my feet,
   and only grace provides the way
   for me to stand complete.
      And your grace clothes me
         in righteousness,
      and your mercy covers me in love;
      your life adorns and beautifies –
      I stand complete in you.

192 Paul Oakley
© 1997 Kingsway's Thankyou Music

1. Here I am, and I have come
   to thank you Lord, for all you've done:
   thank you Lord;
   you paid the price at Calvary,
   you shed your blood, you set me free:
   thank you, Lord;
   no greater love was ever shown,
   no better life ever was laid down.
      And I will always love your name,
      and I will always sing your praise;
      and I will always love your name,
      and I will always sing your praise.

2. You took my sin, you took my shame,
   you drank my cup, you bore my pain;
   thank you Lord;
   you broke the curse,
       you broke the chains,
   in victory from death you rose again:
   thank you, Lord;
   and not by works, but by your grace
   you clothe me now
       in your righteousness.
       And I will always love your name,
       and I will always sing your praise;
       and I will always love your name,
       and I will always sing your praise.

3. You bid me come, you make me whole,
   you give me peace, you restore my soul;
   thank you, Lord;
   you fill me up, and when I'm full
   you give me more till I overflow;
   thank you, Lord;
   you're making me to be like you,
   to do the works of the Father, too.
       And I will always love your name . . .

193 Stuart Townend
© 1995 Kingsway's Thankyou Music

1. How deep the Father's love for us,
   how vast beyond all measure,
   that he should give his only Son
   to make a wretch his treasure.
   How great the pain of searing loss;
   the Father turns his face away
   as wounds, which mar the chosen one,
   bring many sons to glory.

2. Behold the man upon a cross,
   my sin upon his shoulders;
   ashamed, I hear my mocking voice
   call out among the scoffers.
   It was my sin that held him there
   until it was accomplished;
   his dying breath has brought me life –
   I know that it is finished.

3. I will not boast in anything,
   no gifts, no power, no wisdom;
   but I will boast in Jesus Christ,
   his death and resurrection.
   Why should I gain from his reward?
   I cannot give an answer;
   but this I know with all my heart –
   his wounds have paid my ransom.

194 Graham Kendrick
© 1989 Make Way Music

1. My Lord, what love is this
   that pays so dearly:
   that I, the guilty one
   may go free!
       Amazing love, oh what sacrifice,
       the Son of God given for me!
       My debt he pays
           and my death he dies
       that I might live,
       that I might live.

2. And so, they watched him die
   despised, rejected:
   but oh, the blood he shed
   flowed for me!
       Amazing love . . .

3. And now this love of Christ
   shall flow like rivers:
   come, wash your guilt away,
   live again!
       Amazing love . . .

195 Geoff Bullock. © 1997 Watershed
Productions/Kingsway's Thankyou Music

1. Oh, the mercy of God,
       the glory of grace,
   that you chose to redeem us,
       to forgive and restore;
   and you call us your children,
       chosen in him
   to be holy and blameless
       to the glory of God.
       To the praise of his glorious grace,
       to the praise of his glory and power:
       to him be all glory, honour and praise
       for ever and ever and ever, amen!

2. Oh, the richness of grace,
     the depths of his love,
in him is redemption,
     the forgiveness of sin;
you called us as righteous,
     predestined in him
for the praise of his glory,
     included in Christ.
     To the praise of his glorious grace . . .

3. Oh, the glory of God
     expressed in his Son,
his image and likeness
     revealed to us all;
the plea of the ages
     completed in Christ:
that we be presented
     perfected in him.
     To the praise of his glorious grace . . .

196 Gerrit Gustafson. © 1990 Integrity's Hosanna! Music/ Kingsway's Thankyou Music. For UK only

Only by grace can we enter,
only by grace can we stand;
not by our human endeavour,
but by the blood of the Lamb.
Into your presence you call us,
you call us to come;
into your presence you draw us,
and now by your grace we come,
now by your grace we come.

    Lord, if you mark our transgressions,
    who would stand?
    Thanks to your grace we are cleansed
    by the blood of the Lamb.
    Lord, if you mark . . .

Only by grace . . .

197 Martin Smith. © 1994 Curious? Music UK Administered by Kingsway's Thankyou Music Worldwide (excluding USA)

Over the mountains and the sea,
your river runs with love for me,
and I will open up my heart
and let the healer set me free.
I'm happy to be in the truth,
and I will daily lift my hands:
for I will always sing of when
your love come down.

I could sing of your love for ever,
I could sing of your love for ever,
I could sing of your love for ever,
I could sing of your love for ever.

Over the mountains . . .

    Oh, I feel like dancing –
    it's foolishness, I know;
    but, when the world has seen the light,
    they will dance with joy,
    like we're dancing now.

I could sing of your love for ever . . .

198 Graham Kendrick © 1985 Kingsway's Thankyou Music

1. Thank you for the cross,
the price you paid for us;
how you gave yourself
so completely.
Precious Lord, (precious Lord,)
now our sins are gone,
all forgiven,
covered by your blood;
all forgotten –
thank you Lord, (thank you Lord).

    Oh I love you, Lord,
    really love you, Lord.
    I will never understand
    why you love me.
    You're my deepest joy,
    you're my heart's desire,
    and the greatest thing of all,
    O Lord, I see –
    you delight in me!

2. For our healing there,
Lord, you suffered;
and to take our fear
you poured out your love.
Precious Lord, (precious Lord,)
Calvary's work is done,
you have conquered;
able now to save
so completely –
thank you Lord, (thank you Lord).
    Oh I love you, Lord . . .

For other items on this theme, see

HYMNS

379 A purple robe
661 All for Jesus, all for Jesus
662 All-creating heavenly Giver
 26 Amazing grace
168 And can it be that I should gain
553 As water to the thirsty
446 Born by the Holy Spirit's breath
170 Christ whose glory fills the skies
663 Come down O Love divine
453 Dear Christ, uplifted from the earth
527 Eternal light, Eternal light!
 39 Great is your faithfulness
435 Hark the glad sound! – the Saviour comes
 42 How sweet the name of Jesus sounds
437 I cannot tell you why he whom angels worship
406 I know that my redeemer lives
557 It is a thing most wonderful
201 Jesus, lover of my soul
507 Just as I am, without one plea
 49 Let us love and sing and wonder
356 Lord you were rich beyond all splendour
 52 Lord, enthroned in heavenly splendour
383 Man of sorrows!
240 Mercy in our time of failure
537 My hope is built on nothing less
203 My Lord, you called my name
384 My song is love unknown
385 O sacred head surround
150 Rock of ages, cleft for me
 3 Thanks be to God
188 There's a wideness in God's mercy
646 What a friend we have in Jesus
152 What offering shall we give
680 When I survey the wondrous cross
392 When you prayed beneath the trees

PSALMS

513 Because the Lord is my shepherd
 81 Come rejoice before your maker
 82 From all who live beneath
312 Let us gladly with one mind
 93 Praise my soul the king of heaven
205 The king of love my shepherd is
206 The Lord's my shepherd
207 The Lord's my shepherd: I'll not want
100 Timeless love! We sing the story

SONGS

685 All my ways
546 All who are thirsty
610 Far and near
191 God of grace I turn my face
192 Here I am
518 How can I be free from sin
130 My lips shall praise you

194 My Lord what love is this
195 Oh, the mercy of God
216 Such love
137 Thank you for saving me
218 There is none like you
220 We worship and adore you
221 What kind of greatness
141 Who is there like you?
142 Who paints the skies?
165 Who sees it all
696 You know me

ADORATION

HYMNS

199 From the German, Lilian Stevenson
By permission of Oxford University Press

1. Fairest Lord Jesus,
   Lord of all creation,
   Jesus, of God and man the Son;
   you will I cherish,
   you will I honour,
   you are my soul's delight and crown.

2. Fair are the rivers,
   meadows and forests
   clothed in the fresh
      green robes of spring;
   Jesus is fairer,
   Jesus is purer,
   he makes the saddest heart to sing.

3. Fair is the sunrise,
   starlight and moonlight
   spreading their glory across the sky;
   Jesus shines brighter,
   Jesus shines clearer,
   than all the heavenly host on high.

4. All fairest beauty,
   heavenly and earthly,
   Jesus, my Lord, in you I see;
   none can be nearer,
   fairer or dearer,
   than you, my Saviour, are to me.

200 Daniel T. Niles
© Christian Conference of Asia

1. Father in heaven,
   grant to your children
   mercy and blessing,
   songs never ceasing;
   love to unite us,
   grace to redeem us,
      Father in heaven,
      Father, our God.

2. Jesus redeemer,
   may we remember
   your gracious passion,
   your resurrection:
   worship we bring you,
   praise we shall sing you,
      Jesus redeemer,
      Jesus, our Lord.

3. Spirit descending,
   whose is the blessing,
   strength for the weary,
   help for the needy:
   sealing Christ's Lordship,
   blessing our worship,
      Spirit descending,
      Spirit adored.

201 Charles Wesley
© in this version Jubilate Hymns

1. Jesus, lover of my soul,
   let me to your presence fly,
   while the gathering waters roll,
   while the tempest still is high.
   Hide me, O my Saviour, hide,
   till the storm of life is past;
   safe into the haven, guide
   and receive my soul at last.

2. Other refuge have I none,
   all my hope in you I see;
   leave, O leave me, not alone;
   still support and comfort me.
   All my trust on you is stayed,
   all my help from you I bring:
   cover my defenceless head
   with the shadow of your wing.

3. You, O Christ, are all I want,
   more than all in you I find:
   raise the fallen, cheer the faint,
   heal the sick and lead the blind.
   Just and holy is your name,
   I am all unworthiness;
   false and full of sin I am,
   you are full of truth and grace.

4. Plenteous grace with you is found,
   grace to wash away my sin:
   let the healing streams abound;
   make and keep me clean within.
   Living Fountain, now impart
   all your life and purity;
   spring for ever in my heart,
   rise to all eternity!

202 Frederick W. Faber
© in this version Jubilate Hymns

1. My God, how wonderful you are,
   your majesty how bright;
   how beautiful your mercy-seat
   in depths of burning light!

2. Creator from eternal years
   and everlasting Lord,
   by holy angels day and night
   unceasingly adored!

3. How wonderful, how beautiful
   the sight of you must be –
   your endless wisdom, boundless power,
   and awesome purity!

4. O how I fear you, living God,
   with deepest, tenderest fears,
   and worship you with trembling hope
   and penitential tears!

5. But I may love you too, O Lord,
   though you are all-divine,
   for you have stooped to ask of me
   this feeble love of mine.

6. Father of Jesus, love's reward,
   great King upon your throne,
   what joy to see you as you are
   and know as I am known!

203 Martin E. Leckebusch
© Kevin Mayhew

1. My Lord, you called my name
   before the world began,
   and chose that I should be
   included in your plan.

2. How well you know my heart;
   its hidden depths you see;
   and yet you love me still
   and freely pardon me.

3. You feel my every care,
   each hope and each desire;
   my burdens you relieve,
   new visions you inspire.

4. From long before my birth
   my every path you knew –
   I bless you that you turned
   my footsteps back to you!

204 John Monsell
© in this version Jubilate Hymns

1. O worship the Lord
      in the beauty of holiness,
   bow down before him,
      his glory proclaim;
   with gold of obedience
      and incense of lowliness,
   kneel and adore him –
      the Lord is his name.

2. Low at his feet
      lay your burden of carefulness,
   high on his heart he will bear it for you,
   comfort your sorrows
      and answer your prayerfulness,
   guiding your steps
      in the way that is true.

3. Fear not to enter
      his courts in the slenderness
   of the poor wealth
      you would count as your own;
   truth in its beauty
      and love in its tenderness –
   these are the offerings
      to bring to his throne.

4. These, though we bring them
      in trembling and fearfulness,
   he will accept for the name that is dear;
   mornings of joy
      give for evenings of tearfulness,
   trust for our trembling
      and hope for our fear.

5. O worship the Lord
      in the beauty of holiness,
   bow down before him,
      his glory proclaim;
   with gold of obedience
      and incense of lowliness,
   kneel and adore him –
      the Lord is his name.

PSALMS

205 From Psalm 23, Henry Baker
© in this version Jubilate Hymns

1. The king of love my shepherd is,
   whose goodness fails me never;
   I nothing lack if I am his
   and he is mine for ever.

2. Where streams of living water flow
   a ransomed soul, he leads me;
   and where the fertile pastures grow,
   with food from heaven feeds me.

3. Perverse and foolish I have strayed,
   but in his love he sought me;
   and on his shoulder gently laid,
   and home, rejoicing, brought me.

4. In death's dark vale I fear no ill
   with you, dear Lord, beside me;
   your rod and staff my comfort still,
   your cross before to guide me.

5. You spread a banquet in my sight
   of grace beyond all knowing.
   and, oh, the wonder and delight
   from your pure chalice flowing!

6. And so through all the length of days
   your goodness fails me never:
   Good Shepherd, may I sing your praise
   within your house for ever!

206 From Psalm 23, Stuart Townend
© 1996 Kingsway's Thankyou Music

1. The Lord's my shepherd: I'll not want;
   he makes me lie in pastures green,
   he leads me by the still, still waters,
   his goodness restores my soul.

      And I will trust in you alone,
      and I will trust in you alone,
      for your endless mercy follows me,
      your goodness will lead me home.

   (Descant)
      I will trust, I will trust in you,
      I will trust, I will trust in you:
      endless mercy follows me,
      goodness will lead me home.

2. He guides my ways in righteousness,
   and he anoints my head with oil;
   and my cup – it overflows with joy,
   I feast on his pure delights.
      And I will trust in you alone . . .

3. And though I walk the darkest path –
   I will not fear the evil one,
   for you are with me,
      and your rod and staff
   are the comfort I need to know.
      And I will trust in you alone . . .

207 From Psalm 23, William Whittingham and others

1. The Lord's my shepherd: I'll not want;
   he makes me down to lie
   in pastures green: he leadeth me
   the quiet waters by.

2. My soul he doth restore again,
   and me to walk doth make
   within the paths of righteousness,
   e'en for his own name's sake.

3. Yea, though I walk
      through death's dark vale,
   yet will I fear no ill;
   for thou art with me, and thy rod
   and staff me comfort still.

4. My table thou hast furnishèd
   in presence of my foes;
   my head with oil thou dost anoint
   and my cup overflows.

5. Goodness and mercy all my life
   shall surely follow me;
   and in God's house for evermore
   my dwelling-place shall be.

SONGS

208 © Ateliers et Presses de Taizé

Adoramus te Domine.
We adore you, Lord Jesus Christ.

209 From South Africa, traditional liturgical text

Alleluia, alleluia.
Alleluia, alleluia.
Alleluia,
alleluia.
Alleluia, alleluia.

210 From Argentina, unknown
English and Spanish © Copyright Control

Holy, holy, holy,
my heart, my heart adores you!
My heart is glad to say the words:
you are holy, Lord.
Santo, santo, santo
mi corazón te adora!
Mi corazón te sabe decire:
santo eres Sênor.

211 John L. Bell and Graham Maule
© 1988 WGRG, Iona Community, from *Enemy of apathy* (Wild Goose Publications 1988)

Holy, holy, holy Lord of power and might.
Heaven, earth, heaven and earth
   are full of your glory.
All glory to your name,
all glory to your name.
Blessed, blessed is he
   who comes in the name of the Lord.

Blessed, blessed is he
   who comes in the name of the Lord.
Hosanna in the highest,
   hosanna in the highest.

212 Andy Park. © 1995 Mercy/ Vineyard Publishing
Administered by CopyCare.

1. I am standing beneath your wings,
   I am resting in your shelter;
   your great faithfulness has
      been my shield
   and it makes me want to sing:
      Blessed be the name of the Lord,
      blessed be the name of the Lord.
   I will bless your holy name
      for all my days;
      blessed be the name of the Lord.

2. I sing praises to your name, O Lord,
   for you daily bear my burdens;
   your great faithfulness is my reward
   and it makes me want to sing:
      Blessed be the name . . .

213 David Ruis. © 1993 Shade Tree Music/Maranatha!
Music. Administered by CopyCare

1. I will worship (I will worship)
   with all of my heart (with all of my heart);
   I will praise you (I will praise you)
   with all of my strength (all my strength).
   I will seek you (I will seek you)
   all of my days (all of my days);
   I will follow (I will follow)
   all of your ways (all your ways).
      I will give you all my worship,
      I will give you all my praise;
      you alone I long to worship,
      you alone are worthy of my praise.

2. I will bow down (I will bow down) –
   hail you as king (hail you as king);
   I will serve you (I will serve you),
   give you everthing (everything);
   I will lift up (I will lift up)
   my eyes to your throne
      (my eyes to your throne);
   I will trust you (I will trust you),
   I will trust you alone (trust you alone).
      I will give you . . .

214 Sondra Corbett. © 1983 Integrity's Hosanna! Music/Kingsway's Thankyou Music. For UK only

I worship you, almighty God,
there is none like you;
I worship you, O Prince of Peace –
that is what I love to do.
I give you praise,
for you are my righteousness;
I worship you, almighty God,
there is none like you.

215 John Barnett. © 1980 Mercy/Vineyard Publishing Administered by CopyCare

Jesus, Jesus,
holy and anointed One, Jesus;
Jesus, Jesus,
risen and exalted One, Jesus:
  your name is like honey on my lips,
  your Spirit like water to my soul;
  your word is a lamp unto my feet –
  Jesus, I love you, I love you.

Jesus, Jesus . . .

216 Graham Kendrick © 1988 Make Way Music

1. Such love, pure as the whitest snow,
    such love weeps for the shame I know,
    such love, paying the debt I owe –
      O Jesus, such love!

2. Such love, stilling my restlessness,
    such love, filling my emptiness,
    such love, showing me holiness –
      O Jesus, such love!

3. Such love springs from eternity,
    such love, streaming through history,
    such love, fountain of life to me:
      O Jesus, such love!

217 © 1992, 1994 Anne Quigley. Published by OCP Publications

  There is a longing
    in our hearts, O Lord,
  for you to reveal yourself to us.
  There is a longing
    in our hearts for love
  we only find in you, our God.

1. For justice, for freedom,
    for mercy, hear our prayer.
    In sorrow, in grief,
    be near, hear our prayer, O God.
    There is a longing . . .

2. For wisdom, for courage,
    for comfort, hear our prayer.
    In weakness, in fear:
    be near, hear our prayer, O God.
    There is a longing . . .

3. For healing, for wholeness,
    for new life; hear our prayer.
    In sickness, in death;
    be near, hear our prayer, O God.
    There is a longing . . .

4. Lord, save us, take pity,
    light in our darkness.
    We call you, we wait;
    be near, hear our prayer, O God.
    There is a longing . . .

218 Lenny Le Blanc. © 1991 Integrity's Hosanna! Music Administered by Kingsway's Thankyou Music For UK only

  There is none like you –
  no one else can touch
    my heart like you do;
  I could search for all eternity long
  and find there is none like you.

Your mercy flows like a river wide,
and healing comes from your hands.
Suffering children are safe in your arms;
there is none like you.
  There is none like you . . .

219 Viola Grafstrom
© 1996 Kingsway's Thankyou Music

We bow down and confess
you are Lord in this place;
we bow down and confess
you are Lord in this place.

You are all I need,
it's your face I seek;
in the presence of your light
we bow down, we bow down.

We bow down and confess . . .

220 Andy Piercy (verse 3 Cecil Alexander)
© 1994 IQ Music

We worship and adore you, Lord –
hear us when we call,
for there is no god above you,
you are the Lord of all.

1. But how can we begin to express
what's on our hearts?
There are no words enough, Lord,
for us to even start.

2. The tongues of men and angels
we need, to sing your praise,
so that we may glorify your name
through heaven's eternal days.

3. There was no other good enough
to pay the price of sin,
you, only, could unlock
the gate of heaven and let us in.
So, we worship and adore you . . .

221 Graham Kendrick
© 1994 Make Way Music

1. What kind of greatness can this be
that chose to be made small,
exchanging untold majesty
for a world so pitiful;
that God should come as one of us
I'll never understand,
the more I hear the story told
the more amazed I am.

O what else can I do
but kneel and worship you,
and come just as I am –
my whole life an offering.

2. The one in whom we live and move
in swaddling cloths lies bound,
the voice that cried 'let there be light',
asleep without a sound;
the one who strode among the stars
and called each one by name
lies helpless in a mother's arms
and must learn to walk again.
O what else can I do . . .

3. What greater love could he have shown
to shamed humanity,
yet human pride hates to believe
in such deep humility;
but nations now may see his grace,
and know that he is near,
when his meek heart,
his words, his works
are incarnate in us here.
O what else can I do . . .

222 Matt Redman
© 1997 Kingsway's Thankyou Music

When the music fades,
all is stripped away
and I simply come,
longing just to bring
something that's of worth
that will bless your heart.

I'll bring you more than a song,
for a song in itself is not
what you have required.
You search much deeper within,
through the way things appear;
you're looking into my heart.

I'm coming back to the
   heart of worship,
and it's all about you,
all about you, Jesus.
I'm sorry, Lord,
   for the thing I've made it,
when it's all about you,
all about you, Jesus.

King of endless worth,
no-one could express
how much you deserve.
Though I'm weak and poor,
all I have is yours, every single breath.

I'll bring you more . . .

   I'm coming back . . .

For other items on this theme, see

HYMNS
378 Ah, holy Jesus, how have you offended
553 As water to the thirsty
346 Brightest and best of the sons of the morning
348 Come and sing the Christmas story
663 Come down O Love divine
174 Here is love vast as the ocean
290 Holy, holy, holy, Lord God almighty!
406 I know that my redeemer lives
535 Jesus, priceless treasure
356 Lord, you were rich beyond all splendour
384 My song is love unknown
185 There is no moment
392 When you prayed beneath the trees

PSALMS
513 Because the Lord is my shepherd
514 O God, you search me
316 With wonder, Lord, we see your works

SONGS
420 All heaven declares
562 All I once held dear
242 Be still
 18 Be still and know that I am God
393 Come and see
 10 Come, now is the time to worship
547 Faithful one
107 Father God I wonder
108 Give thanks with a grateful heart
193 How deep the Father's love for us
394 Jesus Christ, I think upon your sacrifice
566 Jesus lover of my soul
334 Jesus, what a beautiful name
689 Lord I come to you
125 Lord, I come before your throne of grace
395 Meekness and Majesty
128 My heart is full of admiration
194 My Lord what love is this
427 No scenes of stately majesty
569 O Lord your tenderness
137 Thank you for saving me
198 Thank you for the cross
523 To be in your presence
696 You know me

READING FROM SCRIPTURE

HYMNS

223 © Timothy Dudley-Smith

1. Faith and truth and life bestowing,
     open now the Scriptures, Lord,
   seed to life eternal sowing
     scattered on the wind abroad.
   Let not hearts, your word receiving,
     like a barren field be found,
   choked with thorns and unbelieving,
     shallow earth or stony ground.

2. May the Spirit's power unceasing
     bring to life the hidden grain,
   daily in our hearts increasing,
     bearing fruit that shall remain.
   So in Scripture, song and story,
     Saviour, may your voice be heard.
   Till our eyes behold your glory
     give us ears to hear your word.

224 Anne Steele

1. Father of mercies, in your word
   what endless glory shines!
   For ever be your name adored
   for these celestial lines.

2. Here may the blind and hungry come
   and light and food receive;
   here shall the humble guest find room
   and taste and see and live.

3. Here the redeemer's welcome voice
   spreads heavenly peace around,
   and life and everlasting joys
   attend the glorious sound.

4. Here springs of consolation rise
   to cheer the fainting mind,
   and thirsty souls receive supplies
   and sweet refreshment find.

5. Divine instructor, gracious Lord,
   be now and always near:
   teach us to love your sacred word
   and view our Saviour here.

225 George Briggs
© 1953, renewal 1981 The Hymn Society of America/
Hope Publishing Co. Administered by CopyCare

1. God has spoken – by his prophets,
   spoken his unchanging word;
   each from age to age proclaiming
   God the one, the righteous Lord;
   in the world's despair and turmoil
   one firm anchor still holds fast:
   God is King, his throne eternal,
   God the first and God the last.

2. God has spoken – by Christ Jesus,
   Christ, the everlasting Son;
   brightness of the Father's glory,
   with the Father ever one:
   spoken by the Word incarnate,
   Life, before all time began,
   light of light, to earth descending,
   God, revealed as Son of Man.

3. God is speaking – by his Spirit
   speaking to our hearts again;
   in the age-long word expounding
   God's own message, now as then.
   Through the rise and fall of nations
   one sure faith is standing fast:
   God abides, his word unchanging,
   God the first and God the last.

226 William Reid Jnr
© 1959, renewal 1987 The Hymn Society/
Hope Publishing Co. Administered by CopyCare

1. Help us, O Lord, to learn
   the truths your word imparts,
   to study that your laws may be
   inscribed upon our hearts.

2. Help us, O Lord, to live
   the faith which we proclaim,
   that all our thoughts
     and words and deeds
   may glorify your name.

3. Help us, O Lord, to teach
   the beauty of your ways,
   that yearning souls may find the Christ
   and sing aloud his praise.

227 © Christopher Idle/Jubilate Hymns

1. How sure the Scriptures are!
   God's vital, urgent word,
   as true as steel, and far
   more sharp than any sword:
     So deep and fine,
     at his control
     they pierce where soul
     and spirit join.

2. They test each human thought,
   refining like a fire;
   they measure what we ought
   to do and to desire:
     For God knows all –
     exposed it lies
     before his eyes
     to whom we call.

3. Let those who hear his voice
   confronting them today,
   reject the tempting choice
   of doubting or delay:
     For God speaks still –
     his word is clear,
     so let us hear
     and do his will!

228 © Christopher Idle/Jubilate Hymns

1. Powerful in making us wise to salvation,
   witness to faith in Christ Jesus the Word;
   breathed out for all
     by the life-giving Father –
   these are the scriptures,
     and thus speaks the Lord.

2. Hammer for action
     and compass for travel,
   map in the desert and lamp in the dark;
   teaching, rebuking,
     correcting and training –
   these are the scriptures,
     and this is their work.

3. Prophecy, history, song
     and commandment,
   gospel and letter
     and dream from on high;
   Words of the wise who
     were steered by the Spirit –
   these are the scriptures,
     on them we rely.

4. Gift for God's servants
     to fit them completely,
   fully equipping to walk in his ways;
   guide to good work
     and effective believing –
   these are the scriptures,
     for these we give praise!

229
R. T. Brooks
© 1954, renewal 1982 Hope Publishing Co.
Administered by CopyCare

1. Thanks to God whose word was spoken
   in the deed that made the earth;
   his the voice that called a nation,
   his the fires that tried its worth.
     God has spoken:
   praise him for his open word.

2. Thanks to God whose Word incarnate
   heights and depths of life did share;
   deeds and words and death and rising
   grace in human form declare.
     God has spoken:
   praise him for his open word!

3. Thanks to God whose word was written
   in the Bible's sacred page,
   record of the revelation
   showing God to every age.
     God has spoken:
   praise him for his open word!

4. Thanks to God whose word is published
in the tongues of every race;
see its glory undiminished
by the change of time or place.
God has spoken:
praise him for his open word!

5. Thanks to God whose word is answered
by the Spirit's voice within;
here we drink of joy unmeasured,
life redeemed from death and sin.
God is speaking:
praise him for his open word!

PSALM

230 From Psalm 19, Isaac Watts

1. The heavens declare your glory, Lord!
in every star your wisdom shines;
but when our eyes behold your word,
we read your name in clearer lines.

2. Sun, moon, and stars convey your praise
to all the earth, and never stand;
so when your truth began its race,
it touched and glanced on every land.

3. Nor shall your spreading gospel rest
till through the world your truth has run;
till Christ has all the nations blessed
who see the light or feel the sun.

4. Great Sun of righteousness, arise
and bless the world with heavenly light!
your gospel makes the simple wise,
your laws are pure,
your judgements right.

5. Your noblest wonders here we view
in souls renewed and sins forgiven:
Lord, cleanse my sins, my soul renew,
and make your word
my guide to heaven.

SONGS

231 From Psalm 43:3. John L. Bell
© 1995 WGRG, Iona Community, from *Come all you people* (Wild Goose Publications, 1995)

Send out your light, Lord, send your truth
to be my guide;
then let them lead me to the place
where you reside.

232 Graham Kendrick
© 1991 Make Way Music

1. Now in reverence and awe
we gather round your word;
in wonder we draw near
to mysteries that angels strain to hear,
that prophets dimly saw:
so let your Spirit shine upon the page
and teach me;
open up my eyes
with truth to free me,
light to chase the lies.
Lord Jesus, let me meet you
in your word;
Lord Jesus, let me meet you
in your word.

2. Lord, your truth cannot be chained;
it searches everything –
my secrets, my desires.
Your word is like a hammer and a fire –
it breaks, it purifies:
so let your Spirit shine into my heart
and teach me;
open up my eyes . . .

233 Margaret Old
© Scripture Union

Spirit of God, unseen as the wind,
gentle as is the dove:
teach us the truth
and help us believe,
show us the Saviour's love!

1. You spoke to us – long, long ago –
gave us the written word;
we read it still, needing its truth,
through it God's voice is heard.
Spirit of God . . .

2. Without your help we fail our Lord,
   we cannot live his way;
   we need your power,
      we need your strength,
   following Christ each day.
      Spirit of God . . .

Amy Grant
234 © 1984 Meadowgreen Music/EMI Christian Music
Publishing/Word Music. Administered by CopyCare

Your word is a lamp unto my feet
and a light unto my path;
your word is a lamp unto my feet
and a light unto my path.

1. When I feel afraid, think I've lost my way,
   still you're there right beside me:
      and nothing will I fear
      as long as you are near.
   Please be near me to the end.
      Your word . . .

2. I will not forget your love for me –
      and yet
   my heart for ever is wandering:
      Jesus, be my guide
      and hold me to your side.
   And I will love you to the end.
      Your word . . .

For other items on this theme, see

HYMNS
570 As sons of the day and daughters of light
288 God who created light
238 Great shepherd of your people, hear!
506 Here on the threshold
602 Lord for the years
449 Spirit of holiness, wisdom and faithfulness
450 The Spirit came as promised

SONGS
546 All who are thirsty
687 Alleluia, Word of God
517 Father of life, draw me closer
215 Jesus, Jesus, holy and anointed one
138 We are on the Lord's road
 12 We have come as the family of God

PRAYERS OF INTERCESSION

HYMNS

235 William Whiting and others

1. Eternal Father, strong to save,
   whose arm doth bind the restless wave.
   Who bidst the mighty ocean deep
   its own appointed limits keep;
   O hear us when we cry to thee
   for those in peril on the sea.

2. O Saviour, whose almighty word
   the winds and waves submissive heard.
   Who walkedst on the foaming deep,
   and calm amid its rage didst sleep;
   O hear us when we cry to thee
   for those in peril on the sea.

3. O sacred Spirit, who didst brood
   upon the chaos dark and rude.
   Who badst its angry tumult cease,
   and gavest light and life and peace;
   O hear us when we cry to thee
   for those in peril on the sea.

4. O Trinity of love and power,
   our brethren shield in danger's hour;
   from rock and tempest, fire and foe,
   protect them wheresoe'er they go;
   and ever let there rise to thee
   glad hymns of praise from land and sea.

2. May your kingdom come
     here on earth;
   may your will be done
     here on earth,
   as it is in heaven
     so on earth –
   O Lord, hear our prayer.

3. Give us daily bread
     day by day,
   and forgive our sins
     day by day,
   as we too forgive
     day by day –
   O Lord, hear our prayer.

4. Lead us in your way,
     make us strong;
   when temptations come
     make us strong;
   save us all from sin,
     keep us strong –
   O Lord, hear our prayer.

5. All things come from you,
     all are yours –
   kingdom, glory, power,
     all are yours;
   take our lives and gifts,
     all are yours –
   O Lord, hear our prayer.

236 From *The Lord's Prayer*, James Seddon © Mrs M Seddon/Jubilate Hymns

1. Father God in heaven,
     Lord most high:
   hear your children's prayer,
     Lord most high:
   hallowed be your name,
     Lord most high –
   O Lord, hear our prayer.

237 Love Willis

1. Father, hear the prayer we offer –
   not for ease our prayer shall be,
   but for strength that we may ever
   live our lives courageously.

2. Not for ever in green pastures
   do we ask our way to be;
   but the steep and rugged pathway
   may we tread rejoicingly.

3. Not for ever by still waters
   would we idly rest and stay;
   but would strike the living fountains
   from the rocks along our way.

4. Be our strength in hours of weakness,
   in our wanderings be our guide;
   through endeavour, failure, danger,
   Father, be there at our side.

238 John Newton

1. Great Shepherd of your people, hear!
   your presence now display;
   as you have given a place for prayer,
   so give us hearts to pray.

2. Within these walls let holy peace
   and love and friendship dwell;
   here give the troubled conscience ease,
   the wounded spirit heal.

3. May we in faith receive your word,
   in faith present our prayers;
   and in the presence of our Lord
   unburden all our cares.

4. The hearing ear, the seeing eye,
   the contrite heart bestow;
   and shine upon us from on high,
   that we in grace may grow.

239 Martin E. Leckebusch
© Kevin Mayhew

1. Holy Spirit, will you be
   one who intercedes for me?
   When I wonder what to pray,
   how to phrase the words I say,
   come in might and majesty –
   help me in my frailty.

2. Holy Spirit, will you be
   one who intercedes through me?
   When I lack the words to tell
   what my feelings say too well
   speak through every sigh and groan
   making my emotions known.

3. Holy Spirit, will you be
   one who intercedes with me?
   Come, and search my heart and mind,
   my desires and motives find;
   take my deepest thoughts and cares,
   turn them into fervent prayers.

4. Holy Spirit, you will be
   one who intercedes for me!
   You alone can understand
   what the mind of God has planned –
   and within his will you lead
   all for whom you intercede.

240 Leith Samuel
© Mrs E Samuel

1. Mercy in our time of failure,
   grace to help in time of need:
   this sure promise of our Saviour
   is a word that we may plead.

2. He has passed into the heavens,
   he is seated on the throne,
   ever for us interceding,
   always caring for his own.

3. There is none he will not welcome,
   no request he cannot meet;
   let us not be slow to ask him,
   lay our burdens at his feet.

4. We can never come too often,
   never with a need too great,
   never with a prayer too simple;
   only fear to come too late!

5. Daily on our pilgrim journey
   praise him for his matchless grace,
   live for his immortal glory
   till in heaven we see his face.

241 Philip Doddridge
© in this version Jubilate Hymns

1. O God of Jacob, by whose hand
   your children still are fed;
   who through this earthly pilgrimage
   your people safely led:

2. Our vows, our prayers, we now present
   before your gracious throne;
   as you have been their faithful God,
   so always be our own!

3. Through each perplexing path of life
   our wandering footsteps guide;
   give us today our daily bread,
   and for our needs provide.

4. O spread your covering wings around
   till all our wanderings cease,
   and at our heavenly Father's home
   we shall arrive in peace.

SONGS

242 John L. Bell and Graham Maule
© 1988 WGRG, Iona Community, from *Enemy of apathy* (Wild Goose Publications 1988)

1. LEADER Be still and know that I am God
   ALL   and there is none beside me.
           Be still and know that I am God,
           and there is none beside me.

2. LEADER I am the one
           who calls you my friends . . .

3. LEADER I am the one
           whose love never fails . . .

4. LEADER I am the one
           who says 'follow me' . . .

5. LEADER Be still and know
           that I am God . . .

243 From Psalm 40, John L. Bell and Graham Maule
© 1987 WGRG, Iona Community, from *Heaven shall not wait* (Wild Goose Publications, 1987)

I waited, I waited on the Lord;
I waited, I waited on the Lord.
He bent down low and remembered me
when he heard my prayer.

244 John L. Bell
© 1992 WGRG, Iona Community

Lord, we believe when we call
that you will hear and answer us;
therefore bend down your ear
and listen to our prayer.

245 From BRAZIL. © S. Monteiro/Copyright Control
English Words © 1995 Word & Music/Jubilate Hymns

Merciful Lord,
in your loving-kindness
hear our prayer,
listen to our intercession.
Merciful Lord . . .

Ouve, Senhor,
eu estou clamando,
tem piedade de mim e
me responde.
Ouve, Senhor . . .

246 Taizé Community
© Atéliers et Presses de Taizé

O Lord, hear my prayer;
O Lord, hear my prayer:
when I call, answer me –
O Lord, hear my prayer;
O Lord hear my prayer;
come and listen to me.

247 From *The Lord's Prayer*
© Copyright Control

1. Our Father who is in heaven,
   hallowèd be your name,
   your kingdom come, your will be done,
   hallowèd be your name.

2. On earth as it is in heaven,
   hallowèd be your name,
   give us this day our daily bread,
   hallowèd be your name,

3. Forgive us all our trespasses,
   hallowèd be your name,
   as we forgive those
      who trespass against us,
   hallowèd be your name,

4. And lead us not into temptation,
   hallowèd be your name,
   but deliver us from all that is evil,
   hallowèd be your name,

5. For yours is the kingdom,
   the power and the glory,
   hallowèd be your name,
   for ever and for ever,
   hallowèd be your name,

6. Amen, amen, amen, amen,
   hallowèd be your name,
   amen, amen, amen, amen,
   hallowèd be your name,

John L. Bell and Graham Maule
248 © 1987 WGRG, Iona Community, from *Heaven shall not wait* (Wild Goose Publications, 1987)

With God all things are possible;
all things are possible with God.

249 © 1987 Bernadette Farrell
Published by OCP Publications

1. LEADER   Word of justice,
   ALL   Alleluia.
   LEADER   come to dwell here.
   ALL   Maranatha!

2. LEADER   Word of mercy,
   ALL   Alleluia.
   LEADER   live among us.
   ALL   Maranatha!

3. LEADER   Word of power,
   ALL   Alleluia.
   LEADER   live within us.
   ALL   Maranatha!

4. LEADER   Word of freedom,
   ALL   Alleluia.
   LEADER   save your people.
   ALL   Maranatha!

Additional or alternative verses:

Word of healing . . . heal our sorrow . . .

Word of comfort . . . bring us hope now . . .

Word of gladness . . . fill our hearts now . . .

Word of wisdom . . . come renew us . . .

Word we long for . . . Word we thirst for . . .

For other items on this theme, see

HYMNS
662 All-creating heavenly giver
169 Before the throne of God above
572 Christ is made the sure foundation
 14 Christ is our corner-stone
497 Dear Lord and Father of mankind
447 Gift of Christ from God our Father
500 Give us a sense of wonder, God
666 God be in my head
503 God has promised many things
434 Hail the day that sees him rise
406 I know that my redeemer lives
 16 Jesus, where'er thy people meet
 52 Lord, enthroned in heavenly splendour
579 May the grace of Christ our Saviour
183 Oh the deep, deep love of Jesus!
327 Praise to Christ, the Lord incarnate
 60 Rejoice in God! Let trumpets sound
  3 Thanks be to God
646 What a friend we have in Jesus

PSALMS
651 How long, O Lord
  6 I rejoiced to hear them say
652 Listen to my prayer, Lord
 98 The Lord is king! Lift up your voice

SONG
136 The name of the Lord

PRAYERS FOR THE COMMUNITY

HYMNS

250 Shirley Erena Murray. © 1987 Hope Publishing Co.
Administered by CopyCare

1. O God, we bear the imprint of your face:
   the colours of our skin are your design,
   and what we have of beauty in our race
   as man or woman, you alone define,
   who stretched a living fabric
      on our frame
   and gave to each
      a language and a name.

2. Where we are torn
      and pulled apart by hate
   because our race,
      our skin is not the same,
   while some are judged
      unequal by the state
   and victims made because
      they own their name,
   humanity reduced to little worth,
   dishonoured is your living face on earth.

3. O God, we share the image of your Son
   whose flesh and blood are ours,
      whatever skin,
   in his humanity we find our own,
   and in his family our proper kin:
   Christ is the brother we still crucify,
   his love the language
      we must learn, or die.

251 Margaret Clarkson. © 1987 Hope Publishing Co.
Administered by CopyCare

1. Our cities cry to you, O God,
      from out their pain and strife;
   you made us for yourself alone,
      but we choose alien life.
   Our goals are pleasure, gold and power;
      injustice stalks our earth;
   in vain we seek for rest, for joy,
      for sense of human worth.

2. Yet still you walk our streets O Christ!
      We know your presence here
   where humble Christians love and serve
      in godly grace and fear.
   O Word made flesh, be seen in us!
      May all we say and do
   affirm you God incarnate still
      and turn sad hearts to you!

3. Your people are your hands and feet
      to serve your world today,
   our lives the book our cities read
      to help them find your way.
   Oh pour your sovereign Spirit out
      on heart and will and brain:
   inspire your church with love and power
      to ease our cities' pain!

4. O healing Saviour, Prince of Peace,
      salvation's source and sum,
   for you our broken cities cry:
      O come, Lord Jesus, come!
   With truth your royal diadem,
      with righteousness your rod,
   O come, Lord Jesus, bring to earth
      the city of our God!

SONGS

252 John L. Bell and Graham Maule
© 1989 WGRG, Iona Community, from *Love from below* (Wild Goose Publications, 1989)

1. Christ's is the world in which we move,
   Christ's are the folk
      we're summoned to love,
   Christ's is the voice
      which calls us to care,
   and Christ is the one
      who meets us here.
      To the lost Christ shows his face;
      to the unloved he gives his embrace;
      to those who cry in pain or disgrace
      Christ makes, with his friends,
         a touching place.

2. Feel for the people we most avoid –
   strange or bereaved or never employed;
   feel for the women and feel for the men
   who fear that their living is all in vain.
      To the lost . . .

3. Feel for the parents
         who've lost their child,
   feel for the women
         whom men have defiled,
   feel for the baby
         for whom there's no breast
   and feel for the weary who find no rest.
      To the lost . . .

4. Feel for the lives by life confused,
   riddled with doubt, in loving abused;
   feel for the lonely heart,
         conscious of sin,
   which longs to be pure
         but fears to begin.
      To the lost . . .

253 Graham Kendrick
© 1996 Make Way Music

WOMEN Hear our cry,
          O hear our cry:
MEN   'Jesus, come!'
WOMEN Hear our cry, O hear our cry:
MEN   'Jesus, come!'

1. The tide of prayer is rising,
   a deeper passion burning –
   WOMEN Hear our cry . . .

2. We lift our eyes with longing to see your
   kingdom coming –
   WOMEN Hear our cry . . .

   WOMEN Whoever is thirsty,
             come now and drink
             the waters of life;
   MEN   whoever is thirsty,
             come now and drink
             the waters of life.
   WOMEN Hear our cry, O hear our cry:
   MEN   'Jesus, come!'
   WOMEN Hear our cry, O hear our cry:
   MEN   'Jesus, come!'

3. The streets of teeming cities
   cry out for healing rivers –
   WOMEN Hear our cry . . .

4. Refresh them with your presence,
   give grace for deep repentance –
   WOMEN Hear our cry . . .

   WOMEN Whoever is thirsty . . .

5. Tear back the shroud of shadows
   that covers all the peoples –
   WOMEN Hear our cry . . .

6. Revealing your salvation
   in every tribe and nation –
   WOMEN Hear our cry . . .

   WOMEN Whoever is thirsty . . .

254 Patricia Morgan, Ray Goudie, Ian Townend, Dave
Bankhead. © 1986 Kingsway's Thankyou Music

1. Lord, we long for you to move in power;
   there's a hunger deep within our hearts
   to see healing in our nation:
   send your Spirit to revive us –
      Heal our nation,
      heal our nation,
      heal our nation,
      pour out your Spirit on this land!

2. Lord, we hear your Spirit coming closer –
   a mighty wave to break upon our land,
   bringing justice and forgiveness:
   God, we cry to you, 'Revive us!'
      Heal our nation . . .

255 Graham Kendrick
© 1987 Make Way Music

1. O Lord, the clouds are gathering,
   the fire of judgement burns.
   How we have fallen!
   O Lord, you stand appalled to see
   your laws of love so scorned,
   and lives so broken.
      MEN   Have mercy, Lord,
      WOMEN have mercy, Lord.
      MEN   Forgive us, Lord,
      WOMEN forgive us, Lord.

ALL   Restore us, Lord;
       revive your church again.
MEN   Let justice flow,
WOMEN let justice flow.
MEN   like rivers,
WOMEN like rivers;
ALL   and righteousness
       like a never-failing stream.

2. O Lord, over the nations now,
    where is the dove of peace?
    Her wings are broken,
    O Lord, while precious children starve,
    the tools of war increase,
    their bread is stolen.
       MEN   Have mercy, Lord,
       WOMEN have mercy, Lord.
       MEN   Forgive us, Lord,
       WOMEN forgive us, Lord.
       ALL   Restore us, Lord;
              revive your church again.
       MEN   Let justice flow,
       WOMEN let justice flow.
       MEN   like rivers,
       WOMEN like rivers;
       ALL   and righteousness
              like a never-failing stream.

3. O Lord, dark powers are poised
    to flood our streets with hate and fear.
    We must awaken!
    O Lord, let love reclaim the lives
    that sin would sweep away,
    and let your kingdom come!
       MEN   Have mercy, Lord . . .

4. Yet, O Lord, your glorious cross
    shall tower triumphant in this land,
    evil confounding;
    through the fire, your suffering church
    display the glories of her Christ,
    praises resounding.
       MEN   Have mercy, Lord . . .

    A never-failing stream

256
Noel and Tricia Richards
© 1996 Kingsway's Thankyou Music

       Oh, oh, oh, let your love come down,
       Oh, oh, oh, let your love come down.

1. There is violence in the air,
    fear touches all our lives.
    How much pain can people bear?
    Are we reaping what we've sown –
    voices silent for too long?
    We are calling:
    'let your love come down.'
       Oh, oh, oh, let your love come down . . .

2. There is power in your love,
    bringing laughter out of tears;
    it can heal the wounded soul.
    In the streets where anger reigns
    love will wash away the pain.
    We are calling:
    'heaven's love, come down.'
       Oh, oh, oh, let your love come down . . .

257
Graham Kendrick
© 1988 Make Way Music

1. Who can sound the depths of sorrow
    in the Father heart of God,
    for the children we've rejected,
    for the lives so deeply scarred?
    And each light that we've extinguished
    has brought darkness to our land:
       Upon our nation, upon our nation
       have mercy Lord!

2. We have scorned the truth you gave us,
    we have bowed to other lords,
    we have sacrificed the children
    on the altars of our gods.
    O let truth again shine on us,
    let your holy fear descend:
       Upon our nation, upon our nation
       have mercy Lord!

3. MEN
    Who can stand before your anger;
    who can face your piercing eyes?
    for you love the weak and helpless,
    and you hear the victims' cries.

ALL
Yes, you are a God of justice,
and your judgement surely comes:
  Upon our nation, upon our nation
  have mercy Lord!

4. WOMEN
Who will stand against the violence?
Who will comfort those who mourn?
In an age of cruel rejection,
who will build for love a home?
ALL
Come and shake us into action,
come and melt our hearts of stone:
  Upon your people, upon your people,
  have mercy Lord!

5. Who can sound the depths of mercy
in the Father heart of God?
For there is a Man of sorrows
who for sinners shed his blood.
He can heal the wounds of nations,
he can wash the guilty clean:
  Because of Jesus, because of Jesus
  have mercy Lord!

For other items on this theme, see

HYMNS
624 Jesus Christ is waiting
600 Judge eternal throned in splendour

PSALMS
491 O Lord my God

SONGS
271 Can a nation be changed?
264 Great is the darkness
118 He is the Lord
427 No scenes of stately majesty
260 See your saviour comes

PRAYING FOR PEACE

HYMNS

258 Alan Gaunt
© 1991 Stainer & Bell

1. We pray for peace,
   but not the easy peace,
   built on complacency
   and not the truth of God.
   We pray for real peace,
   the peace God's love alone can seal.

2. We pray for peace,
   but not the cruel peace,
   leaving God's poor bereft
   and dying in distress,
   we pray for real peace,
   enriching all the human race.

3. We pray for peace,
   and not the evil peace,
   defending unjust laws
   and nursing prejudice,
   but for the real peace
   of justice, mercy, truth, and love.

4. We pray for peace;
   holy communion
   with Christ our risen Lord
   and every living thing:
   God's will fulfilled on earth
   and all creation reconciled.

5. We pray for peace,
   and for the sake of peace,
   look to the risen Christ
   who gives the grace we need,
   to serve the cause of peace
   and make our own self-sacrifice.

6. God, give us peace:
   if you withdraw your love,
   there is no peace for us
   nor any hope of it.
   With you to lead us on,
   through death or tumult,
   peace will come.

259 Carl Daw, Jr. © 1982 Hope Publishing Co
Administered by CopyCare

1. O day of peace that dimly shines
   through all our hopes
       and prayers and dreams,
   guide us to justice, truth, and love,
   delivered from our selfish schemes.
   May swords of hate fall from our hands,
   our hearts from envy find release,
   till by God's grace our warring world
   shall see Christ's promised
       reign of peace.

2. Then shall the wolf dwell with the lamb,
   nor shall the fierce devour the small;
   as beasts and cattle calmly graze,
   a little child shall lead them all.
   Then enemies shall learn to love,
   all creatures find their true accord;
   the hope of peace shall be fulfilled,
   for all the earth shall know the Lord.

SONG

260 Graham Kendrick
© 1996 Make Way Music

See, your Saviour comes;
see, your Saviour comes.

1. Desolate cities, desolate homes,
   desolate lives on the streets,
   angry and restless,
   when will you know
   the things that would
       make for your peace?
   See, your Saviour comes . . .

2. Father of mercy, hear as we cry
   for all who live in this place;
   show here your glory, come satisfy
   your longing that all should be saved.
   See, your Saviour comes . . .

3. Where lives are broken,
   let there be hope,
   where there's division bring peace;
   where there's oppression,
       judge and reprove
   and rescue the crushed and the weak.
       See, your Saviour comes . . .

4. Lord, let your glory dwell in this land,
   in mercy restore us again:
   pour out your salvation,
   grant us your peace,
   and strengthen the things that remain.
       See, your Saviour comes . . .

For other items on this theme, see

HYMNS
261 For the healing of the nations
304 It is God who holds the nations
262 We bring you, Lord, our prayer and praise

SONGS
263 Beauty for brokenness
586 Come now, O Prince of peace
264 Great is the Darkness
548 Have you heard the good news
691 Make me a channel of your peace
255 O Lord, the clouds are gathering

PRAYING FOR WORLD NEED

HYMNS

261 Fred Kaan
© 1968 Stainer & Bell

1. For the healing of the nations,
   Lord, we pray with one accord;
   for a just and equal sharing
   of the things that earth affords.
   To a life of love in action
   help us rise and pledge our word.

2. Lead us forward into freedom,
   from despair your world release;
   that, redeemed from war and hatred,
   all may come and go in peace.
   Show us how through care
   and goodness
   fear will die and hope increase.

3. All that kills abundant living,
   let it from the earth be banned:
   pride of status, race or schooling,
   dogmas that obscure your plan.
   In our common quest for justice
   may we hallow life's brief span.

4. You, Creator-God, have written
   your great name on humankind;
   for our growing in your likeness
   bring the life of Christ to mind;
   that by our response and service
   earth its destiny may find.

262 © Timothy Dudley-Smith

1. We bring you, Lord, our prayer and
   praise that every child of earth
   should live and grow in freedom's ways,
   in dignity and worth.

2. We praise for such a task begun
   to serve each other's need,
   for every cause of justice won,
   for every fetter freed.

3. Our prayers are for a world in pain
   where force and fear prevail,
   the plough becomes the sword again,
   and hope and harvests fail.

4. Alike our prayer and praise express
   the wants of humankind,
   that lives in bondage and distress
   their larger freedoms find.

5. So may we still maintain the fight
   till earth's oppressions cease
   before the universal right
   to liberty and peace.

6. In Christ we learn to love and care
   and spread his truth abroad;
   and in his Name we lift our prayer:
   'Your kingdom come, O Lord.'

SONGS

263 Graham Kendrick
© 1993 Make Way Music

1. Beauty for brokenness,
   hope for despair,
   Lord, in your suffering world
   this is our prayer.
   Bread for the children,
   justice, joy, peace,
   sunrise to sunset,
   your kingdom increase!

2. Shelter for fragile lives,
   cures for their ills,
   work for the craftsmen,
   trade for their skills;
   land for the dispossessed,
   rights for the weak,
   voices to plead the cause
   of those who can't speak:

God of the poor,
friend of the weak,
give us compassion we pray;
melt our cold hearts,
let tears fall like rain;
come, change our love
from a spark to a flame.

3. Refuge from cruel wars,
    havens from fear,
    cities for sanctuary,
    freedoms to share.
    Peace to the killing-fields,
    scorched earth to green,
    Christ for the bitterness,
    his cross for the pain.

4. Rest for the ravaged earth,
    oceans and streams
    plundered and poisoned –
    our future, our dreams.
    Lord, end our madness,
    carelessness, greed;
    make us content with
    the things that we need.
        God of the poor . . .

5. Lighten our darkness,
    breathe on this flame
    until your justice burns
    brightly again;
    until the nations
    learn of your ways,
    seek your salvation
    and bring you their praise.
        God of the poor . . .

Come, Lord Jesus, come, Lord Jesus,
pour out your Spirit we pray;
come, Lord Jesus, come, Lord Jesus,
pour out your Spirit on us today.

2. May now your church
    rise with power and love,
    this glorious gospel proclaim;
    in every nation salvation will come
    to those who believe in your name.
    Help us bring light to this world,
    that we may speed your return.
        Come, Lord Jesus . . .

3. Great celebrations on that final day,
    when out of the heavens you come;
    darkness will vanish, all sorrow will end,
    and rulers will bow at your throne;
    our great commission complete,
    then face to face we shall meet.
        Come, Lord Jesus . . .

For other items on this theme, see

HYMNS
304 It is God who holds the nations
602 Lord for the years

PSALM
491 O Lord my God

SONGS
252 Christ's is the world in which we move
 21 Come, light of the world
586 Come now, O Prince of peace
273 Come to be our hope, Lord Jesus
254 Lord we long for you to move in power
255 O Lord the clouds are gathering

264 Gerald Coates and Noel Richards
© 1992 Kingsway's Thankyou Music

1. Great is the darkness
        that covers the earth,
    oppression, injustice and pain;
    nations are slipping in hopeless despair,
    though many have come in your name –
    watching while sanity dies,
    touched by the madness and lies.

PRAYING FOR GOVERNMENTS

HYMNS

265 Unknown

1. God save our gracious Queen,
   long live our noble Queen,
   God save the Queen!
   Send her victorious,
   happy and glorious,
   long to reign over us;
   God save the Queen!

2. Thy choicest gifts in store
   on her be pleased to pour;
   long may she reign!
   May she defend our laws,
   and ever give us cause
   to sing with heart and voice:
   God save the Queen!

266 © Michael Saward/Jubilate Hymns

1. King of the universe, Lord of the ages,
   maker of all things, sustainer of life;
   source of authority,
       wise and just creator,
   hope of the nations:
       we praise and adore.

2. Powerful in majesty,
       throned in the heavens –
   sun, moon and stars
       by your word are upheld;
   time and eternity bow
       within your presence,
   Lord of the nations:
       we praise and adore.

3. Wisdom unsearchable,
       fathomless knowledge
   past understanding by our clever brain;
   ground of reality, basis of all order,
   guide to the nations:
       we praise and adore.

4. Justice and righteousness,
       holy, unswerving –
   all that is tainted
       shall burn in your flame;
   sword-bearing deity, punisher of evil,
   judge of the nations:
       we praise and adore.

5. Ruler and potentate, sage and lawgiver,
   humbled before you, unworthy we bow:
   in our extremity,
       show us your forgiveness,
   merciful Father: we praise and adore.

For other items on this theme, see

HYMNS
304 It is God who holds the nations
600 Judge eternal throned in splendour
262 We bring you, Lord, our prayer and praise

SONGS
263 Beauty for brokenness
273 Come to be our hope, Lord Jesus
118 He is the Lord

PRAYING FOR THOSE WHO SUFFER

HYMN

267 Fred Pratt Green
© 1982 Stainer & Bell

1. Pray for the Church,
       afflicted and oppressed,
   for all who suffer for the gospel's sake,
   that Christ may show us
       how to serve them best
   in that one kingdom
       Satan cannot shake.
   But how much more than us
       they have to give,
   who by their dying show us how to live!

2. Pray for Christ's dissidents,
       who daily wait,
   as Jesus waited in the olive grove,
   the unjust trial, the pre-determined fate,
   the world's contempt
       for reconciling love.
   Shall all they won for us, at such a cost,
   be by our negligence or weakness lost?

3. Pray that if times of testing
       should lay bare
   what sort we are,
       who call ourselves his own,
   we may be counted
       worthy then to wear,
   with quiet fortitude, Christ's only crown;
   the crown that in his saints
       he wears again –
   the crown of thorns
       that signifies his reign.

PSALM

268 From Psalm 69, Michael Perry
© Mrs B Perry/Jubilate Hymns

1. When the waters cover me,
       save me, O God;
   when I look and cannot see,
   when I seek what cannot be,
   when my friends abandon me,
       save me, O God.

2. You know all my guilty fears,
       thank you, O God,
   you have heard with open ears,
   you have seen my contrite tears,
   you will bless me all the years,
       thank you, O God.

For other items on this theme, see

HYMN
250 O God, we bear the imprint of your face

PSALMS
491 O Lord my God
651 How long, O Lord

SONGS
252 Christ's is the world in which we move
253 Hear our cry
691 Make me a channel of your peace
255 O Lord the clouds are gathering
257 Who can sound the depths of sorrow

PRAYING FOR MISSION AND GOD'S KINGDOM

HYMN

269 Lewis Hensley

1. Your kingdom come, O God!
   your rule, O Christ, begin;
   break with your iron rod
   the tyrannies of sin.

2. Where is your reign of peace
   and purity and love?
   When shall all hatred cease
   as in the realms above?

3. When comes the promised time,
   the end of strife and war;
   when lust, oppression, crime
   and greed shall be no more?

4. O Lord our God, arise
   and come in your great might!
   revive our longing eyes
   which languish for your sight.

5. As rebels scorn your name
   and wolves devour your fold,
   by many deeds of shame
   we learn that love grows cold.

6. On nations near and far
   thick darkness gathers yet:
   arise, O Morning Star,
   arise and never set!

PSALM

270 From Psalm 2
© Steve James/Jubilate Hymns

Why are the nations conspiring
   to turn from your name?
Why the rebellion that casts off
   all law and restraint?
   Our God rules in the heavens,
   now hear his word of command:
   Christ is King of the nations,
   our times are in his hand.

Grant us the wisdom
   to live in eternity's light.
Open the eyes of the nations
   to worship the Christ!
   Our God rules . . .

   Who is the Lord? Who is the King?
   Fling wide the gates!
   Let the King of glory in!

Why are the nations conspiring
   to turn from your name?
Why the rebellion that casts off
   all law and restraint?
   Our God rules . . .

   Who is the Lord . . .

   Our God rules in the heavens,
   now hear his word of command;
   Christ is King of the nations,
   our times are in his hand,
   they're in his hand,
   they're in his hand.

SONGS

271 Matt Redman
© 1996 Kingsway's Thankyou Music

Can a nation be changed,
can a nation be saved,
can a nation be turned back to you?
Can a nation be changed . . .

We're on our knees,
   we're on our knees again;
we're on our knees,
   we're on our knees again.

Let this nation be changed,
let this nation be saved,
let this nation be turned back to you.
Let this nation be changed . . .

272 © Steve James/Jubilate Hymns

Christ your glory fills the heavens,
your truth the world must know;
Morning Star,
    you triumph over darkness –
you are Jesus the Lord.
Christ your glory fills the heavens . . .

1. You are the sun
    of righteousness dawning
that shall cause our hearts to sing:
shine upon our faithless
    shadows bringing
healing in your wings.
    Christ your glory fills the heavens . . .

2. You are the final word to be given,
you're the hope that sets us free;
let the earth be filled with your glory
as the waters fill the sea!
    Christ your glory fills the heavens . . .

The light of your face is all we desire:
now walk by our side
and turn our hearts to burn with fire.
    Christ your glory fills the heavens . . .
    . . . you are Jesus the Lord.

273 From Brazil, Jorge Rodriguez
English translation © 1987 Jaci C. Maraschin

1. Come to be our hope, Lord Jesus,
    come to set our people free;
from oppression come, release us,
    turn defeat to victory!
Come, release from every prison
    those who suffer in our land:
in your love we find the reason
    still to live and understand.

2. Come to build your new creation
    through the road of servanthood;
give new life to every nation,
    changing evil into good.
Come and open our tomorrow
    for a kingdom now so near;
take away all human sorrow –
    give us hope in place of fear.

1. Vem, Jesus nossa esperança
    nossas vidas libertar.
Vem, nascer em nós, criança
    vem o teu poder nos dar.
Vem, liberta os prisioneiros
    da injustiça e da aflição;
vem, reúne os brasi leiros
    em amor e em compreensão.

2. Vem tecer um mundo novo
    nos caminhos de verdade;
para que, afinal, o povo
    viva em plena liberdade.
Vem, Jesus, abre o futuro
    do teu reino de alegria.
Vem, derruba o imenso muro
    que sèpara a noite e o dia.

274 Graham Kendrick and Chris Rolinson
© 1981 Kingsway's Thankyou Music

1. Restore, O Lord,
    the honour of your name!
In works of sovereign power
come shake the earth again,
that all may see,
and come with reverent fear
to the living God
whose Kingdom shall outlast the years.

2. Restore, O Lord,
    in all the earth your fame,
and in our time revive
the Church that bears your name;
and in your anger,
Lord, remember mercy –
O living God,
whose mercy shall outlast the years.

3. Bend us, O Lord,
    where we are hard and cold,
in your refiner's fire;
come purify the gold:
though suffering comes,
and evil crouches near,
still our living God
is reigning – he is reigning here!

4. Restore, O Lord,
   the honour of your name!
   In works of sovereign power
   come shake the earth again,
   that all may see,
   and come with reverent fear
   to the living God
   whose Kingdom shall outlast the years.

275 Steve Cantellow and Matt Redman
© 1996 Kingsway's Thankyou Music

We will give ourselves no rest
till your kingdom comes on earth;
you've positioned watchmen on the walls.
Now our prayers will flow like tears,
for you've shared your heart with us;
God of heaven, on our knees we fall,
come down in power,
reveal your heart again;
come, hear our cries,
the tears that plead for rain.

We're knocking, knocking on
   the door of heaven,
we're crying, crying for this generation;
we're praying for your name to be
   known in all of the earth.
We're watching, watching on
   the walls to see you,
we're looking, looking for
   a time of breakthrough;
we're praying for your word to bear fruit
   in all of the earth, in all of the earth.

276 From RUSSIA
© 1980 N. Zabolotski/Copyright Control

Your kingdom come, O Lord.
Your kingdom come, O Lord.
Your kingdom come, O Lord.
Your kingdom come, O Lord.

277 John L. Bell and Graham Maule
© 1987 WGRG, Iona Community, from *Heaven shall not wait* (Wild Goose Publications, 1987)

Through our lives
and by our prayers,
your kingdom come.

For other items on this theme, see

HYMNS
430 Christ brings the kingdom where barrenness
   blooms
236 Father God in heaven
501 Give to me, Lord, a thankful heart
575 In Christ there is no east or west
600 Judge eternal, throned in splendour
262 We bring you, Lord, our prayer and praise

SONGS
106 Blessing and honour
252 Christ's is the world in which we move
264 Great is the darkness
548 Have you heard the good news
253 Hear our cry
613 How do we start?
614 Lord the light of your love is shining
256 Oh, let your love come down

OFFERING OUR GIFTS AND TALENTS TO GOD

HYMN

278 © Brian Hoare/Jubilate Hymns

1. The gifts we bring express our love
   to you, who left the heavens above,
   and showed, through poverty and pain,
   a God who gives and gives again.
   > Freely, freely, freely we have received;
   > gladly, gladly, gladly we love to give.
   > Our gifts we bring to you,
   > our praise we sing to you,
   > giving and giving, and giving again.

2. Though earthly wealth you never knew,
   our greatest riches came from you;
   our needs are all by you supplied,
   and no good thing are we denied.
   > Freely, freely . . .

3. From love of money save us, Lord;
   make us obedient to your word;
   to seek your righteousness and will,
   and all our stewardship fulfil.
   > Freely, freely . . .

4. Lord, you've entrusted to us all
   the wealth we have:
   > some great, some small.
   As you have prospered us, we give,
   and yet in giving we receive.
   > Freely, freely . . .

5. The truth is clear within your word:
   you love a joyful giver, Lord
   so make us joyful as we bring
   our gifts, our lives – an offering.
   > Freely, freely . . .

SONG

279 © Brian Hoare/Jubilate Hymns

Skills and abilities, knowledge and artistry,
power to invent, to create, to achieve;
all come from God
> who has made us so wonderfully,
lavishing on us the gifts we receive.

Different gifts, but only one Giver;
talents that vary, the Giver the same.
Different skills we see in each other,
but give him the glory
> and honour his name!

For other items on this theme, see

HYMNS
662 All-creating heavenly Giver
 27 Angel-voices ever singing
618 Awake, my soul, and with the sun
573 Christ our king in glory reigning
621 Come to us, creative Spirit
623 Forth in your name, O Lord, I go
447 Gift of Christ from God our Father
625 God, who stretched the spangled heavens
306 O Lord of heaven and earth and sea
631 When the Church of Jesus

SONG
 11 Humbly in your sight

SHARING THE PEACE AND FELLOWSHIP WITH ONE ANOTHER

SONGS

280 From Ephesians 4, John L. Bell
© 1993 WGRG, Iona Community

1. One is the body and one is the Head,
   one is the Spirit by whom we are led;
   one God and Father, one faith
      and one call for all.

2. Christ who ascended to heaven above
   is the same Jesus whose nature is love,
   who once descended to bring
      to this earth new birth.

3. Gifts have been given
      well-suited to each;
   some to be prophets,
      to pastor or preach,
   some, through the Gospel,
      to challenge, convert and teach.

4. Called to his service
      are women and men
   so that his body might ever again
   witness through worship,
      through deed and through word
   to Christ our Lord.

282 From BENIN, traditional

SOLO Peace be with you,
ALL peace be with you.
SOLO Peace be with you,
ALL peace be with you,
     with all of us, Amen,
     with all of us, Amen!

SOLO *Na Jijoho,*
ALL *jijoho ni tin.*
SOLO *Na Jijoho,*
ALL *jijoho ni tin.*
     Po omepopo, Amen.
     Po omepopo, Amen!

Other items on this theme, see

HYMN
583 We worship God in harmony

SONG
587 How good and how pleasant it is

281 From ISRAEL, unknown
English version © 1995 Word & Music/Jubilate Hymns

May the peace of God the Father
and the grace of Christ, the Son,
with the blessing of the Spirit –
God the holy Three-in-One:
be upon you always, and remain
now and ever with you. Amen.

AFFIRMING OUR BELIEF

HYMNS

283 © Colin Thompson

1. God's glory fills the universe,
   the heavens proclaim his power;
   but small and weak
     the Word made flesh,
   and dark and brief his hour!
   The mystery sought through ages past
   is born with human face;
   the treasure of eternal love
   dwells with the human race.

2. His words and signs of healing power
   are wonders to the poor,
   blind eyes, cold hearts
     protest and scheme
   till love stands judged by law.
   Let peace and mercy weep apart,
   and justice, truth, take flight
   when God's own Word to silence falls
   and darkness veils the Light.

3. Uplifted on the Cross, Christ bears
   our shame in his disgrace,
   his outstretched arms enfold us all,
   and heaven and earth embrace.
   For Love will know the darkest depths,
   and taste our bitterest pain
   to prove himself their vanquisher,
   and spring from buried grain.

4. The Lord ascends,
     and death bows down
   to his triumphant name.
   The Spirit stirs our sleeping faith
   in wind and tongue of flame.
   Christ strengthens us, calls us to live
   as children of the day,
   to shine where shadows still oppress,
   to walk his risen way.

284 From 1 Corinthians 15 etc
© Michael Saward/Jubilate Hymns

1. These are the facts
     as we have received them,
   these are the truths
     that the Christian believes,
   this is the basis of all of our preaching:
   Christ died for sinners
     and rose from the tomb.

2. These are the facts
     as we have received them:
   Christ has fulfilled
     what the scriptures foretold,
   Adam's whole family
     in death had been sleeping,
   Christ through his rising
     restores us to life.

3. These are the facts
     as we have received them;
   we, with our Saviour,
     have died on the cross;
   now, having risen, our Jesus lives in us,
   gives us his Spirit
     and makes us his home.

4. These are the facts
     as we have received them:
   we shall be changed
     in the blink of an eye,
   trumpets shall sound
     as we face life immortal,
   this is the victory through
     Jesus our Lord.

5. These are the facts
     as we have received them,
   these are the truths
     that the Christian believes,
   this is the basis of all of our preaching:
   Christ died for sinners
     and rose from the tomb.

285 © David Mowbray/Jubilate Hymns

1. We believe in God Almighty,
   maker of the earth and sky;
   all we see and all that's hidden
   is his work unceasingly:
   God our Father's loving kindness
   with us till the day we die –
   evermore and evermore.

2. We believe in Christ the Saviour,
   Son of God and Son of Man;
   born of Mary, preaching, healing,
   crucified, yet risen again:
   he ascended to the Father
   there in glory long to reign –
   evermore and evermore.

3. We believe in God the Spirit,
   present in our lives today;
   speaking hrough the prophets' writings,
   guiding travellers on their way:
   to our hearts he brings forgiveness
   and the hope of endless joy –
   evermore and evermore.

3. We believe in God the Spirit;
   in one church, below, above;
   saints of God in one communion,
   one in holiness and love.
   So by faith, our sins forgiven,
   Christ our Saviour, Lord and Friend,
   we shall rise with him in glory
   to the life that knows no end.

For other items on this theme, see

HYMNS
433 Come see the Lord in his breathtaking
     splendour
288 God who created light
289 I believe in God the Father
306 O Lord of heaven and earth and sea
293 Today I awake
331 We have a gospel to proclaim

SONGS
116 He came down
 12 We have come as the family of God

286 © Timothy Dudley-Smith

1. We believe in God the Father,
   God Almighty, by whose plan
   earth and heaven sprang to being,
   all created things began.
   We believe in Christ the Saviour,
   Son of God in human frame,
   virgin-born, the child of Mary
   upon whom the Spirit came.

2. Christ, who on the cross forsaken,
   like a lamb to slaughter led,
   suffered under Pontius Pilate,
   he descended to the dead.
   We believe in Jesus risen,
   heaven's king to rule and reign,
   to the Father's side ascended
   till as judge he comes again.

AFFIRMING OUR BELIEF IN THE TRINITY

HYMNS

287 John Newman
© in this version Jubilate Hymns.

1. Firmly I believe and truly
   God is Three and God is One;
   and I next acknowledge duly
   manhood taken by the Son.

2. And I trust and hope most fully
   in that manhood crucified;
   and each thought and deed unruly
   do to death, for he has died.

3. Simply to his grace and wholly
   light and life and strength belong;
   and I love supremely, solely,
   Christ the holy, Christ the strong.

4. And I make this affirmation
   for the love of Christ alone:
   holy Church is his creation
   and his teachings are her own.

5. Honour, glory, power, and merit
   to the God of earth and heaven,
   Father, Son, and Holy Spirit –
   praise for evermore be given!

288 © Michael Saward/Jubilate Hymns

1. God who created light
   from his commanding height,
   his voice was heard.
   Through sky and sea
   labouring, came to birth,
   sign of eternal worth,
   life through God's word.

2. Christ who was born to save,
   standing at Lazarus' grave,
   his voice was heard.
   He who had healed the lame
   called to the dead by name,
   and from the tomb there came
   life through God's word.

3. Spirit, whose mighty power
   surges through every hour,
   his voice is heard.
   Strong as the wind he blows,
   swift as a torrent flows,
   and to the church bestows
   life through God's word.

289 Michael Perry
© Mrs B. Perry/Jubilate Hymns

1. I believe in God the Father
   who created heaven and earth;
   holding all things in his power,
   bringing light and life to birth.

2. I believe in God the Saviour,
   Son of Man and Lord most high,
   crucified to be redeemer,
   raised to life that death may die.

3. I believe in God the Spirit,
   wind of heaven and flame of fire,
   pledge of all that we inherit,
   sent to comfort and inspire.

4. Honour, glory, might and merit
   be to God, and God alone!
   Father, Son and Holy Spirit,
   One-in-Three and Three-in-One.

290 Reginald Heber

1. Holy, holy, holy, Lord God almighty!
   early in the morning
     our song shall rise to thee;
   Holy, holy, holy! – merciful and mighty,
   God in three persons, blessèd Trinity.

2. Holy, holy, holy!
     All the saints adore thee,
   casting down their golden crowns
     around the glassy sea;
   cherubim and seraphim
     falling down before thee:
   God from of old who evermore shall be!

3. Holy, holy, holy! –
    though the darkness hide thee,
    though the sinful human eye
      thy glory may not see;
    only thou art holy,
      there is none beside thee
    perfect in power, in love and purity.

4. Holy, holy, holy, Lord God almighty!
    all thy works shall praise thy name,
      in earth and sky and sea:
    Holy, holy, holy! – merciful and mighty,
    God in three persons, blessèd Trinity.

4. O Wind of God, O Wind of God,
      invigorate the dead;
    O Fire of God, O Fire of God,
      your burning radiance spread:
    your fruit our lives renewing,
    your gifts, the church transforming;
      and though . . .

5. O Trinity, O Trinity,
      the uncreated One;
    O Unity, O Unity
      of Father, Spirit, Son:
    you are without beginning,
    your life is never-ending;
      and though . . .

292 © Herbert O'Driscoll

1. Sing of a God in majestic divinity,
      seeding the heavens
        with numberless stars,
    forming our dust
        and our dreams of infinity,
    God of our genes
        and the judge of our wars.

291
From the Lenten Triodion of the Orthodox Church.
© Michael Saward/Jubilate Hymns.

1. O Trinity, O Trinity,
      the uncreated One;
    O Unity, O Unity
      of Father, Spirit, Son:
    you are without beginning,
    your life is never ending:
        and though our tongues
        are earthbound clay,
        light them with flaming fire today.

2. O Majesty, O Majesty,
      the Father of our race;
    O Mystery, O mystery,
      we cannot see your face:
    your justice is unswerving
    your love is overpowering;
      and though . . .

3. O Virgin-born, O Virgin-born,
      of humankind the least;
    O Victim torn, O Victim torn,
      both spotless lamb and priest:
    you died and rose victorious,
    you reign above all-glorious;
      and though . . .

2. Sing of a child
      who was cradled so tenderly,
    sing of a boyhood by Galilee's lake;
    sing of a cross
      and a Saviour who wondrously
    suffered and died for humanity's sake.

3. Sing of a Spirit who daily addresses us,
    lives in our sciences, nature, and arts;
    moving through all of creation
      and blessing us,
    guiding our minds
      and engaging our hearts.

4. Sing of this God
      who in glory and mystery
    chooses to lie in humanity's womb,
    enters the prison
      and pain of our history,
    rises triumphant and opens the tomb.

293

John L. Bell and Graham Maule
© 1989 WGRG, Iona Community, from *Love Below*
(Wild Goose Publications 1989)

1. Today I awake
   and God is before me.
   At night, as I dreamt,
   he summoned the day;
   for God never sleeps
   but patterns the morning
   with slithers of gold
   or glory in grey.

2. Today I arise
   and Christ is beside me.
   He walked through the dark
   to scatter new light.
   Yes, Christ is alive,
   and beckons his people
   to hope and to heal,
   resist and invite.

3. Today I affirm
   the Spirit within me
   at worship and work,
   in struggle and rest.
   The Spirit inspires
   all life which is changing
   from fearing to faith,
   from broken to blest.

4. Today I enjoy
   the Trinity round me,
   above and beneath,
   before and behind;
   the Maker, the Son;
   the Spirit together –
   they called me to life
   and call me their friend.

For other items on this theme, see

HYMNS
662 All-creating heavenly giver
200 Father in heaven, grant to your children
144 Father of heaven, whose love profound
  2 First of the week and finest day
225 God has spoken– by his prophets
301 God lies beyond us
283 God's glory fills the universe
597 God, whose almighty word
640 Lead us, heavenly Father
  1 Sing glory to God the Father
285 We believe in God Almighty
286 We believe in God the Father

AFFIRMING OUR BELIEF IN GOD THE CREATOR

HYMNS

294 Cecil F. Alexander

All things bright and beautiful,
all creatures great and small,
all things wise and wonderful –
the Lord God made them all.

1. Each little flower that opens,
   each little bird that sings –
   he made their glowing colours,
   he made their tiny wings.
   All things bright . . .

2. The purple-headed mountain,
   the river running by,
   the sunset, and the morning
   that brightens up the sky:
   All thing bright . . .

3. The cold wind in the winter,
   the pleasant summer sun,
   the ripe fruits in the garden –
   he made them every one.
   All things bright . . .

4. He gave us eyes to see them,
   and lips that we might tell
   how great is God almighty,
   who has made all things well!
   All things bright . . .

295 Martin E. Leckebusch
© Kevin Mayhew

1. Creation sings! Each plant and tree,
   each bird and beast in harmony;
   the brightest star, the smallest cell,
   God's tender care and glory tell –
   from ocean depths to mountain peaks,
   in praise of God, creation speaks!

2. Creation speaks a message true,
   reminds us we are creatures, too;
   to serve as stewards is our role,

despite our dreams of full control –
when we disparage what God owns,
in turmoil, all creation groans.

3. Creation groans to see the day
   which ends all bondage, all decay:
   frustrated now, it must await
   the Lord who comes to recreate
   till round the universe there rings
   the song his new creation sings!

296 Donald W. Hughes
© Paul Hughes

1. Creator of the earth and skies,
   to whom all truth and power belong:
   grant us your truth to make us wise,
   grant us your power to make us strong.

2. We have not known you: to the skies
   our monuments of folly soar;
   and all our self-wrought miseries
   have made us trust ourselves the more.

3. We have not loved you: far and wide
   the wreckage of our hatred spreads;
   and evils wrought by human pride
   recoil on unrepentant heads.

4. We long to end this worldwide strife:
   how shall we follow in your way?
   Speak to us all your words of life
   until our darkness turns to day!

297 Martin E. Leckebusch
© Kevin Mayhew

1. Do you not know? This is our God!
   Were you not told his holy name?
   Have you not heard? He is the Lord,
   age after age ever the same.

2. To whom will you compare the Lord,
   the God no image can portray?
   No artist has sufficient skill,
   his might or glory to display.

3. Beyond the earth, beyond the skies,
   he reigns, enthroned as King of all;
   though earthly rulers flaunt their power,
   at his command their empires fall.

4. Who is there like the Holy One?
   And who can fathom his design?
   The planets' orbits he decrees,
   and causes sun and stars to shine.

5. How can you worry that your God
   might choose to disregard your prayer?
   He neither slumbers nor forgets,
   and you enjoy his constant care.

6. So trust the everlasting Lord
   your failing vigour to renew –
   then you shall soar on eagles' wings,
   with God himself sustaining you.

298 Folliott Pierpoint

1. For the beauty of the earth,
   for the beauty of the skies,
   for the love which from our birth
   over and around us lies,
      Christ our God, to you we raise
      this our sacrifice of praise.

2. For the beauty of each hour
   of the day and of the night,
   hill and vale, and tree and flower,
   sun and moon and stars of light,
      Christ our God . . .

3. For the joy of ear and eye,
   for the heart and mind's delight,
   for the mystic harmony
   linking sense to sound and sight,
      Christ our God . . .

4. For the joy of human love,
   brother, sister, parent, child,
   friends on earth and friends above,
   pleasures pure and undefiled,
      Christ our God . . .

5. For each perfect gift divine
   to our race so freely given,
   joys bestowed by love's design,
   flowers of earth and fruits of heaven,
      Christ our God . . .

299 Fred Pratt Green
© 1970 Stainer & Bell

1. For the fruits of his creation,
      thanks be to God;
   for his gifts to every nation,
      thanks be to God;
   for the ploughing, sowing, reaping,
   silent growth while we are sleeping,
   future needs in earth's safe-keeping,
      thanks be to God.

2. In the just reward of labour,
      God's will is done;
   in the help we give our neighbour,
      God's will is done;
   in our worldwide task of caring
   for the hungry and despairing,
   in the harvests we are sharing,
      God's will is done.

3. For the harvests of his Spirit,
      thanks be to God;
   for the good we all inherit,
      thanks be to God;
   for the wonders that astound us,
   for the truths that still confound us,
   most of all that love has found us,
      thanks be to God.

300 Fred Pratt Green
© 1973 Stainer & Bell

1. God in his love for us lent us this planet,
   gave it a purpose in time and in space:
   small as a spark
      from the fire of creation,
   cradle of life and the home of our race.

2. Thanks be to God
      for its bounty and beauty,
   life that sustains us in body and mind:
   plenty for all, if we learn how to share it,
   riches undreamed of to fathom and find.

3. Long have our human wars
        ruined its harvest:
    long has earth bowed
        to the terror of force:
    long have we wasted
        what others have need of,
    poisoned the fountain of life
        at its source.

4. Earth is the Lord's: it is ours to enjoy it,
    ours, as his stewards,
        to farm and defend.
    From its pollution,
        misuse, and destruction,
    good Lord, deliver us,
        world without end!

301 © Timothy Dudley-Smith

1. God lies beyond us,
        throned in light resplendent,
    Father eternal, source of all creation.
    To him in glory, timeless
        and transcendent,
    High King of Ages, come with adoration.

2. God walks beside us,
        born to be our neighbour,
    died to redeem us, risen and ascended;
    love the loveless,
        friend of all who labour,
    Christ our Companion,
        till our days are ended.

3. God lives within us,
        breath and life instilling,
    daily transforming ways
        of thought and seeing.
    Spirit all-holy, all our spirits filling,
    blow, Wind, about us!
        burn within our being.

4. God in three persons,
        Trinity of splendour!
    To God the Father, all in all sustaining,
    and God the Saviour, adoration render,
    with God the Spirit,
        One in glory reigning.

302 © Trustees of the late John Arlott

1. God whose farm is all creation,
    take the gratitude we give;
    take the finest of our harvest,
    crops we grow that all may live.

2. Take our ploughing, seeding, reaping,
    hopes and fears of sun and rain,
    all our thinking, planning, waiting,
    ripened in this fruit and grain.

3. All our labour, all our watching,
    all our calendar of care
    in these crops of your creation,
    take, O God – they are our prayer.

303 © David Mowbray/Jubilate Hymns

1. Lord of the changing year,
    patterns and colours bright;
    all that we see and hear,
    sunrise and starlit night;
    the seasons, Lord, in splendour shine,
    your never-failing wise design.

2. Lord of the winter scene,
    hard-frozen ice and snow;
    death where once life has been,
    nothing is seen to grow;
    few creatures roam, few birds will fly
    across the clouded Christmas sky:

3. Lord of unfolding spring,
    promise of life to come;
    nature begins to sing
    where once her tongue was dumb;
    the crocus blooms, the hedgerows wake,
    and Easter Day is soon to break:

4. Lord of the summer days,
    spreading and green the trees;
    songthrush lifts high your praise,
    gulls light on deep-blue seas;
    the warmth and welcome of the sun
    brings happiness to everyone:

5. Lord of the autumn gold,
    reaping and harvest home,
    sheep safely in the fold,
    turn of the year has come:
    the seasons, Lord, in splendour shine,
    your never-failing wise design.

304 Fred Pratt Green
© 1977 Stainer & Bell

1. It is God who holds the nations
    in the hollow of his hand;
    it is God whose light is shining
    in the darkness of the land;
    it is God who builds his City
    on the Rock and not on sand:
    may the living God be praised!

2. It is God whose purpose summons
    us to use the present hour;
    who recalls us to our senses
    when a nation's life turns sour;
    in the discipline of freedom
    we shall know his saving power;
    may the living God be praised!

3. When a thankful nation, looking back,
    has cause to celebrate
    those who win our admiration
    by their service to the state;
    when self-giving is a measure
    of the greatness of the great:
    may the living God be praised!

4. He reminds us every sunrise
    that the world is ours on lease –
    for the sake of life tomorrow,
    may our love for it increase;
    may all races live together,
    share its riches, be at peace:
    may the living God be praised!

305 © Timothy Dudley-Smith

1. Let us sing the God of glory
    who has set the stars in place,
    with the planets in their courses
    as they cross the heaven's face
    and the constellations shining
    to the boundaries of space,
    our God whose Name is love!

Glory, glory, alleluia,
    glory, glory, alleluia,
    glory, glory, alleluia,
    our God whose Name is love!

2. Let us sing the God of beauty
    in the mountains and the seas,
    all the colours of the rainbow
    and the tracery of trees,
    in the thunder of the breakers
    and the whisper of the breeze,
    our God whose name is love!
    Glory, glory . . .

3. Let us sing the God of bounty
    for a fruitful earth and fair,
    who provides for us in plenty
    so that all may have a share,
    and who loves his human family
    and has us in his care,
    our God whose Name is love!
    Glory, glory . . .

4. Let us sing the God of mercy
    for the wonders he has done,
    how he loved us in our sinfulness
    and sent to us his Son,
    who has died for us, and lives for us,
    and life and freedom won,
    our God whose Name is love!
    Glory, glory . . .

5. Let us sing the Saviour Jesus
    as he makes the Father known,
    let us hear his Spirit's call to us
    to come and be his own,
    and to worship him in glory
    on his everlasting throne,
    our God whose Name is love!
    Glory, glory . . .

306 Christopher Wordsworth
© in this version Jubilate Hymns

1. O Lord of heaven and earth and sea,
    to you all praise and glory be,
    who loved us from eternity
    and gave us all.

2. The golden sunshine, gentle air,
    sweet flowers and fruit,
    your love declare;
    when harvests ripen you are there –
    you give us all.

3. For peaceful homes and healthful days,
   for all the blessings earth displays,
   we owe you thankfulness and praise –
   you give us all.

4. Freely you gave your only Son,
   who on the cross salvation won;
   and in the life through him begun
   you give us all.

5. You sent your Spirit from above
   as wind and fire and gentle dove;
   and in his gifts of power and love
   you gave us all.

6. For souls redeemed, for sins forgiven,
   for means of grace
      and hopes of heaven,
   to you, O Lord what can be given?
   you give us all.

7. We lose what on ourselves we spend;
   we have as treasure without end
   whatever, Lord, to you we lend –
   you give us all.

8. Father, from whom we all derive
   our life, our gifts, our power to give:
   O may we ever with you live;
   you give us all.

307 © Paul Wigmore/Jubilate Hymns

1. Praise God for Harvest-Time,
   sing till bells of heaven chime!
   Sing of his love revealed,
   fruit of earth and ocean's yield:
      Alleluia! Alleluia!
      Good harvest safely stored –
      praise our great Creator Lord!

2. Plough turning soil and stone
   by the winter stormwinds blown;
   green buds on bending bough,
   life to bring us harvest now:
      Alleluia! Alleluia! . . .

3. God in the fertile land
   joining with our human hand;
   seed waking in the earth
   stirring at the spring of birth:
      Alleluia! Alleluia! . . .

4. See in our food a sign
   pointing to a love divine;
   strength from a summer sky,
   life bestowed as rainclouds fly:
      Alleluia! Alleluia! . . .

5. Lord, on your gifts we feed:
   show us each the other's need;
   give us the love to share
   in our deeds and in our prayer:
      Alleluia! Alleluia! . . .

6. Lord, from your plenteous field
   land and sea their harvest yield;
   these, Lord, we bring to you,
   gifts that by your goodness grew:
      Alleluia! Alleluia! . . .

308 Brian Wren
© 1974, 1996 Stainer & Bell

1. Praise God for the harvest
      of orchard and field,
   praise God for the people
      who gather their yield,
   the long hours of labour,
      the skills of a team,
   the patience of science,
      the power of machine.

2. Praise God for the harvest
      that's comes from afar,
   from market and harbour,
      the sea and the shore:
   foods packed and transported,
      and gathered and grown
   by God-given neighbours,
      unseen and unknown.

3. Praise God for the harvest
      that's quarried and mined,
   then sifted, and smelted,
      or shaped and refined;
   for oil and for iron, for copper and coal,
   praise God, who in love
      has provided them all.

4. Praise God for the harvest
     of science and skill,
   the urge to discover, create and fulfil:
   for all dreams and inventions
     that promise to gain
   a future more hopeful,
     a world more humane.

5. Praise God for the harvest
     of mercy and love
   from leaders and peoples
     who struggle and serve
   for patience and kindness,
     that all may be led
   to freedom and justice,
     and all may be fed.

309 © David Mowbray/Jubilate Hymns

1. Walk the hills and you will find him,
   lift the stone and he is there;
   rising paths and tumbling water,
   forest pines and mountain air.

2. Search the skies and you will find him;
   eagle's lone majestic flight,
   swirling snow and silent spaces,
   sunrise after stormy night.

3. Sail the seas and you will find him;
   fish the waters, roam the shore;
   wind and waves are at his bidding,
   all creation is God's store.

4. And in Jesus you will find him,
   sent to you with truth and grace;
   for in Christ you find God's likeness
   shining bright upon his face.

310 After William C. Dix.
© in this version Word & Music/Jubilate Hymns

1. To you, O Lord, our hearts we raise
   in hymns of adoration:
   accept our sacrifice of praise,
   our shouts of exultation;
   for by your hand our souls are fed –
   what joys your love has given!
   You give to us our daily bread,
   so give us bread from heaven!

2. And now on this our festal day,
   your love to us expressing
   our gifts before you, Lord, we lay,
   the firstfruits of your blessing:
   bright robes of gold the fields adorn,
   the hills with joy are ringing;
   the valleys stand so thick with corn
   that even they are singing.

3. Yet in your presence we confess,
   O Lord of earth and heaven,
   our pride, our greed and selfishness –
   we ask to be forgiven:
   and where the hungry suffer still
   because of our ambition,
   there let our riches serve your will
   your love be our commission.

4. There is a country bright as day
   beyond the crystal river,
   where hunger will be done away
   and thirst be gone for ever;
   where praises ring out loud and strong
   that now with ours are blending;
   where we shall sing the harvest-song
   that never has an ending.

311 After Matthias Claudius, Jane Campbell

1. We plough the fields, and scatter
   the good seed on the land;
   but it is fed and watered
   by God's almighty hand;
   he sends the snow in winter,
   the warmth to swell the grain;
   the breezes and the sunshine
   and soft refreshing rain.
       All good gifts around us
       are sent from heaven above:
       then thank the Lord, O thank the Lord
       for all his love.

2. He only is the maker
   of all things near and far;
   he paints the wayside flower,
   he lights the evening star:
   the winds and waves obey him,
   by him the birds are fed;
   much more, to us his children
   he gives our daily bread.
   > All good gifts around us
   > are sent from heaven above:
   > then thank the Lord, O thank the Lord
   > for all his love.

3. We thank you, then, our Father,
   for all things bright and good;
   the seed-time and the harvest,
   our life, our health, our food:
   accept the gifts we offer
   for all your love imparts;
   and that which you most welcome
   our humble, thankful hearts!
   > All good gifts . . .

PSALMS

312 From Psalm 136, after John Milton
© in this version Michael Saward/Jubilate Hymns

1. Let us gladly with one mind
   praise the Lord, for he is kind:
   > for his mercy shall endure,
   > ever faithful, ever sure.

2. He has made the realms of space,
   all things have their ordered place:
   > for his mercy . . .

3. He created sky and sea,
   field and mountain, flower and tree:
   > for his mercy . . .

4. Every creature, great and small –
   God alone has made them all:
   > for his mercy . . .

5. Then he fashioned humankind,
   crown of all that he designed:
   > for his mercy . . .

6. He has shaped our destiny –
   heaven for all eternity:
   > for his mercy . . .

7. Glory then to God on high,
   'Glory!' let creation cry:
   > for his mercy . . .

313 From Psalm 65
© Michael Saward/Jubilate Hymns

1. The earth is yours, O God –
   you nourish it with rain;
   the streams and rivers overflow,
   the land bears seed again.

2. The soil is yours, O God –
   the shoots are moist with dew;
   and ripened by the burning sun
   the corn grows straight and true.

3. The hills are yours, O God –
   their grass is lush and green,
   providing pastures for the flocks
   which everywhere are seen.

4. The whole rich land is yours
   for fodder or for plough;
   and so, for rain, sun, soil and seed,
   O God, we thank you now.

314 From Psalm 19
© Timothy Dudley-Smith

1. The stars declare his glory;
   the vault of heaven springs
   mute witness of the master's hand
   in all created things,
   and through the silences of space
   their soundless music sings.

2. The dawn returns in splendour,
   the heavens burn and blaze,
   the rising sun renews the race
   that measures all our days,
   and writes in fire across the skies
   God's majesty and praise.

3. So shine the Lord's commandments
   to make the simple wise;
   more sweet than honey to the taste,
   more rich than any prize,
   a law of love within our hearts,
   a light before our eyes.

4. So order too this life of mine,
    direct it all my days;
  the meditations of my heart
    be innocence and praise,
  my rock, and my redeeming Lord,
    in all my words and ways.

5. All you have made is ours to rule,
    the birds and beasts at will to tame,
  all things to order for the glory
    of your name.

315 From Psalm 29, Michael Perry
© Mrs B Perry/Jubilate Hymns

1. The God of heaven thunders,
  his voice in cadent echoes
  resounds above the waters,
  and all the world sings,
    'Glory, glory, glory!'

2. The desert writhes in tempest,
  wind whips the trees to fury,
  sear lightning splits the forest
  and flame diffuses
    'Glory, glory, glory!'

3. the mighty God eternal,
  is to his throne ascended,
  and we who are his people,
  within these walls cry,
    'Glory, glory, glory!'

316 From Psalm 8, Brian Foley
© 1971 Faber Music

1. With wonder, Lord, we see your works,
  we see the beauty you have made;
  this earth, the skies, all things that are
    in beauty made.

2. With wonder, Lord, we see your works,
  and child-like in our joy we sing
  to praise you, bless you, maker, Lord
    of everything.

3. The stars that fill the skies above,
  the sun and moon which give our light,
  are your designing for our use
    and our delight.

4. We praise your works, yet we ourselves
  are works of wonder made by you;
  not far from you in all we are
    and all we do.

For other items on this theme, see

HYMNS
 23 All creatures of our God and king
 28 Born in song
 30 By every nation, race and tongue
235 Eternal Father, strong to save
 36 For the music of creation
500 Give us a sense of wonder, God
529 God comes to us as one unheard
337 God of God, the uncreated
504 God of gods, we sound his praises
 38 God we praise you! God, we bless you!
288 God who created light
697 God whose love is everywhere
283 God's glory fills the universe
625 God, who stretched the spangled heavens
289 I believe in God the Father
 44 Immortal, invisible, God only wise
266 King of the universe, Lord of the ages
 56 O Lord my God, when I in awesome wonder
291 O Trinity, O Trinity
  1 Sing glory to God the Father
 67 The Lord is king! He set the stars
630 Waterfall and ocean

PSALMS
 80 Fill your hearts with joy and gladness
 82 From all who live beneath the skies
 83 Give to our God immortal praise
  5 God of mercy, God of grace
 84 I'll praise my maker while I've breath
 86 Let us sing to the God of salvation
 90 O worship the king all glorious above
 91 Praise him, praise him
 92 Praise the Lord, you heavens, adore him
230 The heavens declare your glory, Lord!
 99 This earth belongs to God

SONGS
 18 Be still and know that I am God
107 Father God I wonder
115 Have you not known
117 He is exalted
131 Oh, our Lord and King
132 Our God is great
278 Skills and abilities
142 Who paints the skies?
143 You are the fountain of holiness

AFFIRMING OUR BELIEF IN JESUS, THE SON OF GOD

HYMNS

317 Caroline Noel
© in this version Jubilate Hymns

1. At the name of Jesus
     every knee shall bow,
   every tongue confess him
     king of glory now;
   this the Father's pleasure,
     that we call him Lord,
   who from the beginning
     was the mighty word.

2. At his voice creation
     sprang at once to sight,
   all the angel faces, all the hosts of light;
   thrones and dominations,
     stars upon their way,
   all the heavenly orders,
     in their great array.

3. Humbled for a season, to receive a name
   from the lips of sinners
     unto whom he came;
   faithfully he bore it spotless to the last,
   brought it back victorious
     when from death he passed.

4. Bore it up triumphant
     with its human light,
   through all ranks of creatures
     to the central height;
   to the eternal Godhead,
     to the Father's throne,
   filled it with the glory
     of his triumph won.

5. Name him, Christians, name him,
     with love strong as death,
   but with awe and wonder,
     and with bated breath;
   he is God the Saviour,
     he is Christ the Lord,
   ever to be worshipped,
     trusted and adored.

6. In your hearts enthrone him;
     there let him subdue
   all that is not holy, all that is not true;
   crown him as your captain
     in temptation's hour,
   let his will enfold you
     in its light and power.

7. With his Father's glory
     Jesus comes again,
   angel hosts attend him
     and announce his reign;
   for all wreaths of empire
     meet upon his brow,
   and our hearts confess him
     King of glory now.

318 John L. Bell and Graham Maule
© 1987 WGRG, Iona Community, from *Heaven shall not wait* (Wild Goose Publication 1987)

1. Before the world began
     one Word was there;
   grounded in God he was,
     rooted in care;
   by him all things were made;
   in him was love displayed,
   through him God spoke and said,
     'I am for you'.

2. Life found in him its source,
     death found its end;
   light found in him its course,
     darkness its friend;
   for neither death nor doubt
   nor darkness can put out
   the glow of God, the shout
     'I am for you'.

3. The Word was in the world
   which from him came;
   unrecognised was he,
   unknown by name;
   one with all humankind,
   with the unloved aligned,
   convincing sight and mind
   'I am for you'.

4. All who received the Word,
   by God were blessed,
   sisters and brothers they
   of earth's fond guest.
   So did the Word of Grace
   proclaim in time and space,
   and with a human face,
   'I am for you'.

319 © Michael Saward/Jubilate Hymns

1. Christ triumphant, ever reigning,
   Saviour, Master, King!
   Lord of heaven, our lives sustaining,
   hear us as we sing:
      Yours the glory and the crown,
      the high renown, the eternal name.

2. Word incarnate, truth revealing,
   Son of Man on earth!
   power and majesty concealing
   by your humble birth:
      Yours the glory . . .

3. Suffering servant, scorned, ill-treated,
   victim crucified!
   death is through the cross defeated,
   sinners justified:
      Yours the glory . . .

4. Priestly king, enthroned for ever
   high in heaven above!
   sin and death and hell shall never
   stifle hymns of love:
      Yours the glory . . .

5. So, our hearts and voices raising
   through the ages long,
   ceaselessly upon you gazing,
   this shall be our song:
      Yours the glory . . .

320 Jack C. Winslow
© Mrs J. Tyrrell

1. Come sing the praise of Jesus,
   sing his love with hearts aflame,
   sing his wondrous birth of Mary,
   when to save the world he came;
   tell the life he lived for others,
   and his mighty deeds proclaim,
   for Jesus Christ is King.
      Praise and glory be to Jesus,
      praise and glory be to Jesus,
      praise and glory be to Jesus,
      for Jesus Christ is King!

2. When foes arose and slew him,
   he was victor in the fight;
   over death and hell he triumphed
   in his resurrection-might;
   he has raised our fallen manhood
   and enthroned it in the height,
   for Jesus Christ is King.
      Praise and glory be to Jesus . . .

3. There's joy for all who serve him,
   more than human tongue can say;
   there is pardon for the sinner,
   and the night is turned to day;
   there is healing for our sorrows,
   there is music all the way,
   for Jesus Christ is King.
      Praise and glory be to Jesus . . .

4. We witness to his beauty,
   and we spread his love abroad;
   and we cleave the hosts of darkness,
   with the Spirit's piercing sword;
   we will lead the souls in prison
   to the freedom of the Lord,
   for Jesus Christ is King.
      Praise and glory be to Jesus . . .

5. To Jesus be the glory,
   the dominion, and the praise;
   he is Lord of all creation,
   he is guide of all our ways;
   and the world shall be his empire
   in the fullness of the days,
   for Jesus Christ is King.
      Praise and glory be to Jesus . . .

321 Matthew Bridges and Godfrey Thring
© in this version Jubilate Hymns

1. Crown him with many crowns,
   the Lamb upon his throne,
   while heaven's eternal anthem drowns
   all music but its own!
   Awake, my soul, and sing
   of him who died to be
   your saviour and your matchless king
   through all eternity.

2. Crown him the Lord of life
   triumphant from the grave,
   who rose victorious from the strife
   for those he came to save:
   his glories now we sing
   who died and reigns on high;
   he died eternal life to bring
   and lives that death may die.

3. Crown him the Lord of love,
   who shows his hands and side –
   those wounds yet visible above
   in beauty glorified.
   No angel in the sky
   can fully bear that sight,
   but downward bends his burning eye
   at mysteries so bright.

4. Crown him the Lord of peace –
   his kingdom is at hand;
   from pole to pole let warfare cease
   and Christ rule every land!
   A city stands on high,
   his glory it displays,
   and there the nations 'Holy' cry
   in joyful hymns of praise.

5. Crown him the Lord of years,
   the potentate of time,
   creator of the rolling spheres
   in majesty sublime:
   all hail, Redeemer, hail,
   for you have died for me;
   your praise shall never, never fail
   through all eternity!

322 Brian Wren
© 1977, 1995 Stainer & Bell

1. Jesus, on the mountain peak
   stands alone in glory blazing.
   Let us, if we dare to speak,
   the saints and angels praising:
      Alleluia!

2. Trembling at his feet we saw
   Moses and Elijah speaking.
   All the prophets and the law
   shout through them
      their joyful greeting:
      Alleluia!

3. Swift the cloud of glory came,
   God, proclaiming in its thunder,
   Jesus as his Son by name!
   Nations, cry aloud in wonder:
      Alleluia!

4. Jesus is the Chosen One
   living hope of every nation,
   hear and heed him, everyone;
   sing, with earth and all creation,
      Alleluia!

323 Charles Wesley

1. Jesus! the name high over all
   in hell or earth or sky;
   angels again before it fall
      and devils fear and fly,
      and devils fear and fly.

2. Jesus! the name to sinners dear,
   the name to sinners given;
   it scatters all their guilty fear,
      it turns their hell to heaven,
      it turns their hell to heaven.

3. Jesus the prisoner's fetters breaks
   and bruises Satan's head;
   power into strengthless souls he speaks
      and life into the dead,
      and life into the dead.

4. O that the world might taste and see
the riches of his grace!
the arms of love that welcome me
would all mankind embrace,
would all mankind embrace.

5. His righteousness alone I show,
his saving grace proclaim;
this is my work on earth below,
to cry 'Behold the Lamb!'
to cry 'Behold the Lamb!'

6. Happy if with my final breath
I may but gasp his name,
preach him to all, and cry in death,
'Behold, behold the Lamb!'
'Behold, behold the Lamb!.

324 © Timothy Dudley Smith

1. Name of all majesty,
fathomless mystery,
king of the ages
by angels adored;
power and authority,
splendour and dignity,
bow to his mastery,
Jesus is Lord!

2. Child of our destiny,
God from eternity,
love of the Father
on sinners outpoured;
see now what God has done
sending his only Son,
Christ the beloved One,
Jesus is Lord!

3. Saviour of Calvary,
costliest victory,
darkness defeated
and Eden restored;
born as a man to die,
nailed to a cross on high,
cold in the grave to lie,
Jesus is Lord!

4. Source of all sovereignty,
light, immortality,
life everlasting
and heaven assured;
so with the ransomed, we
praise him eternally,
Christ in his majesty,
Jesus is Lord!

325 Martin E. Leckebusch
© Kevin Mayhew

1. No other prophet ever spoke
so clearly to our race;
no bright and shining angel matched
the glory on his face;
through him the universe was made,
by him our debt for sin was paid –
in Christ, at last, we see in full
God's splendour and God's grace.

2. Majestic angels swiftly fly
on wings of wind and flame;
his servants' servants, low they bend
in honour of his name.
The Father's precious Son is he,
the Lord from all eternity –
yet taking human flesh and blood
a baby he became.

3. His throne is built on righteousness,
established firm and sure;
the oil of joy anoints the one
who values what is pure!
The wonder of the Maker's skill
is seen throughout creation still –
but when this age has run its course
his kingdom will endure.

4. God's matchless power
confirms that Christ
is all our life and light;
his word proclaims the solemn truth
dividing wrong from right,
and those who cast that word aside
are lost like driftwood on the tide –
but Jesus reigns eternally
in majesty and might!

326 © Richard Morgan

1. O Firstborn of the Unseen Lord,
   his co-eternal mighty Word,
   all that exists you formed by grace,
   the land and sea, the stars and space:
   things seen and unseen,
       great and small,
   in you, for you, God made them all.

2. You are the bond of unity
   of all that is, and is to be,
   before creation you were there.
   The source of all things good and fair;
   the source of power
       and rule and might,
   you made the day, you made the night.

3. You harmonise the universe,
   and when it fell beneath the curse
   and wandered into sin and death,
   you took for us our mortal breath,
   gave up your life for human sin
   and rose again our peace to win.

4. In you God's fullness wholly lives
   and life and endless glory gives.
   Creator, Ruler, Lover, Friend
   in you creation finds its end:
   the Church's head,
       both source and goal,
   in you, for you, is all made whole.

327 Martin E. Leckebusch © Kevin Mayhew

1. Praise to Christ, the Lord incarnate,
   gift of God by human birth:
   he it is who came among us,
   shared our life and showed our worth;
       ours the turmoil he encountered,
       ours the fight he made his own;
       now within our hearts his Spirit
       makes his way of freedom known.

2. Praise to Christ, the Man of sorrows,
   tasting death for our release:
   his the cup of bitter anguish,
   ours the pardon, ours the peace;
       his the blood that seals forgiveness,
       ours the weight of guilt he bore –
       so by death and resurrection
       Christ has opened heaven's door.

3. Praise to Christ, the Priest eternal;
   still for us he intercedes;
   still he sees our pains and problems –
   how he understands our needs!
       Yesterday, today, forever,
       always he remains the same;
       pledged to bring us to the Father,
       strong in grace and free from blame.

328 Margaret Clarkson. © 1967 Hope Publishing Co. Administered by CopyCare

1. Priest and victim, Jesus dies –
   gives himself in sacrifice.
   Christ, the sinless Son of God,
   offers up for us his blood,
   gives himself in sacrifice –
   Priest and victim, Jesus dies!

2. Mighty Victor, see him rise,
   bringing us to paradise;
   sin and death no more may claim
   those who trust his saving name;
   Bringing us to paradise,
   mighty Victor, see him rise!

3. Lord of life, behold him stand
   now for us at God's right hand.
   Still our human frame he wears,
   feels our woes and heeds our prayers:
   now for us at God's right hand,
   Lord of life, behold him stand!

4. Prince and Saviour, Christ shall come,
   soon to take his ransomed home;
   his the kingdom, his the power,
   his the glory, in that hour –
   soon to take his ransomed home,
   Prince and Saviour, Christ shall come!

5. King forever, he shall reign,
   Lord of death and sin and pain;
   pure and righteous, strong and free,
   he shall rule in equity:
   Lord of death and sin and pain,
   King forever, he shall reign!

329 © Alec Motyer

1. That priceless gift, what tongue can tell?
   Marvel and mystery, incarnate God:
   from highest heaven to lowest earth,
   the Father's Son, a servant's birth:
   our life he lived, our path he trod.

2. That sinless life, what pen can draw?
   Holy perfection, tempted and true:
   to heal the blind, the deaf, the lame;
   dead souls, arise! Dumb lips, proclaim
   that Christ has brought
     good news to you.

3. That saving cross,
     what mind can probe?
   The breadth and length of love,
     its height and depth
   before the world of time and space,
   the Lamb ordained to take our place,
   immortal God in mortal death.

4. That empty tomb, what joy can match –
   word of the angel beyond belief?
   'See here, the place they laid his head,
   the living Lord who once was dead' –
   and Jesus lives to still our grief!

5. That mighty hope, all hopes above:
   in clouds of glory we see him come!
   When saints shall rise with one accord
   to be forever with the Lord;
   when Jesus comes to take us home.

330 Fred Pratt Green
© 1980 Stainer & Bell

1. This is the threefold truth
   on which our faith depends;
   and with this joyful cry
   worship begins and ends;
     Christ has died!
     Christ is risen!
     Christ will come again!

2. Made sacred by long use,
   new-minted for our time,
   our liturgies sum up
   the hope we have in him:
     Christ has died!
     Christ is risen!
     Christ will come again!

3. On this we fix our minds
   as, kneeling side by side,
   we take the bread and wine
   from him, the Crucified:
     Christ has died!
     Christ is risen!
     Christ will come again!

4. By this we are upheld
   when doubt and grief assails
   our Christian fortitude,
   and only grace avails:
     Christ has died!
     Christ is risen!
     Christ will come again!

5. This is the threefold truth
   which, if we hold it fast,
   changes the world and us
   and brings us home at last.
     Christ has died!
     Christ is risen!
     Christ will come again!

331 © Edward Burns

1. We have a gospel to proclaim,
   good news for all throughout the earth;
   the gospel of a saviour's name:
   we sing his glory, tell his worth.

2. Tell of his birth at Bethlehem,
   not in a royal house or hall
   but in a stable dark and dim:
   the Word made flesh, a light for all.

3. Tell of his death at Calvary,
   hated by those he came to save;
   in lonely suffering on the cross
   for all he loved, his life he gave.

4. Tell of that glorious Easter morn;
empty the tomb, for he was free;
he broke the power of death and hell
that we might share his victory.

5. Tell of his reign at God's right hand,
by all creation glorified;
he sends his Spirit on his church
to live for him, the lamb who died.

6. Now we rejoice to name him king;
Jesus is Lord of all the earth;
this gospel-message we proclaim:
we sing his glory, tell his worth.

SONGS

332 Graham Kendrick
© 1995 Make Way Music

1. Above the clash of creeds,
the many voices
that call on so many names,
into these final days
our God has spoken
by sending his only Son.
There is no other way
by which we must be saved;
his name is Jesus, the only Saviour;
no other sinless life,
no other sacrifice,
in all creation – no other way.

2. Before we called he came
to earth from heaven,
our maker became a man;
when no-one else could pay
he bought our freedom,
exchanging his life for ours.
There is no other way . . .

3. Beneath the cross of Christ
let earth fall silent
in awe of this mystery,
then let this song arise
and fill the nations:
O hear him call, 'come to me.'
There is no other way . . .

333 Marc Nelson. © 1987 Mercy/Vineyard Publishing
Administered by CopyCare

1. I believe in Jesus,
I believe he is the Son of God;
I believe he died and rose again,
I believe he paid for us all.

MEN   And I believe he's here now,
WOMEN I believe that he's here,
ALL   standing in our midst.
MEN   Here with the power to heal now,
WOMEN with the power to heal,
ALL   and the grace to forgive.

2. I believe in you, Lord,
I believe you are the Son of God;
I believe you died and rose again,
I believe you paid for us all.

MEN   And I believe you're here now,
WOMEN I believe that you're here,
ALL   standing in our midst.
MEN   Here with the power to heal now,
WOMEN with the power to heal,
ALL   and the grace to forgive.

334 © 1995 Tanya Riches/Hillsongs
Australia/ Kingsway's Thankyou Music

1. Jesus, what a beautiful name –
Son of God, Son of Man,
Lamb that was slain.
Joy and peace, strength and hope,
grace that blows all fear away:
Jesus, what a beautiful name.

2. Jesus, what a beautiful name –
truth revealed, my future sealed,
healed my pain.
Love and freedom, life and warmth,
grace that blows all fear away:
Jesus, what a beautiful name.

3. Jesus, what a beautiful name –
rescued my soul, my stronghold,
lifts me from shame.
Forgiveness, security, power and love,
grace that blows all fear away:
Jesus, what a beautiful name.

For other items on this theme, see

HYMNS

590 All authority is yours
 24 All hail the power of Jesus' name
 25 Alleluia! raise the anthem
458 Alleluia, sing to Jesus
431 Christ holds the keys
591 Christ is the world's Light, he and none other
432 Christ is the world's true light
 33 Come let us join our cheerful songs
199 Fairest Lord Jesus
288 God who created light
 45 Jesus shall reign where'er the sun
 55 O for a thousand tongues to sing
440 Rejoice the Lord is king!
284 These are the facts
 72 To the name of our salvation

SONGS

106 Blessing and honour
272 Christ, your glory
116 He came down
117 He is exalted
118 He is the Lord
122 Jesus is the name we honour
123 Jesus shall take the highest honour
126 Lord, I lift your name on high
127 Lord of lords

AFFIRMING OUR BELIEF
IN THE COMING OF JESUS (ADVENT)

HYMNS

335
Charles Wesley
© in this version Jubilate Hymns

1. Come, O long-expected Jesus,
born to set your people free!
from our fears and sins release us,
Christ in whom our rest shall be.

2. Israel's strength and consolation,
born salvation to impart;
dear desire of every nation,
joy of every longing heart:

3. Born your people to deliver,
born a child and yet a king;
born to reign in us for ever,
now your gracious kingdom bring:

4. By your own eternal Spirit
rule in all our hearts alone;
by your all-sufficient merit
raise us to your glorious throne.

336
From *Nunc Dimittis* Luke 2, Michael Perry
© Mrs B. Perry/Jubilate Hymns

1. Jesus, hope of every nation,
light of heaven upon our way;
promise of the world's salvation,
spring of life's eternal day!

2. Saints by faith on God depending
wait to see Messiah born;
sin's oppressive night is ending
in the glory of the dawn.

3. Look, he comes! – the long-awaited
Christ, redeemer, living Word;
hope and faith are vindicated
as with joy we greet the Lord.

4. Glory in the highest heaven
to the Father, Spirit, Son;
and on earth all praise be given
to our God, the Three-in-One!

337
After Prudentius, John Neale and Henry Baker
© in this version Jubilate Hymns

1. God of God, the uncreated,
love before the world began;
he the source and he the ending,
Son of God and Son of Man,
Lord of all the things that have been,
master of the eternal plan,
   evermore and evermore.

2. He is here, whom generations
sought throughout the ages long;
promised by the ancient prophets,
justice for a world of wrong,
God's salvation for the faithful:
him we praise in endless song
   evermore and evermore.

3. Happy is that day for ever
when, by God the Spirit's grace,
lowly Mary, virgin mother,
bore the saviour of our race.
Man and child, the world's redeemer
now displays his sacred face
   evermore and evermore.

4. Praise him, heaven of the heavens,
praise him, angels in the height;
priests and prophets, bow before him,
saints who longed to see this sight.
Let no human voice be silent,
in his glory hearts unite
   evermore and evermore!

5. Christ be praised with God the Father,
and the Holy Spirit, praised!
hymns of worship, high thanksgiving
echo through a world amazed:
Honour, majesty, dominion!
songs of victory be raised
   evermore and evermore!

338 From the Latin 13th Century, John Neale and others
© in this version Jubilate Hymns. Verses 2, 5, 7 in
this version Michael Saward/Jubilate Hymns

1. O come, O come, Emmanuel,
   and ransom captive Israel
   who mourns in lonely exile here
   until the Son of God draws near.
   Rejoice, rejoice, Emmanuel
   shall come to you, O Israel.

2. O come, true Wisdom from on high,
   who orders all to mind and eye:
   to us the path of knowledge show
   and teach us in her ways to grow.
   Rejoice, rejoice . . .

3. O come, O come, great Lord of might,
   who long ago on Sinai's height,
   gave all your tribes the ancient law
   in cloud and majesty and awe.
   Rejoice, rejoice . . .

4. O come, true Branch of Jesse, free
   your children from this tyranny:
   from depths of hell your people save,
   to rise victorious from the grave.
   Rejoice, rejoice . . .

5. O come, strong Key of David, come
   and open wide our heavenly home;
   upon our journey give relief
   and close the path to pain and grief.
   Rejoice, rejoice . . .

6. O come, bright Daystar, come and cheer
   our spirits by your advent here;
   dispel the long night's lingering gloom
   and pierce the shadows of the tomb.
   Rejoice, rejoice . . .

7. King of the Nations, come, embrace
   and unify the human race;
   command our sad divisions cease
   and be for us the Prince of Peace.
   Rejoice, rejoice . . .

This hymn follows the sequence of the ancient Advent Antiphons
and should not ideally be shortened. If verses have to be omitted
then it is best to leave out verses 2 and 4.

339 After Charles Coffin, John Chandler
© in this version Word & Music/Jubilate Hymns

1. On Jordan's bank the Baptist's cry
   announces that the Lord is nigh:
   awake and listen for he brings
   glad tidings of the King of kings.

2. Let every heart be cleansed from sin,
   make straight the way for God within,
   and so prepare to be the home
   where such a mighty guest may come.

3. For you are our salvation, Lord,
   our refuge and our great reward
   without your grace we waste away
   like flowers that wither and decay.

4. To heal the sick, stretch out your hand,
   and make the fallen sinner stand;
   shine out, and let your light restore
   earth's own true loveliness once more.

5. To you, O Christ, all praises be,
   whose advent sets your people free;
   whom with the Father we adore
   and Holy Spirit evermore!

PSALM

340 From Psalm 98, Isaac Watts
© in this version Jubilate Hymns

1. Joy to the world – the Lord has come!
   let earth receive her king.
   let every heart prepare him room
      and heaven and nature sing,
      and heaven and nature sing,
      and heaven, and heaven
         and nature sing!

2. Joy to the earth – the saviour reigns!
   let songs be heard on high,
   while fields and streams
      and hills and plains
      repeat the sounding joy,
      repeat the sounding joy,
      repeat, repeat the sounding joy.

3. He rules the world with truth and grace,
   and makes the nations prove
   the glories of his righteousness,
      the wonders of his love,
      the wonders of his love,
      the wonders, wonders of his love.

SONGS

341 © Christopher Idle/Jubilate Hymns

Now is the time,
  the time of God's favour,
promise and hope
  for a people restored;
listen, repent and turn back
  to the Saviour
truly to welcome the year of our Lord!

1. This is the day of Jesus' arrival;
here in the desert,
  the threshold of home!
After earth's longings
  comes heaven's revival:
God, make us ready
  this day as you come!
  Now is the time . . .

2. Here is the hour, the hour of salvation;
learn the new song
  for new people to sing:
risen from death
  is the Source of creation;
lift up your heads
  for the hour of the King!
  Now is the time . . .

3. Do not delay, but come now
  to meet him,
Sabbath and Jubilee joining in one:
Christmas and Easter
  and Advent will greet him;
see a fresh universe rise to the Son!
  Now is the time . . .

342 From Isaiah 40 & 41 Andy Piercy and Charlie Groves © 1995 I Q Music

Prepare the way for the Lord;
make straight his path
in the wilderness –
a highway for our God:
every valley shall be raised up,
and every mountain
be made low;
and the glory of the Lord
will be revealed,
and the glory of the Lord
will be revealed.

Do you not know?
Have you not heard?
He sits enthroned
above the earth
and stretches out the heavens:
lift up your voice
and with a shout,
come, lift it up: don't be afraid –
and the glory of the Lord
will be revealed,
and the glory of the Lord
will be revealed,
and the glory of the Lord
will be revealed.

LEADER:
He gives strength to the weary
and power to the weak,
ALL:
he gives strength to the weary
and power to the weak.
LEADER:
Those who hope in the Lord
will renew their strength,
ALL:
those who hope in the Lord
will renew their strength,
and the glory of the Lord
will be revealed.

For other items on this theme, see

HYMNS
504 God of gods, we sound his praises
 38 God we praise you! God, we bless you!
697 God whose love is everywhere
435 Hark the glad sound! – the Saviour comes
438 Jesus comes with clouds descending
472 Let all mortal flesh keep silence
269 Your kingdom come, O God!

AFFIRMING OUR BELIEF IN JESUS, BORN INTO OUR WORLD

HYMNS

343 William Dix
© in this version Jubilate Hymns

1. As with gladness men of old
   did the guiding star behold,
   as with joy they hailed its light,
   leading onward, beaming bright:
   so, most gracious Lord, may we
   evermore your splendour see.

2. As with joyful steps they sped,
   Saviour, to your lowly bed,
   there to bend the knee before
   you, whom heaven and earth adore:
   so with ever-quickening pace
   may we seek your throne of grace.

3. As they offered gifts most rare
   at your cradle plain and bare,
   so may we with holy joy
   pure and free from sin's alloy,
   all our costliest treasures bring,
   Christ, to you, our heavenly king.

4. Holy Jesus, every day
   keep us in the narrow way,
   and when earthly things are past,
   bring our ransomed souls at last:
   where they need no star to guide,
   where no clouds your glory hide.

5. In the heavenly city bright
   none shall need created light –
   you, its light, its joy, its crown,
   you its sun which goes not down;
   there for ever may we sing
   alleluias to our king.

344 James Montgomery
© in this version Jubilate Hymns

1. Angels from the realms of glory,
   wing your flight through all the earth;
   heralds of creation's story
   now proclaim Messiah's birth!
      Come and worship
      Christ, the new-born king;
      come and worship,
      worship Christ the new-born king.

2. Shepherds in the fields abiding,
   watching by your flocks at night,
   God with us is now residing:
   see, there shines the infant light!
      Come and worship . . .

3. Wise men, leave your contemplations!
   brighter visions shine afar;
   seek in him the hope of nations,
   you have seen his rising star:
      Come and worship . . .

4. Though an infant now we view him,
   he will share his Father's throne,
   gather all the nations to him;
   every knee shall then bow down:
      Come and worship . . .

345 Verses 1, 2 unknown
Verse 3 John McFarland

1. Away in a manger, no crib for a bed,
   the little Lord Jesus
      laid down his sweet head;
   the stars in the bright sky
      looked down where he lay;
   the little Lord Jesus asleep on the hay.

2. The cattle are lowing, the baby awakes,
   but little Lord Jesus no crying he makes:
   I love you, Lord Jesus –
      look down from on high
   and stay by my side
      until morning is nigh.

3. Be near me, Lord Jesus; I ask you to stay
close by me for ever and love me, I pray;
bless all the dear children
in your tender care,
and fit us for heaven
to live with you there.

346 Reginald Heber
© in this version Jubilate Hymns

1. Brightest and best
of the sons of the morning,
dawn on our darkness
and come to our aid;
star of the east, the horizon adorning,
guide where our infant redeemer is laid!

2. What shall we give him,
in costly devotion?
Shall we bring incense
and offerings divine,
gems of the mountain
and pearls of the ocean,
myrrh from the forest
or gold from the mine?

3. Vainly we offer each lavish oblation,
vainly with gifts would his favour secure;
richer by far is the heart's adoration,
dearer to God
are the prayers of the poor.

4. Brightest and best
of the sons of the morning,
dawn on our darkness
and come to our aid;
star of the east, the horizon adorning,
guide where our infant redeemer is laid!

347 John Byrom
© in this version Jubilate Hymns

1. Christians, awake!
Salute the happy morn
on which the Saviour
of the world was born;
rise to adore the mystery of love
which hosts of angels
chanted from above:
with them the joyful tidings first begun
of God incarnate and the virgin's Son.

2. First to the watchful shepherds
it was told,
who heard the herald angel's voice:
'Behold,
I bring good news
of your Messiah's birth
to you and all the nations here on earth!
This day has God fulfilled
his promised word;
this day is born a Saviour,
Christ the Lord!'

3. To Bethlehem
these eager shepherds ran
to see the wonder
of our God made man;
they found, with Joseph
and the holy maid,
Jesus, the Saviour, in a manger laid.
Amazed, with joy
this story they proclaim,
the first apostles of his infant fame.

4. Let us, like those good shepherds,
now employ
our grateful voices to declare the joy:
trace we the babe,
who has redeemed our loss,
from his poor manger to his bitter cross;
treading his steps, assisted by his grace,
by faith again we see the Saviour's face.

5. Glory to God! The skies are singing still,
peace on the earth
to people of goodwill!
Christ, who was born on
this most happy day,
round all the earth
his glory shall display.
Saved by his love,
unceasing we shall sing
eternal praise to heaven's almighty King.

348 Michael Perry
© Mrs B. Perry/Jubilate Hymns

1. Come and sing the Christmas story
   this holy night!
   Christ is born: the hope of glory
   dawns on our sight.
   Alleluia! earth is ringing
   with a thousand angels singing –
   hear the message they are bringing
   this holy night.

2. Jesus, Saviour, child of Mary
   this holy night,
   in a world confused and weary
   you are our light.
   God is in a manger lying,
   self effacing, wealth denying,
   life embracing, death defying
   this holy night.

3. Lord of all! Let us acclaim him
   this holy night;
   king of our salvation name him,
   throned in the height.
   Son of Man – let us adore him,
   all the earth is waiting for him;
   Son of God – we bow before him
   this holy night.

349 From *In Dulci Jubilo* (14th Century), John Neale

1. Good Christians all, rejoice
   with heart and soul and voice!
   listen now to what we say,
   Jesus Christ is born today:
   ox and ass before him bow
   and he is in the manger now!
   Christ is born today;
   Christ is born today!

2. Good Christians all, rejoice
   with heart and soul and voice!
   hear the news of endless bliss,
   Jesus Christ was born for this:
   he has opened heaven's door
   and we are blessed for evermore!
   Christ was born for this;
   Christ was born for this.

3. Good Christians all, rejoice
   with heart and soul and voice!
   now you need not fear the grave;
   Jesus Christ was born to save:
   come at his most gracious call
   to find salvation, one and all!
   Christ was born to save;
   Christ was born to save!

350 Traditional
© in this version Jubilate Hymns

1. God rest you merry, gentlemen,
   let nothing you dismay!
   for Jesus Christ our saviour
   was born on Christmas Day,
   to save us all from Satan's power
   when we had gone astray:
   O tidings of comfort and joy,
   comfort and joy;
   O tidings of comfort and joy!

2. At Bethlehem in Judah
   the holy babe was born;
   they laid him in a manger
   on this most happy morn,
   at which his mother Mary
   did neither fear nor scorn;
   O tidings of comfort and joy . . .

3. From God our heavenly Father
   a holy angel came;
   the shepherds saw the glory
   and heard the voice proclaim
   that Christ was born in Bethlehem –
   and Jesus is his name:
   O tidings of comfort and joy . . .

4. 'Fear not,' then said the angel,
   'let nothing cause you fright;
   to you is born a Saviour
   in David's town tonight,
   to free all those who trust in him
   from Satan's power and might:'
   O tidings of comfort and joy . . .

5. The shepherds at these tidings
   rejoiced in heart and mind,
   and on the darkened hillside
   they left their flocks behind,
   and went to Bethlehem straightway
   this holy child to find:
       O tidings of comfort and joy,
       comfort and joy;
       O tidings of comfort and joy!

6. And when to Bethlehem they came
   where Christ the infant lay;
   they found him in a manger
   where oxen fed on hay,
   and there beside her newborn child
   his mother knelt to pray:
       O tidings of comfort and joy . . .

7. Now to the Lord sing praises,
   all people in this place!
   with Christian love and fellowship
   each other now embrace,
   and let this Christmas festival
   all bitterness displace:
       O tidings of comfort and joy . . .

351 © Timothy Dudley-Smith

1. Here is the centre: star on distant star
   shining unheeded
       in the depths of space,
   worlds without number,
       all the worlds there are,
   turn in their travelling to this holy place.
       Here in a stable and an ox's stall
       laid in a manger lies the Lord of all.

2. Now is the moment:
       God in flesh appears,
   down from the splendours
       of his throne sublime,
   High King of Ages, Lord of all the years,
   God, everlasting stoops
       to space and time.
       All that was promised
           now is brought to birth,
       Jesus our Saviour
           come at last to earth.

3. Son of the Father, God's eternal Word,
   emptied of glory,
       born to cross and grave;
   ours is the secret
       ancient prophets heard,
   God in our likeness
       come to seek and save:
       Christ in his passion,
           bearer of our sins;
       and, from his rising, risen life begins.

4. Come then rejoicing!
       Praise be all our songs!
   Love lies among us in the stable bare,
   light in our darkness,
       righting of all wrongs,
   hope for the future, joy enough to share.
       Peace to our hearts
           for God is on the throne!
       Christ our Redeemer
           comes to claim his own.

352 Charles Wesley and others

1. Hark! the herald angels sing
   glory to the new-born King;
   peace on earth and mercy mild,
   God and sinners reconciled!
   Joyful all you nations rise,
   join the triumph of the skies;
   with the angelic host proclaim,
   'Christ is born in Bethlehem'.
       Hark! the herald angels sing
       glory to the new-born King.

2. Christ, by highest heaven adored,
   Christ, the everlasting Lord;
   late in time behold him come,
   offspring of a virgin's womb:
   veiled in flesh the Godhead see,
   hail the incarnate Deity!
   pleased as man with us to dwell,
   Jesus our Emmanuel:
       Hark! the herald . . .

3. Hail the heaven-born Prince of peace,
    hail the Sun of righteousness;
    light and life to all he brings,
    risen with healing in his wings:
    mild, he lays his glory by,
    born that we no more may die;
    born to raise us from the earth,
    born to give us second birth:
    Hark! the herald . . .

353 Christina Rossetti

1. In the bleak mid-winter
        frosty wind made moan,
    earth stood hard as iron,
        water like a stone;
    snow had fallen, snow on snow,
        snow on snow,
    in the bleak mid-winter
        long ago.

2. Heaven cannot hold him,
        nor the earth sustain;
    heaven and earth shall flee away
        when he comes to reign:
    in the bleak mid-winter
        a stable-place sufficed
    God, the Lord almighty,
        Jesus Christ.

3. Enough for him whom cherubim
        worship night and day –
    a breastful of milk,
    and a manger full of hay;
    enough for him whom angels
        fall down before –
    the wise men and the shepherds
        who adore!

4. What can I give him, poor as I am?
    If I were a shepherd
        I would give a lamb,
    if I were a wise man
        I would do my part;
    yet what I can I give him –
        give my heart.

354 Edmund Sears
© in this version Jubilate Hymns

1. It came upon the midnight clear,
    that glorious song of old,
    from angels bending near the earth
    to touch their harps of gold:
    'Through all the earth,
        goodwill and peace
    from heaven's all-gracious king!'
    The world in solemn stillness lay
    to hear the angels sing.

2. With sorrow brought by sin and strife
    the world has suffered long
    and, since the angels sang, have passed
    two thousand years of wrong:
    the nations, still at war, hear not
    the love-song which they bring:
    O hush the noise and cease the strife,
    to hear the angels sing!

3. And those whose journey now is hard,
    whose hope is burning low,
    who tread the rocky path of life
    with painful steps and slow:
    O listen to the news of love
    which makes the heavens ring!
    O rest beside the weary road
    and hear the angels sing!

4. And still the days are hastening on –
    by prophets seen of old –
    towards the fullness of the time
    when comes the age foretold:
    then earth and heaven
        renewed shall see
    the prince of peace, their king;
    and all the world repeat the song
    which now the angels sing.

355 After German authors, Michael Perry
© Mrs B. Perry/Jubilate Hymns

1. Jesus Christ the Lord is born,
    all the bells are ringing!
    angels greet the holy One
        and shepherds hear them singing,
        and shepherds hear them singing:

2. 'Go to Bethlehem today,
   find your king and saviour:
   glory be to God on high,
     to earth his peace and favour,
     to earth his peace and favour!'

3. Held within a cattle stall,
   loved by love maternal,
   see the master of us all,
     our Lord of lords eternal,
     our Lord of lords eternal!

4. Soon shall come the wise men three,
   rousing Herod's anger:
   mothers' hearts shall broken be
     and Mary's son in danger,
     and Mary's son in danger.

5. Death from life and life from death,
   our salvation's story:
   let all living things give breath
     to Christmas songs of glory,
     to Christmas songs of glory!

356 Frank Houghton. © OMF International (IHQ) and in this version Jubilate Hymns

1. Lord, you were rich
     beyond all splendour,
   yet, for love's sake, became so poor;
   leaving your throne in glad surrender,
   sapphire-paved courts for stable floor:
   Lord, you were rich
     beyond all splendour,
   yet, for love's sake, became so poor.

2. You are our God beyond all praising,
   yet, for love's sake, became a man;
   stooping so low, but sinners raising
   heavenwards, by your eternal plan:
   you are our God, beyond all praising,
   yet, for love's sake, became a man.

3. Lord, you are love beyond all telling,
   Saviour and King, we worship you;
   Emmanuel, within us dwelling,
   make us and keep us pure and true:
   Lord, you are love beyond all telling,
   Saviour and King, we worship you.

357 After John Wade, Frederick Oakley and others

1. O come, all ye faithful,
   joyful and triumphant;
   O come ye, O come ye to Bethlehem;
   come and behold him,
     born the king of angels!
   O come, let us adore him,
   O come, let us adore him,
   O come, let us adore him,
     Christ the Lord!

2. God from God,
   Light from light –
   lo, he abhors not the virgin's womb!
   Very God, begotten, not created.
     O come . . .

3. Sing, choirs of angels,
   sing in exultation!
   Sing, all ye citizens of heaven above,
   'Glory to God in the highest!'
     O come . . .

4. Yea, Lord, we greet thee,
   born for our salvation;
   Jesus, to thee be glory given!
   Word of the Father
     now in flesh appearing.
     O come . . .

or on Christmas morning:
4. Yea, Lord we greet thee,
   born this happy morning:
   Jesus, to thee be glory given!
   Word of the Father
     now in flesh appearing.
     O come . . .

358 Phillips Brooks

1. O little town of Bethlehem,
   how still we see you lie!
   Above your deep and dreamless sleep
   the silent stars go by:
   yet in your dark streets shining
   is everlasting light;
   the hopes and fears of all the years
   are met in you tonight.

2. For Christ is born of Mary
   and, gathered all above
   while mortals sleep, the angels keep
   their watch of wondering love:
   O morning stars, together
   proclaim the holy birth,
   and praises sing to God the king,
   and peace to all the earth.

3. How silently, how silently
   the wondrous gift is given!
   So God imparts to human hearts
   the blessings of his heaven;
   no ear may hear his coming,
   but in this world of sin,
   where meek souls will receive him – still
   the dear Christ enters in.

4. O holy child of Bethlehem,
   descend to us, we pray;
   cast out our sin and enter in,
   be born in us today!
   We hear the Christmas angels
   the great glad tidings tell –
   O come to us, abide with us,
   our Lord Emmanuel.

359 Cecil Alexander

1. Once in royal David's city
   stood a lowly cattle shed,
   where a mother laid her baby
   in a manger for his bed:
   Mary was that mother mild,
   Jesus Christ, her little child.

2. He came down to earth from heaven
   who is God and Lord of all;
   and his shelter was a stable
   and his cradle was a stall:
   with the poor and meek and lowly
   lived on earth our Saviour holy.

3. And through all his wondrous childhood
   day by day like us he grew;
   he was little, weak and helpless;
   tears and smiles like us he knew:
   and he feels for all our sadness,
   and he shares in all our gladness.

4. And our eyes at last shall see him,
   through his own redeeming love;
   for that child, so dear and gentle,
   is our Lord in heaven above:
   and he leads his children on
   to the place where he is gone.

5. Not in that poor lowly stable
   with the oxen standing by,
   we shall see him, but in heaven,
   set at God's right hand on high:
   there his children gather round,
   bright like stars, with glory crowned.

360 Edward Caswall
© in this version Jubilate Hymns

1. See, amid the winter snow,
   born for us on earth below;
   see, the gentle Lamb appears,
   promised from eternal years:
   Hail, O ever-blessèd morn;
   hail, redemption's happy dawn;
   sing through all Jerusalem:
   'Christ is born in Bethlehem!'

2. Low within a manger lies
   he who built the starry skies;
   he who, throned in height sublime,
   reigns above the cherubim:
   Hail, O ever-blessèd morn . . .

3. Say, you humble shepherds, say
   what's your joyful news today?
   tell us why you left your sheep
   on the lonely mountain steep:
   Hail, O ever-blessèd morn . . .

4. 'As we watched at dead of night,
   all around us shone a light;
   angels singing Peace on earth
   told us of a Saviour's birth.'
   Hail, O ever-blessèd morn . . .

5. Sacred infant, king most dear,
   what a tender love was here,
   thus to come from highest bliss
   down to such a world as this!
   Hail, O ever-blessèd morn . . .

6. Holy Saviour, born on earth,
   teach us by your lowly birth;
   grant that we may ever be
   taught by such humility.
       Hail, O ever-blessèd morn;
       hail, redemption's happy dawn;
       sing through all Jerusalem:
       'Christ is born in Bethlehem!'

361 Michael Perry
© Mrs B. Perry/Jubilate Hymns

1. See him lying on a bed of straw:
   a draughty stable with an open door;
   Mary cradling the babe she bore –
   the prince of glory is his name.
       O now carry me to Bethlehem
       to see the Lord of love again:
       just as poor as was the stable then,
       the prince of glory when he came.

2. Star of silver, sweep across the skies,
   show where Jesus in the manger lies;
   shepherds, swiftly from your stupor rise
   to see the Saviour of the world!
       O now carry . . .

3. Angels, sing again the song you sang,
   sing the glory of God's gracious plan;
   sing that Bethlehem's little baby can
   be the Saviour of us all.
       O now carry . . .

4. Mine are riches, from your poverty,
   from your innocence, eternity;
   mine, forgiveness by your death for me,
   child of sorrow for my joy.
       O now carry . . .

362 After Joseph Möhr, John Young

1. Silent night! holy night!
   all is calm, all is bright
   round the virgin and her child:
   holy infant, so gentle and mild,
       sleep in heavenly peace;
       sleep in heavenly peace!

2. Silent night! holy night!
   shepherds quail at the sight,
   glory streams from heaven afar:
   heavenly hosts sing, 'Alleluia,
       Christ the Saviour is born,
       Christ the Saviour is born.'

3. Silent night! holy night!
   Son of God, love's pure light:
   radiant beams your holy face
   with the dawn of saving grace,
       Jesus, Lord, at your birth,
       Jesus, Lord, at your birth.

363 © Timothy Dudley-Smith

1. The darkness turns to dawn,
   the dayspring shines from heaven;
   for unto us a child is born,
   to us a Son is given.

2. The Son of God most high,
   before all else began,
   a virgin's son behold him lie,
   the new-born Son of Man.

3. God's Word of truth and grace
   made flesh with us to dwell;
   the brightness of the Father's face,
   the child Emmanuel.

4. How rich his heavenly home!
   How poor his human birth!
   As mortal man he stoops to come,
   the light and life of earth.

5. A servant's form, a slave,
   the Lord consents to share;
   our sin and shame, our cross and grave,
   he bows himself to bear.

6. Obedient and alone
   upon that cross to die,
   and then to share the Father's throne
   in majesty on high.

7. And still God sheds abroad
   that love so strong to send
   a Saviour, who is Christ the Lord,
   whose reign shall never end.

364 © David Mowbray/Jubilate Hymns

1. What if the One who shapes the stars
   and puts the planets in their place
   should set all majesty aside
   and move amongst the human race?
   What if the One who engineers
   the eye, the ear, the heart, the brain,
   should make his home here as a child
   at Mary's breast in Bethlehem?

2. What if the One who spoke the word
   when all was dark, 'Let there be light!'
   should enter this disordered world
   to make our fading hopes more bright?
   What if the God who waits outside
   should all at once be found within,
   and Mary's child be given the strength
   to overturn the power of sin?

3. What if the One who always was,
   creation's hidden energy,
   should – for love's sake – inhabit time,
   God's living Word for all to see?
   Yes, true it is: Christ's Gospel truth,
   the truth on which we all may build!
   So let this be the truth for us
   as now we welcome Mary's child.

365 © Michael Saward/Jubilate Hymns

1. We thank you, God almighty,
   for our salvation won,
   and for that faithful woman,
   the mother of your son.

2. For Mary's true obedience,
   in answer to your call,
   we thank you, God almighty,
   her faith inspires us all.

3. We thank you, God almighty,
   that, virgin at Christ's birth,
   she was upheld by Joseph,
   her husband here on earth.

4. And yet, through pain and sorrow,
   her heart pierced by her loss,
   we thank you, God almighty,
   she stood beside the cross.

5. We thank you, God almighty,
   despite her deepest grief,
   she saw her risen Saviour,
   you honoured her belief.

6. And so, that virgin mother,
   most favoured of our race,
   awaits with us his coming,
   when all shall see your face.

366 © David Mowbray/Jubilate Hymns

1. Who would have dreamed it?
   Mary the Virgin,
   chosen to bear God's only Son.
   Jesus the Saviour,
   Christ the Redeemer,
   freedom for all the world has won.

2. Who would have watched it?
   the Lord's arrival
   in Bethlehem, long years ago.
   Shepherds with reverence,
   wise men with presents,
   angels with anthems' joyous flow.

3. Who would proclaim it?
   Christ's incarnation,
   here in our midst, the Word made flesh –
   unfathomed mystery,
   unending glory,
   Ancient of Days, yet ever fresh.

4. Who would believe it?
   only the childlike,
   theirs is the kingdom of heaven above.
   As in the stillness
   we make Christ welcome
   so God unfolds his feast of love.

367 Nahum Tate

1. While shepherds watched their flocks
   by night
   all seated on the ground,
   the angel of the Lord came down
   and glory shone around.

2. 'Fear not,' said he – for mighty dread
   had seized their troubled mind –
   'Good news of greatest joy I bring
   to you and all mankind.'

3. 'To you in Bethlehem this day
   is born of David's line
   a Saviour, who is Christ the Lord.
   And this shall be the sign:

4. The heavenly babe you there shall find
   to human view displayed,
   all simply wrapped in swathing bands
   and in a manger laid.'

5. Thus spoke the seraph, and forthwith
   appeared a shining throng
   of angels praising God, who thus
   addressed their joyful song:

6. 'All glory be to God on high,
   and to the earth be peace!
   Goodwill henceforth
   from highest heaven
   begin and never cease.'

368 © John Capon/Jubilate Hymns

1. Wise men of old
   came seeking, searching,
   long was their journey, hard their task,
   riding their camels, swaying, lurching,
   losing their way, they stopped to ask.
   Wise men of old
   came seeking, searching,
   long was their journey, hard their task.

2. Led by a star the wise men journeyed
   sure they would see a new king's birth.
   Theirs was a faith profound and learned
   seeking a jewel of priceless worth.
   Led by a star the wise men journeyed
   sure they would see a new king's birth.

3. Inside the house
   the wise men found him,
   this was the King they long had sought.
   Filled with great joy
   they knelt around him
   frankincense, gold
   and myrrh they brought.
   Inside the house
   the wise men found him,
   this was the King they long had sought.

4. Joy to the world, the message ringing,
   homage to Christ, whom we adore;
   praises to God, the whole world singing,
   wise men and humble, rich and poor.
   With them we come,
   our own gifts bringing,
   serving him now and evermore.

369 © Christopher Idle/Jubilate Hymns

1. Wise men, they came to look for wisdom,
   finding one wiser than they knew;
   rich men, they met with one yet richer –
   King of the kings, they knelt to you:
   Jesus, our wisdom from above,
   wealth and redemption, life and love.

2. Pilgrims they were,
   from unknown countries,
   searching for one who knows the world;
   lost are their names,
   and strange their journeys,
   famed is their zeal to find the child:
   Jesus, in you the lost are claimed,
   aliens are found, and known,
   and named.

3. Magi, they stooped
      to see your splendour,
   led by a star to light supreme;
   promised Messiah, Lord eternal,
   glory and peace are in your name.
      Joy of each day, our Song by night,
      shine on our path your holy light.

4. Guests of their God,
      they opened treasures,
   incense and gold and solemn myrrh;
   welcoming one too young to question
   how came these gifts,
      and what they were.
   Gift beyond price of gold or gem,
   make among us your Bethlehem.

SONGS

370 Graham Kendrick
© 1988 Make Way Music

1. Like a candle flame
   flickering small in our darkness;
   uncreated light
   shines through infant eyes.

   MEN: God is with us, alleluia.
   WOMEN: God is with us, alleluia.
   MEN: Come to save us, alleluia.
   WOMEN: Come to save us,
   ALL: Alleluia!

2. Stars and angels sing,
   yet the earth sleeps in shadows;
   can this tiny spark
   set a world on fire?
      MEN: God is with us . . .

3. Yet his light shall shine
   from our lives, Spirit blazing,
   as we touch the flame
   of his holy fire.
      MEN: God is with us . . .

371 Graham Kendrick
© 1988 Make Way Music

1. This child, secretly comes in the night,
   O this child, hiding a heavenly light.
   O this child, coming to us
   like a stranger, this heavenly child.
      This child, heaven come down
      now to be with us here,
      heavenly love and mercy appear,
      softly in awe and wonder come near –
      to this heavenly child.

2. This child, rising on us like the sun,
   O this child, given to light everyone,
   O this child,
      guiding our feet on the pathway
   to peace on earth
      This child, heaven come down . . .

3. This child, raising the humble and poor,
   O this child,
      making the proud ones to fall;
   O this child,
      filling the hungry with good things,
   this heavenly child.
      This child, heaven come down . . .

For other items on this theme, see

HYMNS

PSALM

SONGS

AFFIRMING OUR BELIEF IN JESUS, LIVING AMONG US

HYMNS

372 John Keble and William Hall

1. Blessed are the pure in heart,
   for they shall see our God;
   the secret of the Lord is theirs,
   their soul is Christ's abode.

2. The Lord, who left the heavens
   our life and peace to bring;
   to dwell in lowliness with us,
   our pattern and our king:

3. Still to the lowly soul
   himself he will impart;
   and for his dwelling and his throne
   chooses the pure in heart.

4. Lord, we your presence seek:
   our inner life renew;
   give us a pure and lowly heart,
   a temple fit for you.

373 © Timothy Dudley-Smith

1. Christ our Redeemer
      knew temptation's hour
   in desert places, silent and apart;
   and three times over
      met the tempter's power
   with God's word written,
      hidden in his heart.

2. He makes not bread
      what God has made a stone,
   he at whose bidding
      water turns to wine:
   we are not meant to live by bread alone
   but as God speaks
      the word of life divine.

3. He will not ask the
      fickle crowd's acclaim,
   nor flaunt the Sonship
      which is his by right,
   nor seem distrustful of
      the Father's Name
   who bids us walk by faith
      and not by sight.

4. He seeks no kingdom
      but by cross and grave,
   for love of sinners spurning
      Satan's throne;
   his triumph seen in those
      he died to save
   who, to his glory, worship God alone.

374 © Timothy Dudley-Smith

1. O changeless Christ, for ever new,
   who walked our earthly ways,
   still draw our hearts as once you drew
   the hearts of other days.

2. As once you spoke by plain and hill
   or taught by shore and sea,
   so be today our teacher still,
   O Christ of Galilee.

3. As wind and storm their master heard
   and his command fulfilled,
   may troubled hearts receive your word,
   the tempest-tossed be stilled.

4. And as of old to all who prayed
   your healing hand was shown,
   so be your touch upon us laid,
   unseen but not unknown.

5. In broken bread, in wine outpoured,
   your new and living way
   proclaim to us, O risen Lord,
   O Christ of this our day.

6. O changeless Christ, till life is past
   your blessing still be given;
   then bring us home to taste at last
   the timeless joys of heaven.

375 © Paul Wigmore/Jubilate Hymns

1. New Light has dawned,
   the Son of God is here,
   a holy Light no earthly light outshines;
   the Light has dawned,
   the Light that casts out fear,
   the Light that evil dreads
   and love defines.

2. The Light of glory
   shines to angels' song,
   the shepherds run to where a baby lies;
   a servant of the Lord, who waited long,
   acclaims the Light
   to lighten Gentile eyes.

3. And priestly men sit listening to a boy,
   they see the dawning Light
   within his face.
   Such words they hear those
   Christ-child lips employ!
   Amazing words of wisdom,
   truth and grace.

4. O Christ, the Light
   who came to us on earth,
   shine through the shadow
   cast by human sin;
   renew the faith you gave
   at our new birth,
   destroy the dark,
   and let your Light come in.

376 Christopher Wordsworth
© in this version Jubilate Hymns

1. Songs of thankfulness and praise,
   Jesus, Lord, to you we raise;
   once revealed, when heaven's star
   brought the wise men from afar;
   branch of royal David's stem
   in your birth at Bethlehem,
     Word before the world began,
     God revealed to us in man.

2. God revealed at Jordan's stream,
   prophet, priest and king supreme;
   once revealed in power divine
   changing water into wine;
   Cana's holy wedding guest
   keeping to the last the best;
     Word before . . .

3. God revealed in valiant fight,
   conquering the devil's might;
   sins forgiven, sickness healed,
   life restored and God revealed:
   once revealed in gracious will
   ever bringing good from ill,
     Word before . . .

4. Stars shall fall and heavens fade,
   sun and moon shall dark be made;
   Christ will then like lightning shine,
   all will see the glorious sign;
   all will then the trumpet hear,
   all will see the Son appear,
     Word before . . .

SONG

377 Graham Kendrick
© 1988 Make Way Music

1. He walked where I walk
   (he walked where I walk),
   he stood where I stand
   (he stood where I stand),
   he felt what I feel (he felt what I feel),
   he understands (he understands).
   He knows my frailty
   (he knows my frailty),
   shared my humanity
   (shared my humanity),
   tempted in every way
   (tempted in every way),
   yet without sin (yet without sin).
     God with us, so close to us,
     God with us, Immanuel!
     God with us, so close to us,
     God with us, Immanuel.

2. One of a hated race
       (one of a hated race),
    stung by the prejudice
       (stung by the prejudice),
    suffering injustice (suffering injustice),
    yet he forgives (yet he forgives).
    Wept for my wasted years
       (wept for my wasted years),
    paid for my wickedness
       (paid for my wickedness),
    he died in my place
       (he died in my place),
    that I might live (that I might live).
       God with us, so close to us,
       God with us, Immanuel!
       God with us, so close to us,
       God with us, Immanuel.

For other items on this theme, see

HYMNS
487 At evening, when the sun had set
 28 Born in song
620 Christ who called disciples to him
381 Forty days and forty nights
529 God comes to us as one unheard
 38 God we praise you! God, we bless you!
283 God's glory fills the universe
437 I cannot tell why he whom angels worship
557 It is a thing most wonderful
668 Jesus calls us!
336 Jesus, hope of every nation
509 Lord of all hopefulness
628 My Lord, you wore no royal crown
148 Now let us all with one accord
291 O Trinity, O Trinity
292 Sing of a God in majestic divinity
329 That priceless gift
363 The darkness turns to dawn
331 We have a gospel to proclaim

PSALM
 84 I'll praise my maker while I've breath

SONG
421 Alleluia, alleluia, Jesus, risen Lord of life!

AFFIRMING OUR BELIEF IN JESUS, SUFFERING AND DYING FOR US

HYMNS

378 From *The Yattendon Hymnal.* After Johann Heerman, Robert S. Bridges. By permission of Oxford University Press

1. Ah, holy Jesus, how have you offended
   that man to judge you
      has in hate pretended?
   By foes derided, by your own rejected,
      O most afflicted!

2. Who was the guilty?
      who brought this upon you?
   It is my treason, Lord,
      that has undone you;
   and I, O Jesus, it was I denied you,
      I crucified you.

3. See how the Shepherd
      for the sheep is offered,
   the slave has sinned
      and yet the Son has suffered;
   for our atonement
      hangs the Saviour bleeding
      God interceding.

4. For me, kind Jesus,
      was your incarnation,
   your dying sorrow
      and your life's oblation;
   your bitter passion and your desolation,
      for my salvation.

5. O mighty Saviour, I cannot repay you,
   I do adore you and I will here obey you:
   recall your mercy
      and your love unswerving,
      not my deserving.

379 © Timothy Dudley-Smith

1. A purple robe, a crown of thorn,
   a reed in his right hand;
   before the soldiers' spite and scorn
   I see my Saviour stand.

2. He bears between the Roman guard
   the weight of all our woe;
   a stumbling figure bowed and scarred
   I see my Saviour go.

3. Fast to the cross's spreading span,
   high in the sunlit air,
   all the unnumbered sins of man
   I see my Saviour bear.

4. He hangs, by whom
      the world was made,
   beneath the darkened sky;
   the everlasting ransom paid,
   I see my Saviour die.

5. He shares on high his Father's throne
   who once in mercy came;
   for all his love to sinners shown
   I sing my Saviour's name.

380 After Theodulph, John Neale
© in this version Jubilate Hymns

   All glory, praise and honour,
   to you, Redeemer, King,
   to whom the lips of children
   made sweet hosannas ring.

1. You are the King of Israel,
   great David's greater son;
   you ride in lowly triumph,
   the Lord's anointed one!
      All glory, praise . . .

2. The company of angels
   are praising you on high,
   and we with all creation
   together, make reply:
      All glory, praise . . .

3. The people of the Hebrews
   with palms before you went;
   our praise and prayer and anthems
   before you we present.
      All glory, praise . . .

4. To you before your passion
   they sang their hymns of praise;
   to you, now high exalted,
   our melody we raise:
      All glory, praise and honour,
      to you, Redeemer, King,
      to whom the lips of children
      made sweet hosannas ring.

5. As you received their praises,
   accept the prayers we bring,
   for you delight in goodness
   O good and gracious King!
      All glory, praise . . .

381 George Smyttan
© in this version Jubilate Hymns

1. Forty days and forty nights
   you were fasting in the wild;
   forty days and forty nights
   tempted and yet undefiled.

2. Burning heat throughout the day,
   bitter cold when light had fled;
   prowling beasts around your way,
   stones your pillow, earth your bed.

3. Shall not we your trials share,
   learn your discipline of will;
   and with you by fast and prayer
   wrestle with the powers of hell?

4. So if Satan, pressing hard,
   soul and body would destroy:
   Christ who conquered, be our guard;
   give to us the victor's joy.

5. Saviour, may we hear your voice –
   keep us constant at your side;
   and with you we shall rejoice
   at the eternal Eastertide.

382 Jonathan Evans
© in this version Jubilate Hymns

1. Hark! the voice of love and mercy
   sounds aloud from Calvary;
   see, it tears the temple curtain,
   shakes the earth and veils the sky;
      'It is finished, it is finished!' –
      hear the dying Saviour cry.

2. Finished – all the types and shadows
   of the ceremonial law;
   God fulfils what he has promised –
   death and hell shall reign no more;
      'It is finished, it is finished!' –
      Christ has opened heaven's door.

3. Saints and angels shout his praises,
   his great finished work proclaim;
   all on earth and all in heaven
   join to bless Emmanuel's name:
      'Alleluia, alleluia,
      endless glory to the Lamb!'

383 Philipp Bliss
© in this version Jubilate Hymns

1. Man of sorrows! what a name
   for the Son of God, who came
   ruined sinners to reclaim:
      Alleluia! what a Saviour!

2. Mocked by insults harsh and crude,
   in my place condemned he stood;
   sealed my pardon with his blood:
      Alleluia! what a Saviour!

3. Guilty, helpless, lost were we:
   blameless Lamb of God was he,
   sacrificed to set us free:
      Alleluia! what a Saviour!

4. He was lifted up to die:
   'It is finished!' was his cry;
   now in heaven exalted high:
      Alleluia! what a Saviour!

5. When he comes, our glorious King,
   all his ransomed home to bring;
   then again this song we'll sing:
      'Alleluia! what a Saviour!'

384 Samuel Crossman
© in this version Jubilate Hymns

1. My song is love unknown,
   my Saviour's love for me;
   love to the loveless shown
   that they might lovely be;
   but who am I, that for my sake
   my Lord should take frail flesh and die?

2. He came from heaven's throne
   salvation to bestow;
   but they refused, and none
   the longed-for Christ would know;
   this is my friend, my friend indeed,
   who at my need his life did spend.

3. Sometimes they crowd his way
   and his sweet praises sing,
   resounding all the day
   hosannas to their King;
   then 'crucify' is all their breath,
   and for his death they thirst and cry.

4. Why, what has my Lord done
   to cause this rage and spite?
   he made the lame to run,
   and gave the blind their sight;
   what injuries! yet these are why
   the Lord most high so cruelly dies.

5. They rise and they must have
   my dear Lord done away;
   a murderer they save,
   the prince of life they slay!
   yet, willingly, to shame he goes
   that he his foes, from this, might free.

6. Here might I stay and sing
   of him my soul adores;
   never was love, dear King,
   never was grief like yours! –
   this is my friend in whose sweet praise
   I all my days could gladly spend.

385
After Bernard of Clairvaux and Paul Gerhardt
James Alexander and Henry Baker
© in this version Jubilate Hymns

1. O sacred head surrounded
   by crown of piercing thorn;
   O royal head so wounded,
   reviled and put to scorn;
   death's shadows rise before you,
   the glow of life decays,
   yet angel hosts adore you
   and tremble as they gaze!

2. Your youthfulness and vigour
   are spent, your strength is gone,
   and in your tortured figure
   I see death drawing on:

what agony of dying,
what love, to sinners free!
My Lord, all grace supplying,
O turn your face on me!

3. Your sinless soul's oppression
   was all for sinners' gain;
   mine, mine was the transgression,
   but yours the deadly pain;
   I bow my head, my Saviour,
   for I deserve your place;
   O grant to me your favour,
   and heal me by your grace.

4. What language shall I borrow
   to thank you, dearest Friend,
   for this your dying sorrow,
   your mercy without end?
   Lord, make me yours for ever;
   your servant let me be;
   and may I never, never
   betray your love for me.

386
Henry Milman
© in this version Jubilate Hymns

1. Ride on, ride on in majesty
   as all the crowds 'Hosanna!' cry:
   through waving branches slowly ride,
   O Saviour, to be crucified.

2. Ride on, ride on in majesty,
   in lowly pomp ride on to die:
   O Christ, your triumph now begin
   with captured death, and conquered sin!

3. Ride on, ride on in majesty –
   the angel armies of the sky
   look down with sad and wondering eyes
   to see the approaching sacrifice.

4. Ride on, ride on in majesty,
   the last and fiercest foe defy:
   the Father on his sapphire throne
   awaits his own anointed Son.

5. Ride on, ride on in majesty,
   in lowly pomp ride on to die:
   bow your meek head to mortal pain,
   then take, O God, your power and reign!

387
After the Latin, Venantius Fortunatus, John Neale
© in this version Jubilate Hymns.

1. Sing, my tongue, the glorious battle,
   sing the final, fierce affray!
   how the cross became a triumph
   where our sin was borne away;
   how, the pains of death enduring,
   earth's Redeemer won the day.

2. When at last the appointed fullness
   of the sacred time had come,
   he was sent, the world's Creator,
   from the Father's heavenly home;
   and he came in truest manhood
   from a humble virgin's womb.

3. Now the thirty years are ended
   which on earth he willed to see;
   willingly he goes to suffer,
   born to set his people free;
   on the cross the Lamb is lifted,
   there the sacrifice to be.

4. Gall and vinegar they offer,
   mocking him with thorns and reed;
   nails and spear, the Saviour piercing,
   make his sacred body bleed;
   by that blood the whole creation
   from the stain of sin is freed.

5. Praise and honour to the Father,
   praise and honour to the Son,
   praise and honour to the Spirit,
   ever Three and ever One;
   one in triumph, one in glory
   while eternal ages run! (Amen)

388 Cecil Alexander

1. There is a green hill far away
   outside a city wall,
   where our dear Lord was crucified,
   who died to save us all.

2. We may not know, we cannot tell
   what pains he had to bear,
   but we believe it was for us
   he hung and suffered there.

3. He died that we might be forgiven,
   he died to make us good;
   that we might go at last to heaven,
   saved by his precious blood.

4. There was no other good enough
   to pay the price of sin;
   he, only, could unlock the gate
   of heaven – and let us in.

5. Lord Jesus, dearly you have loved;
   and we must love you too,
   and trust in your redeeming blood
   and live our lives for you.

389
Peter Abélard, translated Richard Sturch
© 1990 Stainer & Bell

1. This is the night, dear friends,
       the night for weeping,
   when darkness' power
       overcome the day,
   the night the faithful mourn
       the weight of evil
   whereby our sins the Son of Man betray.

2. This night the traitor,
       wolf within the sheepfold,
   betrays himself into his victim's will;
   the Lamb of God for sacrifice preparing,
   sin brings about the cure
       for sin's own ill.

3. This night Christ institutes
       his holy supper,
   blest food and drink for heart
       and soul and mind;
   this night injustice joins
       its hand to treason's,
   and buys for death the ransom
       of mankind.

4. This night the Lord by slaves
       shall be arrested,
   he who destroys our slavery to sin;
   accused of crime, to criminals be given,
   that judgement on the
       righteous judge begin.

5. O make us sharers, Saviour,
   of your passion,
   that we may share your glory
   that shall be;
   let us pass through these three
   dark nights of sorrow
   to Easter's laughter and its liberty.

390 Thomas Kelly

1. We sing the praise of him who died,
   of him who died upon the cross;
   the sinner's hope let none deride –
   for this we count the world but loss.

2. Inscribed upon the cross we see
   in shining letters, 'God is Love',
   he bears our sins upon the tree,
   he brings us mercy from above.

3. The cross – it takes our guilt away,
   it holds the fainting spirit up;
   it cheers with hope the gloomy day
   and sweetens every bitter cup:

4. It makes the coward spirit brave
   and nerves the feeble arm for fight;
   it takes the terror from the grave
   and gilds the bed of death with light:

5. The balm of life, the cure of woe,
   the measure and the pledge of love;
   the sinner's refuge here below,
   the angels' theme in heaven above.

391 © Elizabeth Cosnett

1. What have we to show our Saviour
   as he dies to make us free?
   All the shame of our behaviour,
   countless years of treachery.
   We have broken his commandment,
   made his love a mockery.
   So we stand beneath his judgement,
   once for all on Calvary.

2. See the soldiers pierce and leave him,
   one dead body on a cross.
   See his mother's arms receive him,
   final fruit of Eden's loss.
   To what end did she conceive him?
   Why did angels hail his birth?
   Must the friends he loved believe him
   gone for ever, earth to earth?

3. When to Caesar he had tendered
   everything that was his due,
   to his God alone he rendered,
   what from God alone he drew.
   He accepted our condition,
   all that human sin could do:
   we accept his full submission,
   made in faith to One he knew.

4. In this last humiliation
   God is strong to meet our need,
   brings to birth a new creation,
   fills with hope the life we lead.
   Here the great retaliation
   promised once to Adam's seed
   through divine renunciation
   ends in victory indeed.

392 © Christopher Idle/Jubilate Hymns

1. When you prayed beneath the trees,
   it was for me, O Lord;
   when you cried upon your knees,
   how could it be, O Lord?
   When in blood and sweat and tears
   you dismissed your final fears,
   when you faced the soldiers' spears,
   you stood for me, O Lord.

2. When their triumph looked complete,
   it was for me, O Lord;
   when it seemed like your defeat,
   they could not see, O Lord!
   When you faced the mob alone
   you were silent as a stone
   and a tree became your throne;
   you came for me, O Lord.

3. When you stumbled up the road,
     you walked for me, O Lord,
   when you took your deadly load,
     that heavy tree, O Lord;
   when they lifted you on high
     and they nailed you up to die,
   and when darkness filled the sky,
     it was for me, O Lord.

4. When you spoke with kingly power,
     it was for me, O Lord
   in that dread and destined hour,
     you made me free, O Lord;
   earth and heaven heard you shout,
     death and hell were put to rout,
   for the grave could not hold out;
     you are for me, O Lord.

SONGS

393 Graham Kendrick
© 1989 Make Way Music

1. Come and see, come and see,
   come and see the King of love;
   see the purple robe
     and crown of thorns he wears.
   Soldiers mock, rulers sneer,
   as he lifts the cruel cross;
   lone and friendless now
     he climbs towards the hill.
     We worship at your feet,
     where wrath and mercy meet,
     and a guilty world is washed
     by love's pure stream;
     for us he was made sin,
     O, help me take it in!
     Deep wounds of love cry out,
     'Father, forgive!'
     I worship, I worship,
     the Lamb who was slain.

2. Come and weep, come and mourn
   for your sin that pierced him there;
   so much deeper
     than the wounds of thorn and nail.
   All our pride, all our greed,
   all our fallenness and shame!
   And the Lord has laid
     the punishment on him.
     We worship at your feet . . .

3. Man of heaven, born to earth
   to restore us to your heaven:
   here we bow in awe
     beneath your searching eyes.
   From your tears comes our joy,
   from your death our life shall spring:
   by your resurrection power we shall rise.
     We worship at your feet . . .

394 Matt Redman
© 1995 Kingsway's Thankyou Music

1. Jesus Christ, I think upon your sacrifice:
   you became nothing,
     poured out to death.
   Many times I've wondered
     at your gift of life,
   and I'm in that place once again,
   I'm in that place once again.
     And once again I look upon
       the cross where you died:
     I'm humbled by your mercy
       and I'm broken inside,
     once again I thank you,
     once again I pour out my life.

2. Now you are exalted
     to the highest place –
   King of the heavens –
     where one day I'll bow,
   but for now, I marvel
     at this saving grace,
   and I'm full of praise once again,
   I'm full of praise once again.
     And once again . . .

395 Graham Kendrick
© 1986 Kingsway's Thankyou Music

1. Meekness and majesty,
   manhood and deity,
   in perfect harmony –
   the man who is God:
   Lord of eternity
   dwells in humanity,
   kneels in humility
   and washes our feet.
     Oh what a mystery –
     meekness and majesty:
     bow down and worship,
     for this is your God,
     this is your God!

2. Father's pure radiance,
   perfect in innocence,
   yet learns obedience
   to death on a cross:
   suffering to give us life,
   conquering through sacrifice –
   and as they crucify,
   prays, 'Father, forgive'.
      Oh what a mystery . . .

3. Wisdom unsearchable,
   God the invisible,
   love indestructible
   in frailty appears:
   Lord of infinity,
   stooping so tenderly,
   lifts our humanity
   to the heights of his throne.
      Oh what a mystery . . .

396 Melody Green. © 1982 Birdwing Music/
BMG Songs Inc/Ears to Hear Music/EMI Christian
Music Publishing. Administered by CopyCare

1. There is a Redeemer,
   Jesus, God's own Son,
   precious Lamb of God, Messiah,
   holy One.
      Thank you, O my Father,
      for giving us your Son,
      and leaving your Spirit
      till the work on earth is done.

2. Jesus, my Redeemer,
   name above all names,
   precious Son of God, Messiah,
   Lamb for sinners slain:
      Thank you . . .

3. When I stand in glory
   I will see his face,
   and there I'll serve my King for ever
   in that holy place.
      Thank you . . .

For other items on this theme, see

HYMNS
  25 Alleluia! raise the anthem
317 At the name of Jesus
462 At the supper, Christ the Lord
  28 Born in song
591 Christ is the world's light, he and none other
319 Christ triumphant, ever reigning
321 Crown him with many crowns
622 Empty he came
200 Father in heaven, grant to your children
146 Glory be to Jesus
504 God of gods, we sound his praises
  38 God we praise you! God, we bless you!
697 God whose love is everywhere
173 He lives in us, the Christ of God
174 Here is love vast as the ocean
289 I believe in God the Father
437 I cannot tell you why he whom angels worship
557 It is a thing most wonderful
627 Lord Christ, we praise your sacrifice
641 Lord, in our lonely hours
324 Name of all majesty
642 O Christ of all the ages, come!
673 O Christ, the Master Carpenter
674 O dearest Lord, thy sacred head
  56 O Lord my God, when I in awesome wonder
291 O Trinity, O Trinity
  58 Praise to the Holiest in the height
328 Priest and victim, Jesus dies
292 Sing of a God in majestic divinity
645 'Take up your cross,' the Saviour said
329 That priceless gift
363 The darkness turns to dawn
  67 The Lord is king! He set the stars
  70 This is the day the Lord has made
331 We have a gospel to proclaim
680 When I survey the wonderous cross
187 With loving hands

SONGS
332 Above the clash of creeds
190 Behold the Lamb of God
632 From heaven you came
377 He walked where I walk
193 How deep the Father's love for us
424 Led like a lamb
194 My Lord, what love is this
427 No scenes of stately majesty
198 Thank you for the cross
139 We sing your mercies

AFFIRMING OUR BELIEF IN JESUS, RISEN FROM THE DEAD

HYMNS

397 © Timothy Dudley-Smith

1. All shall be well!
   for on our Easter skies
   see Christ the sun
      of righteousness arise.

2. All shall be well!
   the sacrifice is made;
   the sinner freed,
      the price of pardon paid.

3. All shall be well!
   the cross and passion past;
   dark night is done,
      bright morning come at last.

4. All shall be well!
   within our Father's plan
   death has no more
      dominion over man.

5. Jesus alive!
   rejoice and sing again,
   'All shall be well
      for evermore, Amen!'

398 After Christopher Wordsworth
Verses 2 and 3 © Jubilate Hymns

1. Alleluia, alleluia!
      hearts to heaven and voices raise:
   sing to God a hymn of gladness,
      sing to God a hymn of praise;
   he who on the cross a victim
      for the world's salvation bled –
   Jesus Christ, the King of glory,
      now is risen from the dead.

2. Alleluia, Christ is risen!
      death at last has met defeat:
   see the ancient powers of evil
      in confusion and retreat;

once he died, and once was buried:
   now he lives for evermore,
Jesus Christ, the world's redeemer,
   whom we worship and adore.

3. Christ is risen, we are risen!
      set your hearts on things above;
   there in all the Father's glory
      lives and reigns our king of love;
   hear the word of peace he brings us,
      see his wounded hands and side!
   now let every wrong be ended,
      every sin be crucified.

4. Alleluia, alleluia!
      glory be to God on high:
   alleluia to the Saviour
      who has gained the victory;
   alleluia to the Spirit,
      fount of love and sanctity:
   alleluia, alleluia
      to the Triune Majesty!

399 Frank von Christierson

1. Christ is risen! Raise your voices
   jubilant with joy and praise,
   Christ is risen! Earth rejoices!
   To the Lord your anthems raise.
   Over sin and death victorious,
   Christ is risen! Hail your King!
   Ever may his praise be glorious;
   let the world his triumph sing!

2. Lord of life, our Saviour risen,
   bid the shadows flee away;
   death no more a darkened prison,
   death the door to life's new day.
   This the resurrection chorus,
   lift its music on the air;
   Jesus lives, our Lord victorious,
   Tell it! Tell it everywhere.

3. Life eternal! joy of heaven;
life abundant – joy of earth;
life which God in Christ has given
brings to us new hope, new worth.
Lift your hearts from sin and sadness,
trust this joyful sacred word,
fill the earth with holy gladness:
Christ is risen! Christ our Lord!

400 After Michael Weisse, Catherine Winkworth

1. Christ the Lord is risen again,
Christ has broken every chain;
hear the angel voices cry,
singing evermore on high:
Alleluia!

2. He who gave for us his life,
who for us endured the strife,
is our paschal lamb today;
we too sing for joy and say:
Alleluia!

3. He who bore all pain and loss
comfortless upon the cross
lives in glory now on high,
pleads for us and hears our cry:
Alleluia!

4. He who slumbered in the grave
is exalted now to save;
through the universe it rings
that the Lamb is King of kings:
Alleluia!

5. Now he bids us tell abroad
how the lost may be restored,
how the penitent forgiven,
how we too may enter heaven:
Alleluia!

6. Christ, our paschal Lamb indeed,
all your ransomed people feed!
take our sins and guilt away;
let us sing by night and day:
Alleluia!

401 From John 20, Michael Perry
© Mrs B. Perry/Jubilate Hymns

1. Comes Mary to the grave:
no singing bird has spoken,
nor has the world awoken,
and in her grief all love lies lost
and broken.

2. Says Jesus at her side,
no longer Jesus dying,
'Why, Mary, are you crying?'
She turns, with joy, 'My Lord! my love!'
replying.

3. With Mary on this day
we join our voices praising
the God of Jesus' raising,
and sing the triumph of his love
amazing.

402 © David Mowbray/Jubilate Hymns

1. Exult, archangels bright
and angels round God's throne
for Christ, at morning light,
steps past the rolled-back stone
To God all praise and glory be,
life-giving holy Trinity.

2. Exult, both earth and sky!
the powers of death have fled
with anthems magnify
Christ, first-born from the dead.
To God all praise . . .

3. Exult, saints near and far,
God's Easter people sing!
Christ is the morning star
and shining hope shall bring.
To God all praise . . .

4. Exult, wide world that waits
for justice and for love:
Christ's gifts are at your gates,
the risen Christ above!
To God all praise . . .

403
© Christopher Idle/Jubilate Hymns

1. Exult, creation round God's throne!
   All heaven, rejoice! All angels, sing!
   Salvation's trumpet sound aloud
   for Jesus Christ, our risen King.

2. Exult, O earth, in radiant hope;
   in Christ's majestic splendour shine!
   The Lord is here, the victory won,
   the darkness drowned in light divine.

3. Exult, all Christians, one in praise
   with our Jerusalem above!
   This roof shall ring with Easter songs
   that echo Christ's redeeming love.

404
Cyril Alington
© Hymns Ancient & Modern

1. Good Christians all, rejoice and sing!
   now is the triumph of our king;
   to all the world glad news we bring:
      Alleluia, alleluia, alleluia!

2. The Lord of life is risen today;
   death's mighty stone is rolled away:
   let every tongue rejoice and say,
      'Alleluia, alleluia, alleluia!'

3. We praise in songs of victory
   that love, that life, which cannot die,
   and sing with hearts uplifted high,
      'Alleluia, alleluia, alleluia!'

4. Your name we bless, O risen Lord,
   and sing today with one accord
   the life laid down, the life restored:
      Alleluia, alleluia, alleluia!

405
After Edmond Budry, Richard Hoyle
© in this version Jubilate Hymns

1. Glory to Jesus! risen, conquering Son;
   endless is the victory
      over death you won;
   angels robed in splendour
   rolled the stone away,
   kept the folded grave clothes
   where your body lay:
      Glory to Jesus! risen, conquering Son:
      endless is the victory over death
         you won.

2. See! Jesus meets us,
      risen from the tomb,
   lovingly he greets us,
      scatters fear and gloom;
   let the church with gladness
   hymns of triumph sing!
   for her Lord is living,
      death has lost sting:
      Glory to Jesus! risen . . .

3. No more we doubt you,
      glorious prince of life:
   what is life without you?
      aid us in our strife;
   make us more than conquerors
   through your deathless love,
   bring us safe through Jordan
   to your home above:
      Glory to Jesus! risen . . .

See also traditional version no. 417

406
Samuel Medley

1. I know that my redeemer lives –
   what comfort this assurance gives!
   he lives, he lives, who once was dead,
   he lives, my everlasting Head.

2. He lives, triumphant from the grave,
   he lives, eternally to save;
   he lives, to bless me with his love,
   and intercedes for me above.

3. He lives to help in time of need,
   he lives, my hungry soul to feed;
   he lives, and grants me daily breath,
   he lives, and I shall conquer death.

4. He lives, my kind, wise, constant friend,
   who still will guard me to the end;
   he lives, and while he lives I'll sing,
   Jesus, my prophet, priest, and king.

5. He lives, my saviour, to prepare
   a place in heaven, and lead me there;
   he lives, all glory to his name,
   Jesus, unchangeably the same.

407 © Christopher Idle/Jubilate Hymns

1. If Christ had not been raised from death
   our faith would be in vain,
   our preaching but a waste of breath,
   our sin and guilt remain.
      But now the Lord is risen indeed;
      he rules in earth and heaven:
      his Gospel meets a world of need –
      in Christ we are forgiven.

2. If Christ still lay within the tomb
   then death would be the end,
   and we should face our final doom
   with neither guide nor friend.
      But now the Saviour is raised up,
      so when a Christian dies
      we mourn, yet look to God in hope –
      in Christ the saints arise!

3. If Christ had not been truly raised
   his church would live a lie;
   his name should never more be praised,
   his words deserve to die.
      But now our great Redeemer lives;
      through him we are restored;
      his word endures, his church revives
      in Christ, our risen Lord.

408 After a 14th Century author, unknown (18th Century)

1. Jesus Christ is risen today,
      Alleluia,
   our triumphant holy day;
      alleluia,
   he who once upon the cross
      alleluia,
   suffered to redeem our loss.
      alleluia!

2. Hymns of joy then let us sing
      Alleluia,
   praising Christ our heavenly king;
      alleluia,
   who endured the cross and grave
      alleluia,
   sinners to redeem and save!
      alleluia!

3. But the pains which he endured
      Alleluia,
   our salvation have procured;
      alleluia,
   now above the sky he's King
      alleluia,
   where the angels ever sing.
      alleluia!

409 After Christian Gellert, Frances Cox © in this version Jubilate Hymns

1. Jesus lives! Your terrors now
   can, O death, no more appal us:
   Jesus lives! – by this we know
   you, O grave, cannot enthral us:
      Alleluia!

2. Jesus lives! – henceforth is death
   but the gate of life immortal;
   this shall calm our trembling breath
   when we pass its gloomy portal:
      Alleluia!

3. Jesus lives! – for us he died:
   then, alone to Jesus living,
   pure in heart may we abide,
   glory to our Saviour giving;
      Alleluia!

4. Jesus lives! – this bond of love
   neither life nor death shall sever,
   powers below, around, above
   tear us from his keeping never:
      Alleluia!

5. Jesus lives! – to him the throne
   over all the world is given;
   may we go where he is gone,
   rest and reign with him in heaven:
      Alleluia!

410 © Timothy Dudley-Smith

1. Jesus, Prince and Saviour,
   Lord of life who died,
   Christ, the friend of sinners,
   mocked and crucified;
   for a world's salvation
   he his body gave,
   lay at last death's victim
   lifeless in the grave.

Lord of life triumphant,
risen now to reign!
King of endless ages,
Jesus lives again!

2. In his power and Godhead
every victory won,
pain and passion ended,
all his purpose done:
Christ the Lord is risen!
sighs and sorrows past,
death's dark night is over,
morning comes at last!
    Lord of life triumphant . . .

3. Resurrection morning,
sinners' bondage freed!
Christ the Lord is risen,
he is risen indeed!
Jesus, Prince and Saviour,
Lord of life who died,
Christ the King of glory
now is glorified!
    Lord of life triumphant . . .

411 Robert Lowry

1. Low in the grave he lay,
Jesus my Saviour,
waiting the coming day,
Jesus my Lord!
    Up from the grave he arose,
    and, triumphant over all his foes,
    he arose a victor from
        the dark domain,
    and he lives for ever
    with his saints to reign –
    he arose, he arose,
    Alleluia – Christ arose!

2. Vainly they guard his bed,
Jesus my Saviour;
vainly they seal the dead,
Jesus my Lord!
    Up from the grave he arose . . .

3. Death cannot keep his prey,
Jesus my Saviour;
he tore the bars away,
Jesus my Lord!
    Up from the grave he arose . . .

412 Charles Wesley
© in this version Jubilate Hymns

1. Love's redeeming work is done;
fought the fight, the battle won:
see, our Sun's eclipse has passed;
see, the dawn has come at last!

2 Vain the stone, the watch, the seal:
Christ has burst the gates of hell;
death in vain forbids his rise –
Christ has opened paradise:

3. Now he lives, our glorious King;
now, O death, where is your sting?
Once he died, our souls to save –
where's your victory, boasting grave?

4. We are raised where Christ has led,
following our exalted head;
made like him, like him we rise –
ours the cross, the grave, the skies:

5. Hail the Lord of earth and heaven!
praise to you by both be given;
every knee to you shall bow,
risen Christ, triumphant now:

413 From The Easter Anthems
© David Mowbray/Jubilate Hymns

1. Now lives the Lamb of God,
our Passover, the Christ,
who once with nails and wood
for us was sacrificed:
    Come, keep the feast, the anthem sing
    that Christ indeed is Lord and king!

2. Now risen from the dead
Christ never dies again;
in us, with Christ as head,
sin nevermore shall reign:
    Come, keep the feast . . .

3. In Adam all must die,
forlorn and unforgiven;
in Christ all come alive,
the second Man from heaven.
    Come, keep the feast . . .

4. Give praise to God alone
   who life from death can bring;
   whose mighty power can turn
   the winter into spring:
       Come, keep the feast . . .

414 John M. C. Crum. © Oxford University Press from *The Oxford Book of Carols*

1. Now the green blade rises
   from the buried grain,
   wheat that in dark earth
   many days has lain;
   love lives again,
   that with the dead has been:
       Love is come again,
       like wheat that springs up green.

2. In the grave they laid him,
   love whom men had slain,
   thinking that he never
   would awake again,
   laid in the earth
   like grain that sleeps unseen:
       Love is come again . . .

3. Forth he came at Easter,
   like the risen grain,
   he that for the three days
   in the grave had lain,
   back from the dead
   my risen Lord is seen:
       Love is come again . . .

4. When our hearts are wintry,
   grieving, or in pain,
   then your touch can call us
   back to life again,
   field of our hearts
   that dead and bare have been:
       Love is come again . . .

415 After John of Damascus, John Neale

1. The day of resurrection!
   Come, spread the news abroad;
   the passover of gladness,
   the passover of God:

from death to life eternal,
from earth up to the sky,
our Christ has brought us over
with hymns of victory.

2. Now let the skies be joyful
   and earth sing back her praise;
   let all the nations worship
   the God of endless days:
   let all things seen and unseen
   their joyful music blend,
   for Christ the Lord has risen –
   our triumph knows no end!

416 From the Latin, Francis Pott
© in this version Jubilate Hymns

1. The strife is past, the battle done;
   now is the victor's triumph won –
   O let the song of praise be sung,
       Alleluia!

2. Death's mightiest powers have done
       their worst;
   and Jesus has his foes dispersed –
   let shouts of praise and joy outburst,
       Alleluia!

3. The three sad days have quickly sped,
   he rises glorious from the dead,
   all glory to our risen head,
       Alleluia!

4. Lord over death, our wounded King,
   save us from Satan's deadly sting
   that we may live for you and sing,
       Alleluia!

417 After Edmond Budry, Richard Hoyle

1. Thine be the glory!
       risen, conquering Son;
   endless is the victory
       thou o'er death hast won;
   angels in bright raiment
       rolled the stone away,
   kept the folded grave clothes
       where thy body lay;

Thine be the glory!
risen, conquering Son:
endless is the victory thou
over death hast won.

2. Lo, Jesus meets us, risen from the tomb,
lovingly he greets us,
scatters fear and gloom;
let the church with gladness
hymns of triumph sing!
for her Lord now liveth,
death has lost its sting:
Thine be the glory . . .

3. No more we doubt thee,
glorious prince of life;
life is naught without thee:
aid us in our strife;
make us more than conquerors,
through thy deathless love,
bring us safe through Jordan
to thy home above.
Thine be the glory . . .

See also revised version no. 405

418 Rory Cooney
© 1987, North American Liturgy Resources (NALR)

1. Up from the earth,
and surging like a wave,
rise up, O Christ!
your God defies the grave.
Up from the earth push blade
and leaf and stem,
they rise for Christ,
and we shall rise with them!

2. Up from the cross a billion voices strain,
cry for a hand to lift them
from their pain.
Up from the cross but scarred
in limbs and side,
a wounded church brings
healing far and wide!

3. Up from the night
Christ Morning Star awakes.
O what a light upon earth's
darkness breaks!
Up from the night Christ
sows his life like wheat,
and death itself lies fallow at his feet!

4. Up from the tomb of all
the past conceals!
See how our God a brighter day reveals.
Up from the tomb!
Though death had bound us tight,
like Lazarus, we stumble into light!

5. Cry to the cross where tyrants
work their dread!
Shout to the tombs where parents
mourn their dead!
Sing to the earth,
for God all newness gives!
Alleluia! Christ Liberator lives!

419 After Fulbert of Chartres, Robert Campbell

1. You choirs of new Jerusalem,
your sweetest notes employ
the paschal victory to hymn
in songs of holy joy!

2. For Judah's Lion burst his chains
and crushed the serpent's head;
he cries aloud through death's domains
to wake the imprisoned dead.

3. Devouring depths of hell their prey
at his command restore;
his ransomed hosts pursue their way
where Jesus goes before.

4. Triumphant in his glory now –
to him all power is given;
to him in one communion bow
all saints in earth and heaven.

5. All glory to the Father be,
the Spirit and the Son:
all glory to the One-in-Three
while endless ages run.

SONGS

420 Noel and Tricia Richards
© 1987 Kingsway's Thankyou Music

1. All heaven declares
   the glory of the risen Lord.
   Who can compare
   with the beauty of the Lord?
   For ever he will be
      the Lamb upon the throne:
   I gladly bow the knee
   and worship him alone.

2. I will proclaim
   the glory of the risen Lord,
   who once was slain
   to reconcile us to God.
   For ever you will be
   the Lamb upon the throne:
   I gladly bow the knee
   and worship you alone.

421 © 1988, 1990 Bernadette Farrell
Published by OCP Publications

> Alleluia, alleluia,
> Jesus, risen Lord of life!
> Alleluia, alleluia, alleluia!

LEADER: Word of the Father:
ALL: Jesus Christ!
LEADER: Hope of the world:
ALL: Jesus Christ!
LEADER: Broken and buried:
ALL: Jesus Christ!
LEADER: Risen to life:
ALL: Jesus Christ!
> Alleluia, alleluia . . .

LEADER: Light of the nations:
ALL: Jesus Christ!
LEADER: Way, Truth and Life:
ALL: Jesus Christ!
LEADER: Bearing our sorrows:
ALL: Jesus Christ!
LEADER: With us through time:
ALL: Jesus Christ!
> Alleluia, alleluia . . .

LEADER: Living among us:
ALL: Jesus Christ!
LEADER: Word in our flesh:
ALL: Jesus Christ!
LEADER: Servant of others:
ALL: Jesus Christ!
LEADER: Friend of the poor:
ALL: Jesus Christ!
> Alleluia, alleluia . . .

422 © Steve James/Jubilate Hymns

Behold, I am the first
   and the last,
I am the living one,
I died, now I'm alive ever more!

Glory! Glory! Glory to you!
Glory! Glory! Glory to you:
behold I am the first
and the last!

423 Chris Rolinson
© 1989 Kingsway's Thankyou Music

> Christ is risen —
> hallelujah, hallelujah!
> Christ is risen,
> risen indeed — hallelujah!

1. Love's work is done,
   the battle is won.
   Where now, O death, is your sting?
   He rose again
   to rule and to reign,
   Jesus our conquering King.
      Christ is risen . . .

2. Lord over sin,
   Lord over death,
   at his feet Satan must fall!
   Every knee, bow!
   All will confess
   Jesus is Lord over all!
      Christ is risen . . .

3. Tell it abroad,
   'Jesus is Lord!'
   Shout it and let your praise ring!
   Gladly we raise
   our songs of praise
   worship is our offering.
      Christ is risen . . .

424 Graham Kendrick
© 1983 Kingsway's Thankyou Music

1. Led like a lamb to the slaughter
   in silence and shame,
   there on your back
   you carried a world
   of violence and pain,
       bleeding, dying,
       bleeding, dying.
       You're alive – you're alive,
       you have risen –
          Alelluia . . .
       and the power
       and the glory is given –
          alleluia . . .
       Jesus to you.

2. At break of dawn – poor Mary,
   still weeping, she came:
   when through her grief
   she heard your voice
   now speaking her name.
       MEN: 'Mary!' WOMEN: 'Master!'
       MEN: 'Mary!' WOMEN: 'Master!'
       You're alive . . .

3. At the right hand of the Father,
   now seated on high,
   you have begun your eternal reign
   of justice and joy:
       Glory, glory,
       glory, glory!
       You're alive . . .

425 Eugene Greco
© 1995 His Banner Publishing/Music Lifeline

My Redeemer lives,
and I will see his glory
as he works all things
   together for my good –
whatever things occur,
   of this I can be sure:
I know my Redeemer lives.

Even though I walk through the valley,
I will fear no evil,
he is with me;
and on the battlefield,
      although the pain is real,
my struggles soon will fade
as his glory is revealed.
      My Redeemer lives . . .

      . . . I know my Redeemer lives,
I know my Redeemer lives.

426 © 1983, 1984 Christopher Walker
Published by OCP Publications

1. No more weeping,
   joy has come into the world –
   he is risen!

2. Do not fear, Jesus has conquered –
   he is risen from the dead!

3. Jesus lives – the Lord of lords
   fills the world with his glory;
   he is risen from the dead!
   in joyfulness we greet the risen Lord,
   singing Jesus lives – the Lord of lords . . .

4. The Lord is calling his disciples
   to send us out into the world;
   for we love him, we believe him,
   and will follow him till we rise with him.
   The Lord is calling . . .

5. Sing him praise all of our days –
   blessings on him for ever;
   sing him praise all of our days,
   for his name is Wonderful Counsellor.
   So sing his praise . . .

6. Glory in the highest heaven!

427 From the *Millennium Chorus*. Graham Kendrick
© 1997 Ascent Music

1. No scenes of stately majesty
     for the King of kings;
   no nights aglow with candle flame
     for the King of love.
   no flags of empire hung in shame
     for Calvary
   no flowers perfumed the lonely way
     that led him to
   a borrowed tomb for Easter Day.

2. No wreaths upon the ground were laid
     for the King of kings;
   only a crown of thorns remained
     where he gave his love,
   a message scrawled in irony –
     'King of the Jews', –
   lay trampled where they turned away,
     and no one knew
   that it was the first Easter Day.

3. Yet nature's finest colours blaze
     for the King of kings:
   and stars in jewelled clusters say
     'Worship heaven's King',
   Two thousand springtimes more
     have bloomed – is that enough?
   Oh, how can I be satisfied
     until he hears
   the whole world sing of Easter love.

4. My prayers shall be a fragrance sweet
     for the King of kings;
   my love, the flowers at his feet,
     for the King of love.
   My vigil is to watch and pray
     until he comes;
   my highest tribute to obey
     and live to know
   the power of that first Easter Day.

5. I long for scenes of majesty
     for the risen King,
   for nights aglow with candle flame
     for the King of love.

A nation hushed upon its knees
   at Calvary:
where all our sins and griefs were nailed
   and hope was born
of everlasting Easter Day.

428 Craig Musseau. © 1989 Mercy/Vineyard Publishing
Administered by CopyCare

You are mighty, you are holy,
you are awesome in your power;
you have risen, you have conquered,
you have beaten the power of death.
   Hallelujah, we will rejoice;
   hallelujah, we will rejoice!
You are mighty . . .
. . . you are mighty!

For other items on this theme, see

HYMNS
  25 Alleluia! raise the anthem
526 As Jesus walked the Emmaus Road
317 At the name of Jesus
318 Before the world began
  28 Born in song
  32 Christ is alive! Let Christians sing
319 Christ triumphant, ever reigning
321 Crown him with many crowns
200 Father in heaven, grant to your children
    2 First of the week and finest day
528 From the apple in the garden
504 God of gods, we sound his praises
  38 God we praise you! God, we bless you!
283 God's glory fills the universe
173 He lives in us, the Christ of God
289 I believe in God the Father
533 In Christ shall all be made alive, we sing!
558 Lord of the cross of shame
324 Name of all majesty
642 O Christ of all the ages, come!
291 O Trinity, O Trinity
328 Priest and victim, Jesus dies
  60 Rejoice in God! Let trumpets sound
292 Sing of a God in majestic divinity
329 That priceless gift
363 The darkness turns to dawn
  67 The Lord is king! He set the stars
284 These are the facts
  70 This is the day the Lord has made
331 We have a gospel to proclaim

SONGS
562 All I once held dear
686 All that I am
609 Come see a vision
215 Jesus, Jesus, holy and anointed one

AFFIRMING OUR BELIEF IN JESUS, ASCENDED AND COMING AGAIN

HYMNS

429 © Christopher Idle/Jubilate Hymns

1. Ascended Christ, who gained
   the glory that we sing,
   anointed and ordained,
   our prophet, priest, and king:
     by many tongues
     the church displays
     your power and praise
     in all her songs.

2. No titles, thrones, or powers
   can ever rival yours;
   no passing mood of ours
   can turn aside your laws:
     you reign above
     each other name
     of worth or fame,
     the Lord of love.

3. Now from the Father's side
   you make your people new;
   since for our sins you died
   our lives belong to you:
     from our distress
     you set us free
     for purity
     and holiness.

4. You call us to belong
   within one body here;
   in weakness we are strong
   and all your gifts we share:
     in you alone
     we are complete
     and at your feet
     with joy bow down.

5. All strength is in your hand,
   all power to you is given;
   all wisdom to command
   in earth and hell and heaven:
     beyond all words
     creation sings
     the King of kings
     and Lord of lords.

430 Martin E. Leckebusch
© Kevin Mayhew

1. Christ brings the kingdom
     where barrenness blooms:
   see how the image of God is restored,
   yielding a harvest of talents and skills
   when we acknowledge
     our maker as Lord.

2. Come to his kingdom
     of weakness made strong,
   brokenness mended,
     the blind given sight;
   welcome and dignity
     crown the despised,
   darkness is banished by glorious light.

3. Come to his kingdom
     where righteousness reigns –
   God has commanded:
     repent and believe!
   Children of dust in his glory may share,
   penitent rebels his favour receive.

4. Come to his kingdom
     of laughter and hope,
   savour the freedom
     its fullness will bring:
   no more oppression, injustice or fear –
   come to the kingdom
     where Jesus is King!

431 © Richard Bewes/Jubilate Hymns

1. Christ holds the keys of death and hell,
   The First and Last, and Living One.
   His rule proclaim, his triumph tell!
   For through his Cross his work is done.

2. Though powers of darkness
      make their claim
   Though wars may rage
      and kingdoms fall,
   The throne of Christ shall stay the same:
   And all must heed his trumpet call.

3. Christ breaks the seal around the scroll,
   unfolds the meaning of our world.
   He leads us forward to our goal,
   The secrets of all life unfurled.

4. See death and famine riding by,
   With war and sickness drawing near.
   We'll ride with Christ until we die,
   And wait his reign in glory here.

432 From *Enlarged Songs of Praise* 1931, George Briggs
By permission of Oxford University Press

1. Christ is the world's true light,
      its captain of salvation,
   our daystar clear and bright;
   desire of every nation:
   new life, new hope awakes
   where we accept his way;
   freedom her bondage breaks
   and night is turned to day.

2. In Christ all races meet,
      their ancient feuds forgetting,
   the whole round world complete
   from sunrise to its setting:
   when Christ is known as Lord
   all shall forsake their fear,
   to ploughshare beat the sword,
   to pruning-hook the spear.

3. One Lord, in one great name
   unite all who have known you,
   cast out our pride and shame
   that hinder to enthrone you:
   the world has waited long,
   has laboured long in pain;
   to heal its ancient wrong
   come, Prince of peace, and reign!

433 Martin E. Leckebusch
© Kevin Mayhew

1. Come, see the Lord
      in his breathtaking splendour:
   gaze at his majesty – bow and adore!
   Enter his presence
      with wonder and worship –
   he is the King, and enthroned evermore.

2. He is the Word
      who was sent by the Father,
   born as a baby, a child of our race:
   God here among us,
      revealed as a servant,
   walking the pathway
      of truth and of grace.

3. He is the Lamb
      who was slain to redeem us –
   there at the cross
      his appearance was marred;
   though he emerged
      from the grave as the victor,
   still from the nails
      and the spear he is scarred.

4. He is the Lord who ascended in triumph –
   ever the sound of his praises shall ring!
   Hail him the First
      and the Last, the Almighty:
   Jesus, our Prophet,
      our Priest and our King.

5. Come, see the Lord
      in his breathtaking splendour:
   gaze at his majesty – bow and adore!
   Come and acknowledge him
      Saviour and Sovereign:
   Jesus our King is enthroned evermore.

434 Charles Wesley and Thomas Cotterill

1. Hail the day that sees him rise
   Alleluia,
   to his throne beyond the skies,
   alleluia,
   Christ, the Lamb for sinners given,
   alleluia,
   enters now the highest heaven:
   alleluia!

2. There for him high triumph waits:
   Alleluia,
   lift your heads, eternal gates,
   alleluia,
   he has conquered death and sin,
   alleluia,
   take the King of glory in:
   alleluia!

3. See! the heaven its Lord receives,
   Alleluia,
   yet he loves the earth he leaves;
   alleluia,
   though returning to his throne,
   alleluia,
   still he calls mankind his own.
   alleluia!

4. Still for us he intercedes,
   Alleluia,
   his prevailing death he pleads,
   alleluia,
   near himself prepares our place,
   alleluia,
   he the first-fruits of our race.
   alleluia!

5. Lord, though parted from our sight
   Alleluia,
   far beyond the starry height,
   alleluia,
   lift our hearts that we may rise
   alleluia,
   one with you beyond the skies:
   alleluia!

6. There with you we shall remain,
   Alleluia,
   share the glory of your reign,
   alleluia,
   there your face unclouded view,
   alleluia,
   find our heaven of heavens in you.
   alleluia!

435 Philip Doddridge

1. Hark the glad sound! –
   the Saviour comes,
   the Saviour promised long;
   let every heart prepare a throne
   and every voice a song.

2. He comes the prisoners to release
   in Satan's bondage held;
   the gates of brass before him burst,
   the iron fetters yield.

3. He comes the broken heart to bind,
   the wounded soul to cure;
   and with the treasures of his grace
   to enrich the humble poor.

4. Our glad hosannas, Prince of peace,
   your welcome shall proclaim;
   and heaven's eternal arches ring
   with your beloved name.

436 From the Latin, Edward Caswall

1. Hark! a trumpet call is sounding,
   'Christ is near,' it seems to say:
   'Cast away the dreams of darkness,
   children of the dawning day!'

2. Wakened by the solemn warning,
   let our earth-bound souls arise;
   Christ, our sun, all harm dispelling,
   shines upon the morning skies.

3. See! the Lamb, so long expected,
   comes with pardon down from heaven;
   let us haste, with tears of sorrow,
   one and all to be forgiven:

4. That, when next he comes in glory
   and the world is wrapped in fear
   with his mercy he may shield us,
   and with words of love draw near.

5. Honour, glory, might and blessing
   to the Father, and the Son,
   with the everlasting Spirit,
   while eternal ages run!

437 William Fullerton

1. I cannot tell why
   he whom angels worship
   should set his love
   upon the sons of men,
   or why as shepherd
   he should seek the wanderers,
   to bring them back,
   they know not how nor when.
   But this I know,
   that he was born of Mary
   when Bethlehem's manger
   was his only home,
   and that he lived at Nazareth
   and laboured;
   and so the saviour, saviour of the world,
   has come.

2. I cannot tell how silently he suffered
   as with his peace he graced
   this place of tears,
   nor how his heart upon the cross
   was broken,
   the crown of pain to three
   and thirty years.
   But this I know,
   he heals the broken-hearted
   and stays our sin
   and calms our lurking fear,
   and lifts the burden from
   the heavy-laden;
   for still the saviour, saviour of the world,
   is here.

3. I cannot tell how he will win the nations,
   how he will claim his earthly heritage,
   how satisfy the needs and aspirations
   of east and west, of sinner and of sage.
   But this I know,
   all flesh shall see his glory,
   and he shall reap the harvest
   he has sown,
   and some glad day
   his sun will shine in splendour
   when he the saviour, saviour of the
   world, is known.

4. I cannot tell how all the lands
   shall worship,
   when at his bidding every storm
   is stilled,
   or who can say how great the jubilation
   when all our hearts
   with love for him are filled.
   But this I know,
   the skies will sound his praises,
   ten thousand thousand human
   voices sing,
   and earth to heaven, and heaven to
   earth, will answer,
   'At last the saviour, saviour of the world,
   is king!'

438 After John Cennick, Charles Wesley and Martin Madan
© in this version Jubilate Hymns

1. Jesus comes with clouds descending –
   see the Lamb for sinners slain!
   thousand thousand saints attending
   join to sing the glad refrain:
   Alleluia, alleluia, alleluia!
   God appears on earth to reign.

2. Every eye shall then behold him
   robed in awesome majesty;
   those who jeered at him and sold him,
   pierced and nailed him to the tree,
   shamed and grieving . . .
   shall their true Messiah see.

3. All the wounds of cross and passion
   still his glorious body bears;
   cause of endless exultation
   to his ransomed worshippers.
   With what gladness . . .
   we shall see the Saviour's scars!

4. Yes, Amen! let all adore you
   high on your eternal throne;
   crowns and empires fall before you –
   claim the kingdom for your own.
   Come, Lord Jesus . . .
   everlasting God, come down!

439 © James Quinn S. J. reprinted by permission of Cassell & Co.

1. Now from the heavens descending,
   is seen a glorious light,
   the bride of Christ in splendour,
   arrayed in purest white.
   She is the holy city,
   whose radiance is the grace
   of all the saints in glory,
   from every time and place.

2. This is the hour of gladness
   for bridegroom and for bride.
   The Lamb's great feast is ready,
   his bride is at his side.
   How blessed are those invited
   to share his wedding feast;
   the least become the greatest,
   the greatest are the least.

3. He who is throned in heaven
   takes up his dwelling place
   among his chosen people,
   who see him face to face.
   No sound is heard of weeping,
   for pain and sorrow cease,
   and sin shall reign no longer,
   but love and joy and peace.

4. See how a new creation
   is brought at last to birth,
   a new and glorious heaven,
   a new and glorious earth.
   Death's power for ever broken,
   its empire swept away,
   the promised dawn of glory
   begins its endless day.

440 Charles Wesley

1. Rejoice the Lord is king!
   your Lord and king adore:
   mortals, give thanks and sing,
   and triumph evermore:
   Lift up your heart, lift up your voice:
   rejoice! – again I say, rejoice!

2. Jesus, the Saviour, reigns,
   the God of truth and love;
   when he had purged our stains
   he took his seat above:
   Lift up your heart . . .

3. His kingdom cannot fail,
   he rules both earth and heaven;
   the keys of death and hell
   are to our Jesus given:
   Lift up your heart . . .

4. He sits at God's right hand,
   till all his foes submit
   and bow to his command
   and fall beneath his feet:
   Lift up your heart . . .

5. Rejoice in glorious hope!
   Jesus the judge shall come
   and take his servants up
   to their eternal home:
   We soon shall hear the
   archangel's voice:
   God's trumpet call shall sound –
   rejoice!

441
Albert Bayly
© 1988 Oxford University Press

1. Rejoice, the Lord of life ascends
   in triumph from earth's battlefield:
   his strife with human hatred ends,
   as sin and death their conquests yield.

2. No more his mortal form we see;
   he reigns invisible but near:
   for in the midst of two or three
   he makes his glorious presence clear.

3. He reigns, but with a love that shares
   the troubles of our earthly life;
   he takes upon his heart the cares,
   the pain, and shame of human strife.

4. He reigns in heaven until the hour
   when he, who once was crucified,
   shall come in all love's glorious power
   to rule the world for which he died.

442
Thomas Kelly

1. The head that once
       was crowned with thorns
   is crowned with glory now;
   a royal diadem adorns
   the mighty victor's brow.

2. The highest place that heaven affords
   is his, is his by right;
   the King of kings and Lord of lords
   and heaven's eternal light.

3. The joy of all who dwell above,
   the joy of all below;
   to whom he manifests his love
   and grants his name to know.

4. To them the cross with all its shame,
   with all its grace is given;
   their name, an everlasting name,
   their joy, the joy of heaven.

5. They suffer with their Lord below,
   they reign with him above;
   their profit and their joy to know
   the mystery of his love.

6. The cross he bore is life and health,
   though shame and death to him;
   his people's hope, his people's wealth,
   their everlasting theme.

SONGS

443
Michael Sandeman
© 1997 Kingsway's Thankyou Music

Here is the risen Son,
riding out in glory,
radiating light all around.
Here is the Holy Spirit,
poured out for the nations,
glorifying Jesus the Lamb.
Here is the risen Son . . .

We will stand as a people
who are upright and holy,
we will worship the Lord of Hosts.
We will watch, we will wait
on the walls of the city,
we will look
       and see what he will say to us.

Here is the risen Son . . .

We will stand . . .

   Every knee shall bow before him,
   every tongue confess
       that he is King of kings,
   Lord of lords,
   and ruler of the earth.

Here is the risen Son . . .

444
Matt Redman
© 1996 Kingsway's Thankyou Music

1. There is a louder shout to come,
   there is a sweeter song to hear;
   all the nations with one voice,
   all the people with one fear.
   Bowing down before your throne,
   every tribe and tongue we'll be:
   all the nations with one voice,
   all the people with one king.
   And what a song we'll sing
       upon that day!

O what a song we'll sing, and
O what a tune we'll bear –
you deserve an anthem
of the highest praise;
O what a joy will rise, and
O what a sound we'll make –
you deserve an anthem
of the highest praise.

2. Now we see a part of this,
one day we shall see in full;
all the nations with one voice,
all the people with one love.
No one else will share your praise,
nothing else can take your place;
all the nations with one voice,
all the people with one Lord.
And what a song we'll sing
upon that day!
O what a song we'll sing . . .

3. Even now upon the earth,
there's a glimpse of all to come;
many people with one voice,
harmony of many tongues.
We will all confess your name,
you will be our only praise;
all the nations with one voice,
all the people with one God.
And what a song we'll sing
upon that day!
O what a song we'll sing . . .

445
From CHILE, Santiago Stevenson
© Copyright Control. English words Michael Perry
© Mrs B. Perry/Jubilate Hymns

1. When the stars in their flight
fall from the heavens,
and the world has surrendered to night,
and the pillars of earth
have been shaken,
and the sun and the moon
lose their light:
Then we'll see the Lord
come in his glory,
in the clouds he'll descend
from his throne;
he will send all his angels before him,
and with joy they will gather his own.

2. Be on guard!
Be prepared for Jesus' coming;
for we don't know the day or the hour,
but we'll hear of the wars
of the nations,
when the kings of the earth
lose their power.
Then we'll see the Lord . . .

3. We can trust in the presence
of the Spirit,
he will teach us what we are to say;
and we need not be fearful or anxious,
for his grace will provide in that day.
Then we'll see the Lord . . .

4. When the leaves of the fig tree
are emerging,
then we see that the summer is near,
even so, as these things start to happen
then you know that the Son will appear.
Then we'll see the Lord . . .

1. *La venida de Cristo se acerca.*
Pronto viene su iglesia a buscar.
No durmamos, estemos alertos;
¡Vigilad, vigilad, vigilad!
Pronto viene Jesús y nos lleva
a la hermosa mansión celestial.
Pronto viene Jesús a la tierra;
nos iremos con él a morar.

2. *Si queremos que Cristo nos lleve*
a los cielos con él a morar.
No seamos jamás negligentes;
¡Trabajad, trabajad, trabajad!
Pronto viene . . .

3. *Arreglemos, estemos a cuentas*
con Jesús, el Cordero de Dios.
Del que ofende tengamos clemencia;
¡Perdonad, perdonad, perdonad!
Pronto viene . . .

4. *Perdonando, Jesús nos perdona,*
y nos lleva con él a reinar.
Ganaremos también la corona;
¡Vigilad, trabajad, perdonad!
Pronto viene . . .

For other items on this theme, see

HYMNS
590 All authority is yours
317 At the name of Jesus
 28 Born in song
 32 Christ is alive! Let Christians sing
 31 Christ is the king! O friends rejoice
573 Christ our king in glory reigning
319 Christ triumphant, ever reigning
321 Crown him with many crowns
504 God of gods, we sound his praises
 38 God we praise you! God, we bless you!
283 God's glory fills the universe
174 Here is love vast as the ocean
533 In Christ shall all be made alive, we sing!
354 It came upon the midnight clear
472 Let all mortal flesh keep silence
 48 Let hymns of joyful praise abound
383 Man of sorrows!
259 O day of peace
491 O Lord my God
291 O Trinity, O Trinity
327 Praise to Christ, the Lord Incarnate
328 Priest and victim, Jesus dies
440 Rejoice the Lord is king!
441 Rejoice the Lord of life ascends
376 Songs of thankfulness and praise
329 That priceless gift
363 That darkness turns to dawn
 67 The Lord is king! He sets the stars in space
538 Through the darkness of the ages
331 We have a gospel to proclaim
269 Your kingdom come, O God

PSALMS
315 The God of heaven thunders
 98 The Lord is king! Lift up your voice
 99 This earth belongs to God

SONGS
420 All heaven declares
609 Come see a vision
394 Jesus Christ, I think upon your sacrifice
424 Led like a lamb
341 Now is the time, the time of God's favour

AFFIRMING OUR BELIEF IN THE HOLY SPIRIT

HYMNS

446 From Romans 8
© Timothy Dudley-Smith

1. Born by the Holy Spirit's breath,
   loosed from the law of sin and death,
   now cleared in Christ from every claim
   no judgement stands against our name.

2. In us the Spirit makes his home
   that we in him may overcome;
   Christ's risen life, in all its powers,
   its all-prevailing strength, is ours.

3. Children and heirs of God most high,
   we by his Spirit 'Father' cry;
   that Spirit with our spirit shares
   to frame and breathe
       our wordless prayers.

4. One is his love, his purpose one:
   to form the likeness of his Son
   in all who, called and justified,
   shall reign in glory at his side.

5. Nor death nor life, nor powers unseen,
   nor height nor depth
       can come between;
   we know through peril, pain and sword,
   the love of God in Christ our Lord.

2. Gift of Chirst to guide and teach us,
   come, Spirit, come!
   Counsellor so swift to reach us,
   come, Spirit, come!
   Christ is Lord, so may we name him:
   never fearfully disclaim him
   but to all the world proclaim him.
   come, Spirit, come!

3. Gift of Christ to help us praying,
   come, Spirit, come!
   Advocate beside us staying,
   come, Spirit, come!
   In the work of intercession,
   in the healing of confession,
   in success and in depression,
   come, Spirit, come!

4. Gift of Christ for our salvation,
   come, Spirit, come!
   Bring to birth your new creation,
   come, Spirit, come!
   All the devil's work undoing,
   Christ's own ministry pursuing,
   glory in the Church renewing!
   come, Spirit, come!

447 © David Mowbray/Jubilate Hymns

1. Gift of Christ from God our Father,
   come, Spirit, come!
   Well of life and generous Giver,
   come, Spirit, come!
   With your light our minds enlighten,
   with your grace our talents heighten,
   with your joy our worship brighten:
   come, Spirit, come!

448 Henriette Auber
© in this version Jubilate Hymns

1. Our blest Redeemer, as he breathed
   his tender last farewell,
   a guide, a comforter, bequeathed
       with us to dwell.

2. He came in tongues of living flame
   to teach, convince, subdue;
   unseen as rushing wind he came –
       as powerful too.

3. He comes sweet influence to impart –
   a gracious, willing guest;
   when he can find one humble heart
      where he may rest.

4. And every virtue we possess,
   and every victory won,
   and every thought of holiness
      are his alone.

5. Spirit of purity and grace,
   our failing strength renew;
   and make our hearts a worthier place
      to welcome you.

449 © Christopher Idle/Jubilate Hymns

Spirit of holiness,
wisdom and faithfulness.
Wind of the Lord,
blowing strongly and free:
strength of our serving
and joy of our worshipping –
Spirit of God,
bring your fullness to me!

1. You came to interpret
      and teach us effectively
   all that the Saviour
      has spoken and done;
   to glorify Jesus is all your activity –
   Promise and Gift of the Father and Son:
      Spirit of holiness . . .

2. You came with your gifts
      to supply all our poverty,
   pouring your love on the church
      in her need;
   you came with your fruit
      for our growth to maturity,
   richly refreshing the souls that you feed:
      Spirit of holiness . . .

450 James Seddon
© Mrs M. Seddon/Jubilate Hymns

1. The Spirit came, as promised,
   in God's appointed hour;
   and now to each believer
   he comes in love and power;
   and by his Holy Spirit,
   God seals us as his own;
   and through the Son and Spirit
   makes access to his throne.

2. The Spirit makes our bodies
   the temple of the Lord;
   he binds us all together
   in faith and true accord:
   the Spirit in his greatness,
   brings power from God above;
   and with the Son and Father
   dwells in our hearts in love.

3. He bids us live together
   in unity and peace,
   employ his gifts in blessing,
   and let base passions cease:
   we should not grieve the Spirit
   by open sin or shame;
   nor let our words and actions
   deny his holy name.

4. The word, the Spirit's weapon,
   will bring all sin to light;
   and prayer, by his directing,
   will add new joy and might:
   be filled then with his Spirit,
   live out God's will and word;
   rejoice with hymns and singing,
   make music to the Lord!

For other items on this theme, see

HYMNS

662 All-creating heavenly Giver
 28 Born in song
554 Breathe on me, breath of God
663 Come down O Love divine
555 Come Holy Ghost, our souls inspire
621 Come to us, creative Spirit
527 Eternal light, eternal light!
200 Father in heaven, grant to your children
593 Filled with the Spirit's power
 2 First of the week and finest day
171 Freedom and life are ours
288 God who created light
597 God, whose almighty word
173 He lives in us, the Christ of God
289 I believe in God the Father
576 Let every Christian pray
 17 Like the murmur of the dove's song
672 May we, O Holy Spirit, bear your fruit
560 O thou who camest from above
291 O Trinity, O Trinity
292 Sing of a God in majestic divinity
677 Spirit of God within me
 67 The Lord is king! He set the stars in space
331 We have a gospel to proclaim
681 Wind of God, dynamic Spirit

SONGS

 19 Come Holy Spirit
 20 Come, O Holy Spirit, come
517 Father of life, draw me closer
118 He is the Lord
233 Spirit of God, unseen as the wind
396 There is a redeemer

AFFIRMING OUR BELIEF IN THE WORLDWIDE CHURCH

HYMNS

451 Arthur Ainger
© in this version Jubilate Hymns

1. God is working his purpose out,
   as year succeeds to year:
   God is working his purpose out,
   and the time is drawing near:
   nearer and nearer draws the time,
   the time that shall surely be,
       when the earth shall be filled
       with the glory of God,
       as the waters cover the sea.

2. From utmost east to utmost west,
   wherever foot has trod,
   by the mouth of many messengers
   rings out the voice of God:
   Listen to me you continents,
   you islands look to me,
       that the earth may be filled . . .

3. We shall march in the strength of God,
   with the banner of Christ unfurled,
   that the light of the glorious
       gospel of truth
   may shine throughout the world;
   we shall fight with sorrow and sin
   to set their captives free,
       that the earth may be filled . . .

4. All we can do is nothing worth
   unless God blesses the deed;
   vainly we hope for the harvest-tide
   till God gives life to the seed:
   nearer and nearer draws the time,
   the time that shall surely be,
       when the earth shall be filled . . .

452 © Michael Saward/Jubilate Hymns

1. Jesus Christ gives life and gladness
   to a world of death and grief;
   love, to conquer human madness,
   and, to broken hearts, relief;
   hope for doubt and joy for sadness,
   faith to silence unbelief.

2. Jesus works through us, expressing
   to the nations in their need
   his great love; that all possessing
   faith and hope, from bondage freed,
   round the globe may join, confessing
   'Jesus Christ is life indeed'.

453 Brian Wren
© 1973, 1996 Stainer & Bell

1. Dear Christ, uplifted from the earth,
   your arms stretched out above
   through every culture, every birth,
   to draw an answering love.

2. Still east and west your love extends
   and always, near and far,
   you call and claim us as your friends
   and love us as we are.

3. Where age and gender, class and race,
   divides us to our shame,
   you see a person and a face,
   a neighbour with a name.

4. May we, accepted as we are,
   yet called in grace to grow,
   reach out to others, near and far
   your healing love to show.

For other items on this theme, see

HYMNS
 28 Born in song
575 In Christ there is no east or west
 45 Jesus shall reign where'er the sun
601 Lift high the cross
 65 The day you gave us, Lord, is ended
 67 The Lord is king! He set the stars
649 Your hand, O God, has guided

SONG
444 There is a louder shout

AFFIRMING OUR BELIEF IN HEAVEN

HYMNS

454 From Revelation 4-5
© Christopher Idle/Jubilate Hymns

1. Come and see the shining hope
       that Christ's apostle saw;
   on the earth, confusion,
       but in heaven an open door,
   where the living creatures
       praise the Lamb for evermore:
   Love has the victory for ever!
     Amen, he comes!
       to bring his own reward!
     Amen, praise God!
       for justice now restored;
   kingdoms of the world
   become the kingdom of the Lord:
   Love has the victory for ever!

2. All the gifts you send us, Lord,
       are faithful, good, and true;
   holiness and righteousness
       are shown in all you do:
   who can see your greatest Gift
       and fail to worship you?
   Love has the victory for ever!
     Amen, he comes! . . .

3. Power and salvation
       all belong to God on high!
   So the mighty multitudes of heaven
       make their cry,
   singing, Alleluia!
       where the echoes never die:
   Love has the victory for ever!
     Amen, he comes! . . .

455 From Revelation 7
© Christopher Idle/Jubilate Hymns

1. Here from all nations, all tongues,
       and all peoples,
   countless the crowd
       but their voices are one;
   vast is the sight
       and majestic their singing –
   'God has the victory:
       he reigns from the throne!'

2. These have come
       out of the hardest oppression,
   now they may stand
       in the presence of God,
   serving their Lord
       day and night in his temple,
   ransomed and cleansed
       by the Lamb's precious blood.

3. Gone is their thirst
       and no more shall they hunger,
   God is their shelter,
       his power at their side;
   sun shall not pain them,
       no burning will torture,
   Jesus the Lamb
       is their shepherd and guide.

4. He will go with them
       to clear living water
   flowing from springs
       which his mercy supplies;
   gone is their grief
       and their trials are over –
   God wipes away every tear
       from their eyes.

5. Blessing and glory
       and wisdom and power
   be to the Saviour again and again;
   might and thanksgiving
       and honour for ever
   be to our God: Alleluia! Amen.

456 © Christopher Idle/Jubilate Hymns

1. Then I saw a new heaven and earth
   for the first had passed away,
   and the holy city, come down from God,
   like a bride on her wedding day.
   And I know how he loves his own
   for I heard his great voice tell
   they would be his people
      and he their God,
   and among them he came to dwell.

2. He will wipe away every tear,
   even death shall die at last;
   there'll be no more crying,
      or grief, or pain,
   they belong to the world that's past.
   And the One on the throne said 'Look!
   I am making all things new';
   he is A and Z, he is first and last,
   and his words are exact and true.

3. So the thirsty can drink their fill
   at the fountain giving life;
   but the gates are shut on all evil things,
   on deceit and decay and strife.
   With foundations and walls and towers
   like a jewel the city shines,
   with its streets of gold
      and its gates of pearl
   in a glory where each combines.

4. As they measured its length and breadth
   I could see no temple there,
   for its only temple is God the Lord
   and the Lamb, in that city fair.
   And it needs neither sun nor moon
   in a place which knows no night,
   for the city's lamp is the Lamb himself
   and the glory of God its light.

5. And I saw by the sacred throne
   flowing water, crystal clear,
   and the tree of life
      with its healing leaves
   and its fruit growing all the year.

So the worshippers of the Lamb
bear his name, and see his face;
and they reign and serve
   and for ever live
to the praise of his glorious grace.

SONG

457 Paul Oakley
© 1995 Kingsway's Thankyou Music

1. There's a place where the streets shine
   with the glory of the Lamb.
   There's a way we can go there,
   we can live there beyond time.
   Because of you, because of you,
   because of your love,
   because of your blood.

2. No more pain, no more sadness,
   no more suffering, no more tears,
   no more sin, no more sickness,
   no injustice, no more death.
   Because of you, because of you,
   because of your love,
   because of your blood.
      All our sins are washed away
      and we can live for ever;
      now we have this hope because of you;
      O, we'll see you face to face,
      and we will dance together
      in the city of our God –
      because of you.

3. There is joy everlasting,
   there is gladness, there is peace,
   there is wine ever flowing,
   there's a wedding, there's a feast.
   Because of you, because of you,
   because of your love,
   because of your blood.
      All our sins . . .

For other items on this theme, see

HYMNS

 28 Born in song
 29 Bright the vision that delighted
321 Crown him with many crowns
638 Guide me, O my great Redeemer
435 Hark the glad sound! – the Saviour comes
436 Hark! a trumpet call is sounding
 40 Heavenly hosts in ceaseless worship
437 I cannot tell why he whom angels worship
406 I know that my redeemer lives
533 In Christ shall all be made alive, we sing!
472 Let all mortal flesh keep silence
578 Let saints on earth together sing
179 Love divine, all loves excelling
324 Name of all majesty
 39 Now from the heavens descending
 56 O Lord my God, when I in awesome wonder
675 Rejoice in God's saints
440 Rejoice the Lord is king!
 66 The God of Abraham praise
 67 The Lord is king! He set the stars
310 To you, O Lord, our hearts we raise
539 We shall see him in the morning

SONGS

609 Come see a vision
444 There is a louder shout
138 We are on the Lord's road

CELEBRATING HOLY COMMUNION

HYMNS

458
William Dix
© in this version Jubilate Hymns

1. Alleluia, sing to Jesus!
his the sceptre, his the throne:
Alleluia! – his the triumph,
his the victory alone.
Hear the songs of holy Zion
thunder like a mighty flood:
'Jesus out of every nation
has redeemed us by his blood!'

2. Alleluia! – not as orphans
are we left in sorrow now:
Alleluia! – he is near us;
faith believes, but knows not how.
Though the cloud
   from sight received him
whom the angels now adore,
shall our hearts forget his promise,
'I am with you evermore'?

3. Alleluia! – bread of heaven,
here on earth our food, our stay:
Alleluia! – here the sinful
come to you from day to day.
Intercessor, friend of sinners,
earth's redeemer, plead for me,
where the songs of all the sinless
sweep across the crystal sea.

4. Allelulia! – King eternal,
you, the Lord of lords we own;
Alleluia! – born of Mary,
earth your footstool,
   heaven your throne:
you, within the veil have entered,
robed in flesh, our great high priest;
yours the blood and yours the body,
in our eucharistic feast.

*If not used at communion, omit verse 4
and repeat verse 1 as final verse*

459
William Bright
© in this version Jubilate Hymns

1. And now, O Father, mindful of the love
which bought us once for all
   on Calvary's tree,
and having with us Christ
   who reigns above,
we celebrate with joy for all to see
that only offering perfect in your eyes:
the one true, pure, immortal sacrifice.

2. Look, Father, look on his anointed face,
and only look on us as found in him;
look not on our misusings
   of your grace,
our prayer so feeble
   and our faith so dim;
for, set between our sins
   and their reward,
we see the cross of Christ,
   your Son, our Lord.

3. And so we come:
   O draw us to your feet,
most patient Saviour,
   who can love us still;
and by this food, so awesome
   and so sweet,
deliver us from every touch of ill;
for your glad service, Master, set us free,
and make of us what you
   would have us be.

460
Fred Kaan
© 1968 Stainer & Bell

1. As we break the bread
   and taste the life of wine,
we bring to mind our Lord,
   Man of all time.

2. Grain is sown to die;
   it rises from the dead,
becomes through human toil
   our daily bread.

3. Pass from hand to hand
   the living love of Christ!
   Machines and people raise
   bread for this feast.

4. Jesus binds in one
   our daily life and work;
   he is of humankind
   symbol and mark.

5. Having shared the bread
   that died to rise again,
   we rise to serve the world,
   scattered as grain.

461 Carl P. Daw Jnr. © 1989 Hope Publishing Co.
Administered by CopyCare

1. As we gather at your table,
   as we listen to your word,
   help us know, O God, your presence:
   let our hearts and minds be stirred.
   Nourish us with sacred story
   till we claim it as our own;
   teach us through this holy banquet
   how to make Love's victory known.

2. Turn our worship into witness
   in the sacrament of life:
   send us forth to love and serve you,
   bringing peace where there is strife.
   Give us, Christ, your great compassion
   to forgive as you forgave:
   may we still behold your image
   in the world you died to save.

3. Gracious Spirit, help us summon
   other guests to share that feast
   where triumphant Love will welcome
   those who had been last and least.
   There no more will envy bind us
   nor will pride our peace destroy,
   as we join with saints and angels
   to repeat the sounding joy.

462 © David Mowbray/Jubilate Hymns

1. At the supper, Christ the Lord
   gathered friends and said the blessing;
   bread was broken, wine was poured,
   faith in Israel's God expressing:
   signs of the forthcoming passion,
   tokens of a great salvation.

2. After supper, Jesus knelt,
   taking towel and bowl of water;
   washing the disciples' feet,
   servant now as well as master:
   'You,' said he, 'have my example –
   let your way of life be humble!'

3. In the fellowship of faith
   Christ himself with us is present;
   supper of the Lord in truth,
   host and master all-sufficient!
   From this table, gladly sharing,
   send us, Lord, to love and caring.

463 John L. Bell and Graham Maule
© 1989 WGRG, Iona Community, from *Love from
Below* (Wild Goose Publications, 1989)

1. Before I take the body of my Lord,
   before I share his life in bread and wine,
   I recognise the sorry things within –
   these I lay down.

2. The words of hope I often failed to give,
   the prayers of kindness
        buried by my pride,
   the signs of care I argued out of sight:
   these I lay down.

3. The narrowness of vision and of mind,
   the need for other folk to serve my will,
   and every word and silence
        meant to hurt:
   these I lay down.

4. Of those around
        in whom I meet my Lord,
   I ask their pardon and I grant them mine
   that every contradiction
        to Christ's peace
   might be laid down.

5. Lord Jesus Christ,
    companion at this feast,
I empty now my heart
    and stretch my hands,
and ask to meet you here
    in bread and wine
which you lay down.

464 Josiah Conder
© in this version Jubilate Hymns

1. Bread of heaven, on you we feed,
    for your flesh is food indeed;
always may our souls be fed
with this true and living bread;
day by day our strength supplied
through your life, O Christ, who died.

2. Vine of heaven, your precious blood
seals today our peace with God;
Lord, your wounds our healing give,
to your cross we look and live:
grafted, rooted, built in you,
Jesus, here our souls renew.

465 Reginald Heber

1. Bread of the world in mercy broken,
wine of the soul in mercy shed;
by whom the words of life were spoken
and in whose death our sins are dead:

2. Look on the heart by sorrow broken,
look on the tears by sinners shed,
and make your feast to us the token
that by your grace our souls are fed.

466 Louis Benson

1. For the bread which you have broken,
for the wine which you have poured,
for the words which you have spoken,
now we give you thanks, O Lord.

2. By these pledges that you love us,
by your gift of peace restored,
by your call to heaven above us,
consecrate our lives, O Lord:

3. In your service, Lord, defend us,
help us to obey your word;
in the world to which you send us
let your kingdom come, O Lord!

467 © Christopher Porteous and in this version
Jubilate Hymns

1. He gave his life in selfless love,
    for sinners once he came;
he had no stain of sin himself
    but bore our guilt and shame:
he took the cup of pain and death,
    his blood was freely shed;
we see his body on the cross,
    we share the living bread.

2. He did not come to call the good
    but sinners to repent;
it was the lame, the deaf, the blind
    for whom his life was spent:
to heal the sick, to find the lost –
    it was for such he came,
and round his table all may come
    to praise his holy name.

3. They heard him call his Father's name –
    then 'Finished!' was his cry;
like them we have forsaken him
    and left him there to die:
the sins that crucified him then
    are sins his blood has cured;
the love that bound him to a cross
    our freedom has ensured.

4. His body broken once for us
    is glorious now above;
the cup of blessing we receive,
    a sharing of his love:
as in his presence we partake,
    his dying we proclaim
until the hour of majesty
    when Jesus comes again.

468 Horatius Bonar

1. Here, O my Lord, I see you face to face,
   here faith can touch and handle
      things unseen:
   here I will grasp with firmer hand
      your grace
   and all my weariness upon you lean.

2. Here I will feed upon the bread of God,
   here drink with you the royal wine
      of heaven:
   here I will lay aside each earthly load,
   here taste afresh the calm
      of sin forgiven.

3. I have no help but yours, nor do I need
   another arm but yours to lean upon;
   it is enough, my Lord, enough indeed,
   my hope is in your strength,
      your strength alone.

4. Mine is the sin,
      but yours the righteousness;
   mine is the guilt,
      but yours the cleansing blood:
   here is my robe, my refuge,
      and my peace;
   your blood, your righteousness,
      O Lord my God.

5. Too soon we rise,
      the symbols disappear;
   the feast, though not the love,
      is past and done:
   gone are the bread and wine,
      but you are here,
   nearer than ever, still my shield and sun.

6. Feast after feast thus comes
      and passes by,
   yet, passing,
      points to that glad feast above;
   giving sweet foretaste of the festal joy,
   the Lamb's great bridal feast
      of bliss and love.

469 Brian Wren
© 1971, 1995 Stainer & Bell

1. I come with joy, a child of God,
   forgiven, loved, and free,
   the life of Jesus to recall,
   in love laid down for me.

2. I come with Christians far and near
   to find, as all are fed,
   the new community of love
   in Christ's communion bread.

3. As Christ breaks bread
      and bids us share,
   each proud division ends.
   The love that made us, makes us one,
   and strangers now are friends.

4. The Spirit of the risen Christ,
   unseen, but ever near,
   is in such friendship better known,
   alive among us here.

5. Together met, together bound
   by all that God has done,
   we'll go with joy, to give the world
   the love that makes us one.

470 John Monsell

1. I hunger and I thirst,
   Jesus, my manna be:
   O living waters, burst
   out of the rock for me!

2. O bruised and broken bread,
   my life-long needs supply:
   as living souls are fed,
   so feed me, or I die.

3. O true life-giving vine,
   let me your goodness prove:
   by your life sweeten mine,
   refresh my soul with love.

4. Rough paths my feet have trod
   since first their course began:
   renew me, bread of God,
   restore me, Son of man.

5. For still the desert lies
   behind me and before:
   O living waters, rise
   within me evermore!

471 From the Latin (12th Century), Ray Palmer

1. Jesus, the joy of loving hearts,
   true source of life, our lives sustain:
   from the best bliss that earth imparts
   we turn unfilled to you again.

2. Your truth unchanged has ever stood,
   you rescue those who on you call:
   to those yet seeking, you are good –
   to those who find you, all-in-all.

3. We taste of you, the living bread,
   and long to feast upon you still;
   we drink from you, the fountain-head,
   our thirsty souls from you we fill.

4. Our restless spirits long for you,
   whichever way our lot is cast,
   glad when your gracious smile we view,
   blessed when our faith
        can hold you fast.

5. Jesus, for ever with us stay,
   make all our moments calm and bright;
   chase the dark night of sin away,
   spread through the world
        your holy light.

472 After the *Liturgy of James*, Gerard Moultrie
© in this version Jubilate Hymns

1. Let all mortal flesh keep silence,
   and with fear and trembling stand;
   set your minds on things eternal,
   for with blessing in his hand
   Christ our God to earth descending
   comes our homage to command.

2. King of kings, yet born of Mary,
   once upon the earth he stood;
   Lord of lords we now perceive him
   in his body and his blood –
   he will give to all the faithful
   his own self for heavenly food.

3. Rank on rank the host of heaven
   stream before him on the way;
   as the Light of light decending
   from the realms of endless day
   vanquishes the power of evil,
   clears the gloom of hell away.

4. At his feet the six-winged seraphs,
   cherubim with sleepless eye,
   veil their faces in his presence
   as with ceaseless voice they cry:
   Alleluia, alleluia,
   alleluia, Lord most high!

473 From a Syriac liturgy, John Neale, Charles Humphreys
and Percy Dearmer, by permission of Oxford
University Press

1. Make strong for service, Lord, the hands
   that holy things have taken;
   let ears that now have heard your songs
   to clamour never waken.

2. Lord, may the tongues which 'Holy' sang
   keep free from all deceiving;
   the eyes which saw your love be bright,
   the glorious hope perceiving:

3. The feet that tread your holy courts
   from light be never banished;
   the bodies by your Body fed,
   be with new life replenished.

474 Philip Doddridge
© in this version Jubilate Hymns

1. My God, now is your table spread,
   your cup with love still overflows:
   so may your children here be fed
   as Christ to us his goodness shows.

2. This holy feast, which Jesus makes
   a banquet of his flesh and blood –
   how glad each one
        who comes and takes
   this sacred drink, this royal food!

3. His gifts that richly satisfy
   are yet to some in vain displayed:
   did not for them the Saviour die –
   may they not share the children's bread?

4. My God, here let your table be
   a place of joy for all your guests,
   and may each one salvation see
   who now its sacred pledges tastes.

475
Fred Kaan
© 1968 Stainer & Bell

1. Now let us from this table rise
   renewed in body, mind and soul;
   with Christ we die and rise again,
   his selfless love has made us whole.

2. With minds alert, upheld by grace,
   to spread the Word in speech and deed,
   we follow in the steps of Christ,
   at one with all in hope and need.

3. To fill each human house with love,
   it is the sacrament of care;
   the work that Christ began to do
   we humbly pledge ourselves to share.

4. Then give us grace, Companion-God,
   to choose again the pilgrim way
   and help us to accept with joy
   the challenge of tomorrow's day!

476
William Turton. © Hymns Ancient & Modern
and in this version Jubilate Hymns

1. O Christ,
   at your first eucharist you prayed
   that all your church
   might be for ever one;
   at every eucharist this prayer is made
   with longing heart and soul,
   'Your will be done':
   O may we all one bread, one body be
   through this blessed sacrament
   of unity.

2. For all your church,
   O Lord, we intercede
   that you will make
   our sad divisions cease:
   O draw us nearer
   each to each, we plead,
   by drawing all to you,
   the prince of peace.
   Thus may we all
   one bread, one body be
   through this blessed sacrament
   of unity.

3. We pray for those who wander
   from your fold:
   O bring them back,
   great Shepherd of the sheep –
   back to the faith
   which saints believed of old,
   the faith for all your holy church to keep.
   Soon may we all
   one bread, one body be
   through this blessed sacrament
   of unity.

4. So, Lord, at length
   when sacraments shall cease,
   may we be one
   with all your church above;
   one with your saints
   in one unbroken peace,
   one with your saints
   in one unbounded love:
   Far happier then,
   in peace and love to be
   one with the Trinity-in-Unity!

477
© Andrew King

1. O Lord, sustaining all who live
   by fertile field and fruitful vine,
   we bow before you now to give
   our heartfelt thanks for bread and wine.

2. For bread and wine as food – but more,
   as signs of Jesus' flesh and blood;
   we thank you for the one who bore
   our sin and gave us peace with God.

478 © Michael Saward/Jubilate Hymns

1. O Sacrifice of Calvary,
   O Lamb whose sacred blood was shed,
   O great High Priest on heaven's throne,
   O Victor from the dead!
   here I recall your agony,
   here see again your bloodstained brow:
   beyond the sign of bread and wine
   I know your presence now.

2. Your royal presence intercedes
   eternally for me above,
   and here my hungry spirit feeds
   upon these gifts of love;
   before your holy table laid
   I kneel once more in hope and peace,
   your blood and flesh my soul refresh
   with joy that shall not cease.

479 Fred Kaan © 1989 Stainer & Bell

1. Put peace into each other's hands
   and like a treasure hold it,
   protect it like a candle-flame,
   with tenderness enfold it.

2. Put peace into each other's hands
   with loving expectation;
   be gentle in your words and ways,
   in touch with God's creation.

3. Put peace into each other's hands,
   like bread we break for sharing;
   look people warmly in the eye:
   our life is meant for caring.

4. As at communion, shape your hands
   into a waiting cradle;
   the gift of Christ receive, revere,
   united round the table.

5. Put Christ into each other's hands:
   he is love's deepest measure;
   in love make peace, give peace a chance
   and share it like a treasure.

480 © Michael Saward/Jubilate Hymns

1. 'Peace be with you all,' we sing;
   peace from Christ, our Lord and King,
   he it is who makes us one,
   God's eternal rising Son.

2. Bound together in his name,
   welded by the Spirit's flame;
   at his table here we kneel
   and his living presence feel.

3. Bread is broken for our food;
   wine we share in gratitude.
   His the flesh and blood he gave
   for the world he died to save.

4. So, with empty hands, we bow
   welcoming our Saviour now
   and, renewed in mind and heart,
   in the peace of Christ depart.

481 © Stephen Horsfall/Jubilate Hymns

1. The life within the standing corn,
   cut down and crushed, for us is made
   the symbol of a hope reborn.
   New seed is sown: a debt is paid.

2. The life within the swelling grape,
   cut down and crushed,
     becomes the wine:
   shed blood wherein is all our hope.
   New buds will grow upon the vine.

3. We drink this wine and eat this bread,
   sustaining soul and body still,
   as we recall the blood once shed
   at Calvary, upon that hill.

4. The body racked with agony,
   cut down and crushed
     with blood and pain:
   but death shall not have mastery,
   for what was crushed now lives again.

482 © Basil Bridge

1. The Son of God proclaim!
   the Lord of time and space,
   the God who bade the light break forth
   now shines in Jesus' face.

2. He, God's creative Word,
   the church's Lord and head,
   here bids us gather as his friends
   and share his wine and bread.

3. The Lord of life and death
   with wondering praise we sing;
   we break the bread at his command
   and name him God and King.

4. We take this cup in hope,
   for he who gladly bore
   the shameful cross, is risen again
   and reigns for evermore.

483 © Michael Saward/Jubilate Hymns

1. Welcome to another day!
   night is blinded;
   'Welcome', let creation say;
   darkness ended.
   Comes the sunshine after dew,
   time for labour;
   time to love my God anew
   and my neighbour.

2. Welcome to the day of prayer
   with God's people;
   welcome is the joy we share
   at his table.
   Bread and wine from heaven fall:
   come, receive it
   that the Christ may reign in all
   who believe it.

3. Welcome is the peace that's given,
   sure for ever;
   welcome is the hope of heaven
   when life's over.
   As we work and as we pray,
   trust God's story:
   come then, as the dawning day
   heralds glory!

SONGS

484 © 1982, 1987 Bernadette Farrell
Published by OCP Publications

ALL: Bread of life, hope of the world,
Jesus Christ our brother:
feed us now, give us life,
lead us to one another.

SOLO/GROUP
1. As we proclaim your death,
   as we recall your life,
   we remember your promise
   to return again,
   ALL: Bread of life . . .

SOLO/GROUP
2. This bread we break and share
   was scattered once as grain:
   just as now it is gathered,
   make your people one.
   ALL: Bread of life . . .

SOLO/GROUP
3. We eat this living bread,
   we drink this saving cup:
   sign of hope in our broken world,
   source of lasting love.
   ALL: Bread of life . . .

Alternative verses for Christmas:

1. A child is born for us,
   a Son is given to us;
   in our midst Christ our Lord and God
   comes as one who serves.
   ALL: Bread of life . . .

2. With our own eyes we see,
   with our own ears we hear
   the salvation of all the world,
   God's incarnate Word.
   ALL: Bread of life . . .

3. You are the hope of all,
   our promise and our call,
   radiant light in our darkness,
   truth to set us free.
   ALL: Bread of life . . .

485
Janet Lunt
© 1978 Sovereign Music UK

Broken for me, broken for you,
the body of Jesus broken for you.

1. He offered his body,
   he poured out his soul,
Jesus was broken
   that we might be whole:
Broken for me . . .

2. Come to my table and with me dine,
   eat of my bread and drink of my wine:
   Broken for me . . .

3. This is my body given for you,
   eat it remembering I died for you:
   Broken for me . . .

4. This is my blood I shed for you,
   for your forgiveness, making you new:
   Broken for me . . .

For other items on this theme, see

HYMNS
571 By the sacrifice of Jesus
 2 First of the week and finest day
 37 Glory in the highest
638 Guide me, O my great Redeemer
 4 Here in this place
670 Lord Jesus Christ, you have come to us
 52 Lord, enthroned in heavenly splendour
180 Love is his word, love is his way
374 O changeless Christ, for ever new
 61 Sing of the Lord's goodness
186 The love of God comes close
 69 There's a spirit in the air
389 This is the night, dear friends
330 This is the threefold truth

SONGS
112 Glory, glory
160 Lamb of God

486
From *The Alternative Service Book 1980*
© 1988 The Central Board of Finance of the Church
of England; 1999 The Archbishop's Council

1. MEN: We break this bread
               to share in the body of Christ;
   WOMEN: we break this bread
               to share in the body of Christ.
   ALL: Though we are many,
            we are one body,
            because we all share,
            we all share in one bread.
            Though we are many . . .

2. MEN: We drink this cup
               to share in the body of Christ;
   WOMEN: we drink this cup
               to share in the body of Christ.
   ALL: Though we are many . . .

HEALING SERVICES

HYMNS

487 Henry Twells
© in this version Jubilate Hymns

1. At evening, when the sun had set,
   the sick, O Lord, around you lay:
   in what distress and pain they met,
   but in what joy they went away!

2. Once more the evening comes, and we
   oppressed with various ills draw near;
   and though your form we cannot see,
   we know and feel that you are here.

3. O Saviour Christ, our fears dispel –
   for some are sick and some are sad,
   and some have never loved you well,
   and some have lost the love they had.

4. And none, O Lord, has perfect rest,
   for none is wholly free from sin;
   and those who long to serve you best
   are conscious most of wrong within.

5. O Saviour Christ, the Son of Man,
   you have been troubled, tempted, tried;
   your kind but searching glance can scan
   the very wounds that shame would hide.

6. Your touch has still its ancient power;
   no word from you can fruitless fall:
   meet with us in this evening hour
   and in your mercy heal us all!

488 Michael Perry
© Mrs B. Perry/Jubilate Hymns

1. Heal me, hands of Jesus,
   and search out all my pain;
   restore my hope, remove my fear
   and bring me peace again.

2. Cleanse me, blood of Jesus,
   take bitterness away;
   let me forgive as one forgiven
   and bring me peace today.

3. Know me, mind of Jesus,
   and show me all my sin;
   dispel the memories of guilt,
   and bring me peace within.

4. Fill me, joy of Jesus:
   anxiety shall cease
   and heaven's serenity be mine,
   for Jesus brings me peace!

489 Fred Pratt Green
© 1969 Stainer & Bell

1. O Christ, the Healer, we have come
      to pray for health, to plead for friends.
   How can we fail to be restored,
      when reached by love that never ends?

2. From every ailment flesh endures
      our bodies clamour to be freed;
   yet in our hearts we would confess
      that wholeness is our deepest need.

3. How strong, O Lord, are our desires,
      how weak our knowledge of ourselves!
   Release in us those healing truths
      unconscious pride resists or shelves.

4. In conflicts that destroy our health
      we diagnose the world's disease;
   Our common life declares our ills:
      is there no cure, O Christ, for these?

5. Grant that we all, made one in faith;
      in your community may find
   the wholeness that, enriching us,
      shall reach the whole of humankind.

490 © 1989, 1996 WGRG Iona Community

1. We cannot measure how you heal
   or answer every sufferer's prayer,
   yet we believe your grace responds
   where faith and doubt unite to care.

Your hands,
> though bloodied on the cross,
> survive to hold and heal and warn,
> to carry all through death to life
> and cradle children yet unborn.

2. The pain that will not go away,
> the guilt that clings
> > from things long past,
> the fear of what the future holds,
> are present as if meant to last.
> But present too is love which tends
> the hurt we never hoped to find,
> the private agonies inside,
> the memories that haunt the mind.

3. So some have come who need your help
> and some have come to make amends,
> as hands which shaped
> > and saved the world
> are present in the touch of friends.
> Lord, let your Spirit meet us here
> to mend the body, mind and soul,
> to disentangle peace from pain
> and make your broken people whole.

PSALM

491 From Psalm 22, John L. Bell and Graham Maule
© 1988 WGRG, Iona Community, from *Enemy and Apathy* (Wild Goose Publications, 1988)

ALL
O Lord my God, O Lord my God,
why do you seem so far from me,
O Lord my God?

GROUP/SOLO
1. Night and morning I make my prayer:
> peace for this place, and help for there;
> > waiting and wondering,
> > waiting and wondering –
> does God care; does God care?
> > ALL: O Lord my God . . .

GROUP/SOLO
2. Pain and suffering unbound and blind
> plague the progress of humankind,
> > always demanding,
> > always demanding –
> does God mind; does God mind?
> > ALL: O Lord my God . . .

GROUP/SOLO
3. Why, oh why do the wicked thrive,
> poor folk perish, the rich survive;
> > begging the question,
> > begging the question –
> is God alive; is God alive?
> > ALL: O Lord my God . . .

GROUP/SOLO
4. Turn again as you hear my plea,
> tend the torment in all I see;
> > loving and healing,
> > loving and healing –
> set me free, set me free.
> > ALL: O Lord my God . . .

For other items on this theme, see

HYMNS
620 Christ who called disciples to him
447 Gift of Christ from God our Father
597 God, whose almighty word
638 Guide me, O my great Redeemer
467 He gave his life in selfless love
505 His eyes will guide my footsteps
406 I know that my redeemer lives
176 Immortal love for ever full
201 Jesus, lover of my soul
 52 Lord, enthroned in heavenly splendour
374 O changeless Christ, for ever new
489 O Christ, the Healer, we have come
 55 O for a thousand tongues to sing
339 On Jordan's bank the Baptist's cry
 73 When all your mercies, O my God
187 With loving hands

PSALMS
 84 I'll praise my maker while I've breath
 93 Praise my soul, the King of heaven

SONGS
  7 Be still, for the presence of the Lord
252 Christ's is the world in which we move
333 I believe in Jesus
658 Kindle a flame to lighten the dark
522 Say the word
217 There is a longing
166 You are merciful to me
696 You know me

CHRISTIAN INITIATION

HYMNS

492 © Michael Saward/Jubilate Hymns

1. Baptized in water,
    sealed by the Spirit,
    cleansed by the blood of Christ our king;
    heirs of salvation,
    trusting his promise –
    faithfully now God's praise we sing.

2. Baptized in water,
    sealed by the Spirit,
    dead in the tomb with Christ our king;
    one with his rising,
    freed and forgiven
    thankfully now God's praise we sing.

3. Baptized in water,
    sealed by the Spirit,
    marked with the sign of Christ our king;
    born of one Father,
    we are his children –
    joyfully now God's praise we sing.

493 © Paul Wigmore/Jubilate Hymns

1. Lord, bless and keep this little child,
    your blessing be *her* joy,
    your keeping, *her* most certain strength
    that nothing can destroy.

2. So look upon this little child
    and make your face to shine,
    that *she* may see,
    through hopes and fears,
    your countenance divine.

3. Thus may this precious little child
    grow in that heavenly grace
    which little children long ago
    found in your holy face.

4. Your peace be with this little child –
    not as the world would give;
    for yours is peace that will not fail
    as long as *she* may live.

5. We dedicate this little child
    in deepest joy and praise;
    prepare our hearts to love *her* well
    and guide *her* in your ways.

The words *her* and *she* may be sung as *him* and *he*

494 © Michael Saward/Jubilate Hymns

1. This is the truth which we proclaim,
    God makes a promise firm and sure;
    marked by this sign made in his name,
    here, for our sickness, God's own cure.

2. This is the grave in which we lie:
    dead to a world of sin and shame
    raised with our Lord, to self we die
    and live to praise God's holy name.

3. This is the sacrament of birth:
    sealed by a Saviour's death for sin,
    trust in his mercy all on earth,
    open your hearts and let him in!

4. This is the covenant of grace –
    God, to the nations, shows his love;
    people of every tribe and race,
    born, by his Spirit, from above.

5. This is the badge we proudly wear:
    washed by our God, the Three-in-One;
    welcomed, in fellowship we share
    hope of eternal life begun.

Other item on this theme

601 Lift high the cross

RESPONDING TO GOD: IN FAITH AND TRUST

HYMNS

495 Henry Francis Lyte

1. Abide with me, fast falls the eventide;
   the darkness deepens:
       Lord, with me abide.
   When other helpers fail
       and comforts flee,
   help of the helpless, O abide with me.

2. Swift to its close
       ebbs out life's little day;
   earth's joys grow dim,
       its glories pass away.
   Change and decay in all around I see –
   you never change,
       O Lord: abide with me!

3. I need your presence
       every passing hour:
   what but your grace can foil
       the tempter's power?
   Who like yourself my guide
       and strength can be?
   Through cloud and sunshine,
       Lord, abide with me!

4. I have no fear with you at hand to bless;
   ills have no weight
       and tears no bitterness.
   Where is death's sting?
       Where, grave, your victory?
   I triumph still if you abide with me.

5. Hold now your cross
       before my closing eyes;
   shine through the gloom
       and point me to the skies!
   Heaven's morning breaks
       and earth's vain shadows flee:
   in life, in death, O Lord, abide with me!

496 © Elizabeth Cosnett

1. Can we by searching find out God
   or formulate his ways?
   Can numbers measure what he is
   or words contain his praise?

2. Although his being is too bright
   for human eyes to scan,
   his meaning lights our shadowed world
   through Christ, the Son of Man.

3. Our boastfulness is turned to shame,
   our profit counts as loss,
   when earthly values stand beside
   the manger and the cross.

4. We there may recognise his light,
   may kindle in its rays,
   find there the source of penitence,
   the starting-point for praise.

5. There God breaks in upon our search,
   makes birth and death his own:
   he speaks to us in human terms
   to make his glory known.

497 John Whittier © in this version Jubilate Hymns

1. Dear Lord and Father of mankind,
   forgive our foolish ways:
   reclothe us in our rightful mind;
   in purer lives your service find,
       in deeper reverence praise,
       in deeper reverence praise.

2. In simple trust like theirs who heard,
   beside the Syrian sea,
   the gracious calling of the Lord –
   let us, like them, obey his word:
       'Rise up and follow me,
       rise up and follow me!'

3. O sabbath rest by Galilee!
   O calm of hills above,
   when Jesus shared on bended knee
   the silence of eternity
       interpreted by love,
       interpreted by love!

4. With that deep hush subduing all
   our words and works that drown
   the tender whisper of your call,
   as noiseless let your blessing fall
       as fell your manna down,
       as fell your manna down.

5. Drop your still dews of quietness,
   till all our strivings cease;
   take from our souls
       the strain and stress,
   and let our ordered lives confess
       the beauty of your peace,
       the beauty of your peace.

6. Breathe through the heats of our desire
   your coolness and your balm;
   let sense be dumb, let flesh retire,
   speak through the earthquake,
       wind and fire,
       O still small voice of calm,
       O still small voice of calm!

498
Thomas Pollock
© in this version Jubilate Hymns

1. Faithful Shepherd, feed me
   in the pastures green;
   faithful Shepherd, lead me
   where your steps are seen:

2. Hold me fast, and guide me
   in the narrow way;
   so, with you beside me,
   I need never stray:

3. Daily bring me nearer
   to the heavenly shore;
   make my faith grow clearer,
   help me love you more;

4. Consecrate each pleasure,
   every joy and pain;
   you are all my treasure,
   all I hope to gain:

5. Day by day prepare me
   as you purpose best,
   then to heaven bear me
   to my promised rest.

499
John Eddison
© Scripture Union

1. Father, although I cannot see
       the future you have planned,
   and though the path is sometimes dark
       and hard to understand:
   yet give me faith, through joy and pain,
       to trace your loving hand.

2. When I recall that in the past
       your promises have stood
   through each perplexing circumstance
       and every changing mood,
   I rest content that all things work
       together for my good.

3. Whatever, then, the future brings
       of good or seeming ill,
   I ask for strength to follow you
       and grace to trust you still;
   and I would look for no reward,
       except to do your will.

500
© Jocelyn Marshall

1. Give us a sense of wonder, God,
       perceptive child-like eyes
   that seeing beauty fresh revealed
       blend marvel with surprise.

2. Give us the gift of laughter, God,
       spontaneous, generous, shared,
   the vital spark that kindles warmth,
       your joy in us declared.

3. Give us the gift of peace profound,
　　that listening we perceive
　eternal truths, unspoken words;
　　enlightment receive.

4. We see you in the billowing clouds,
　　the stamen of a flower,
　reflections on a tranquil lake,
　　a mighty river's power.

5. We hear you in a thrush's song,
　　the surging of the sea,
　the wind which makes
　　the tree tops dance:
　a world of harmony.

6. Enlarge our vision, glorious God,
　　with expectations new.
　give us the grace to see afresh;
　　bring wonder to our view.

501 © Caryl Micklem

1. Give to me, Lord, a thankful heart
　　and a discerning mind:
　give, as I play the Christian's part,
　the strength to finish what I start
　　and act on what I find.

2. When, in the rush of days, my will
　　is habit-bound and slow,
　help me to keep in vision still
　　what love and power
　　and peace can fill
　a life that trusts in you.

3. By your divine and urgent claim,
　　and by your human face,
　kindle our sinking hearts to flame
　and as you teach the world your name
　　let it become your place.

4. Jesus, with all your Church I long
　　to see your kingdom come:
　show me your way of righting wrong
　and turning sorrow into song
　　until you bring me home.

502 Thomas Ken
© in this version Jubilate Hymns

1. Glory to you, my God, this night
　for all the blessings of the light;
　keep me, O keep me, King of kings,
　beneath your own almighty wings.

2. Forgive me, Lord,
　　through your dear Son,
　the wrong that I this day have done,
　that peace with God and man may be,
　before I sleep, restored to me.

3. Teach me to live, that I may dread
　the grave as little as my bed;
　teach me to die, that so I may
　rise glorious at the judgement day.

4. O may my soul on you repose
　and restful sleep my eyelids close;
　sleep that shall me more vigorous make
　to serve my God when I awake.

5. If in the night I sleepless lie,
　my mind with peaceful thoughts supply;
　let no dark dreams disturb my rest,
　no powers of evil me molest.

6. Praise God from whom all blessings flow
　in heaven above and earth below;
　one God, three persons, we adore –
　to him be praise for evermore!

503 Martin E. Leckebusch
© Kevin Mayhew

1. God has promised many things –
　treasures from a heavenly store;
　now in Christ the echo sounds:
　'Yes' to all he said before.
　　Think of how he gave his Son –
　　such a precious gift indeed!
　　How will he not also give
　　all that we could ever need?

2. Faith unlocks the power of God
　in the face of doubt and fear;
　access to his throne is ours –
　what can stop us drawing near?
　　God has pledged to hear our prayers
　　when we ask in Jesus' name,
　　so we come with eager hearts
　　and his promise boldly claim.

3. Faith enjoys the peace of God –
   freedom from anxiety!
   What can earthly riches give?
   Christ is our security!
       Faith will therefore never cling
       to the wealth we now possess,
       but will find the better way –
       giving freely, keeping less.

4. God has promised many things –
   treasures from a heavenly store;
   now in Christ the echo sounds:
   'Yes' to all he said before.
       So we raise a loud 'Amen!'
       as we make his word our own
       and, with faith to guide our lives,
       make his promised riches known.

504 From *Te Deum*
© Timothy Dudley-Smith

1. God of gods, we sound his praises,
   highest heaven its homage brings;
   earth and all creation raises
   glory to the King of kings.
   Holy, holy, holy, name him,
   Lord of all his hosts proclaim him;
   to the everlasting Father
   every tongue in triumph sings.

2. Christians in their hearts enthrone him,
   tell his praises wide abroad;
   prophets, priests, apostles own him
   martyrs' crown and saints' reward.
   Three-in-One his glory sharing,
   earth and heaven his praise declaring,
   praise the high majestic Father,
   praise the everlasting Lord!

3. Hail the Christ, the king of glory,
   he whose praise the angels cry;
   born to share our human story,
   love and labour, grieve and die:
   by his cross his work completed,
   sinners ransomed, death defeated;
   in the glory of the Father
   Christ ascended reigns on high.

4. Lord, we look for your returning;
   teach us so to walk your ways,
   hearts and minds your will discerning,
   lives alight with joy and praise:
   in your love and care enfold us,
   by your constancy uphold us;
   may your mercy, Lord and Father,
   keep us now and all our days!

505 © Christopher Porteous/Jubilate Hymns

1. His eyes will guide my footsteps
   when faltering age is near;
   his light will lift my darkness
   and help my ears to hear;
   in faith I claim the promise
   of Jesus' love for me;
   the Lord of hope and healing
   who made the blind to see.

2. When others fail or leave me,
   he comes to me in prayer;
   when life no longer needs me
   I find my comfort here:
   his promises are faithful –
   he lives, my closest friend;
   I know that he will keep me
   until my days shall end.

3. He comes when I am weary,
   in pain or in distress;
   with patient understanding
   and perfect gentleness:
   he was far more forsaken
   than I shall ever be;
   the presence of my saviour
   is everything to me.

506 © Timothy Dudley Smith

1. Here on the threshold
       of a new beginning,
   by grace forgiven, now we leave behind
   our long-repented selfishness
       and sinning,
   and all our blessings call again to mind:
   Christ to redeem us,
       ransom and restore us,

the love that holds us
  in a Saviour's care,
faith strong to welcome all
  that lies before us,
our unknown future,
  knowing God is there.

2. May we, your children,
  feel with Christ's compassion
an earth disordered, hungry and in pain;
then, at your calling,
  find the will to fashion
new ways where freedom,
  truth and justice reign;
where wars are ended,
  ancient wrongs are righted,
and nations value human life and worth;
where in the darkness
  lamps of hope are lighted
and Christ is honoured
  over all the earth.

3. So may your wisdom shine
  from scripture's pages
to mould and make us stones
  with which to build
God's holy temple, through eternal ages,
one church united,
  strong and Spirit-filled;
heirs to the fulness
  of your new creation
in faith we follow,
  pledged to be your own;
yours is the future, ours the celebration,
for Christ is risen! God is on the throne!

507 Charlotte Elliott
© in this version Jubilate Hymns

1. Just as I am, without one plea
but that you died to set me free,
and at your bidding 'Come to me!'
  O Lamb of God, I come.

2. Just as I am, without delay
your call of mercy I obey –
your blood can wash my sins away:
  O Lamb of God, I come.

3. Just as I am, though tossed about
with many a conflict, many a doubt,
fightings within and fears without,
  O Lamb of God, I come.

4. Just as I am, poor, wretched, blind!
Sight, riches, healing of the mind –
all that I need, in you to find:
  O Lamb of God, I come.

5. Just as I am! You will receive,
will welcome, pardon, cleanse, relieve:
because your promise I believe,
  O Lamb of God, I come.

6. Just as I am! Your love unknown
has broken every barrier down:
now to be yours, yes, yours alone,
  O Lamb of God, I come.

7. Just as I am! Of that free love
the breadth, length, depth
  and height to prove,
here for a time and then above,
  O Lamb of God, I come.

508 © Timothy Dudley-Smith

1. Lighten our darkness
  now the day is ended:
Father in mercy,
  guard your children sleeping;
from every evil, every harm defended,
safe in your keeping:

2. To that last hour,
  when heaven's day is dawning,
far spent the night
  that knows no earthly waking;
keep us as watchmen,
  longing for the morning,
till that day's breaking.

509 From *Enlarged Songs of Praise* 1931, Jan Struther
By permission of Oxford University Press

1. Lord of all hopefulness, Lord of all joy,
   whose trust, ever childlike,
     no cares could destroy:
   be there at our waking,
     and give us, we pray,
   your bliss in our hearts, Lord,
     at the break of the day.

2. Lord of all eagerness, Lord of all faith,
   whose strong hands were skilled
     at the plane and the lathe:
   be there at our labours,
     and give us, we pray,
   your strength in our hearts, Lord,
     at the noon of the day.

3. Lord of all kindliness, Lord of all grace,
   your hands swift to welcome,
     your arms to embrace:
   be there at our homing,
     and give us, we pray,
   your love in our hearts, Lord,
     at the eve of the day.

4. Lord of all gentleness, Lord of all calm,
   whose voice is contentment,
     whose presence is balm:
   be there at our sleeping,
     and give us, we pray,
   your peace in our hearts, Lord,
     at the end of the day!

510 Edith Cherry
© in this version Jubilate Hymns

1. We trust in you,
     our shield and our defender;
   we do not fight alone against the foe:
   strong in your strength,
     safe in your keeping tender,
   we trust in you,
     and in your name we go.
     Strong in your strength . . .

2. We trust in you, O Captain of salvation!
   in your dear name,
     all other names above:
   Jesus our righteousness,
     our sure foundation,
   our prince of glory and our king of love.
     Jesus, our righteousness . . .

3. We go in faith,
     our own great weakness feeling,
   and needing more each day
     your grace to know;
   yet from our hearts a song
     of triumph pealing,
   'We trust in you,
     and in your name we go.'
     Yet from our hearts . . .

4. We trust in you,
     our shield and our defender:
   yours is the battle –
     yours shall be the praise!
   when passing through
     the gates of dazzling splendour,
   victors, we rest in you
     through endless days.
     When passing through . . .

511 © Edward Burns

1. O God, who gives to humankind
   a searching heart and questing mind:
   grant us to find your truth and laws,
   and wisdom to perceive their cause.

2. In all our learning give us grace
   to bow ourselves before your face;
   as knowledge grows, Lord, keep us free
   from self-destructive vanity.

3. Sometimes we think we understand
   the working of your mighty hand;
   then through your Spirit help us know
   those truths which you alone can show.

4. Teach us to joy in things revealed,
   to search with care all yet concealed;
   as through Christ's light
     your truth we find
   and worship you with heart and mind.

PSALMS

512 From Psalm 17, Isaac Williams
© in this version Jubilate Hymns

1. Be now our guardian and our guide,
   be near us when we call;
   uphold us when our footsteps slide,
   and raise us when we fall.

2. The world, the flesh and Satan dwell
   around the path we tread;
   O save us from the snares of hell,
   Deliverer from the dead!

3. And if we tempted are to sin,
   and evil powers are strong;
   be present, Lord, keep watch within
   and save our souls from wrong.

4. Still let us always watch and pray,
   and know that we are frail;
   that if the tempter cross our way,
   yet he shall not prevail.

513 From Psalm 23. © 1985 Christopher Walker
Published by OCP Publications

1. Because the Lord is my shepherd
   I have everything I need;
   he lets me rest in the meadow
   and leads me to the quiet streams;
   he restores my soul
   and he leads me in the paths
       that are right.
     Lord, you are my shepherd,
     you are my friend:
     I want to follow you always –
     just to follow my friend.

2. And when the road leads to darkness,
   I shall walk there unafraid;
   even when death is close
   I have courage, for your help is there;
   you are close beside me with comfort,
   you are guiding my way.
     Lord, you are my shepherd . . .

3. In love you make me a banquet
   for my enemies to see;
   you make me welcome,
   pouring down honour
       from your mighty hand;
   and this joy fills me with gladness –
   it is too much to bear.
     Lord, you are my shepherd . . .

4. Your goodness always is with me,
   and your mercy I know;
   your loving-kindness
       strengthens me always
   as I go through life;
   I shall dwell in your presence for ever,
   giving praise to your name.
     Lord, you are my shepherd . . .

514 From Psalm 139. © 1993 Bernadette Farrell
Published by OCP Publications

1. O God, you search me
       and you know me,
   all my thoughts lie open to your gaze;
   when I walk or lie down
       you are before me:
   ever the maker and keeper of my days.

2. You know my resting and my rising,
   you discern my purpose from afar;
   and with love everlasting
       you besiege me:
   in every moment of life
       or death, you are.

3. Before a word is on my tongue, Lord,
   you have known its meaning
       through and through;
   you are with me
       beyond my understanding;
   God of my present,
       my past and future, too.

4. Although your Spirit is upon me,
   still I search for shelter from your light
   there is nowhere on earth
       I can escape you:
   even the darkness is radiant
       in your sight.

5. For you created me and shaped me,
   gave me life within my mother's womb;
   for the wonder of who I am I praise you:
   safe in your hands,
       all creation is made new.

515 From Psalm 121
© Timothy Dudley-Smith

1. I lift my eyes
   to the quiet hills
   in the press of a busy day;
       as green hills stand
       in a dusty land
   so God is my strength and stay.

2. I lift my eyes
   to the quiet hills
   to a calm that is mine to share;
       secure and still
       in the Father's will
   and kept by the Father's care.

3. I lift my eyes
   to the quiet hills
   with a prayer as I turn to sleep;
       by day, by night,
       through the dark and light
   my Shepherd will guard his sheep.

4. I lift my eyes
   to the quiet hills
   and my heart to the Father's throne;
       in all my ways
       to the end of days
   the Lord will preserve his own.

516 From Psalm 91
© Timothy Dudley-Smith

1. Safe in the shadow of the Lord
   beneath his hand and power,
       I trust in him,
       I trust in him,
   my fortress and my tower.

2. My hope is set on God alone
   though Satan spreads his snare;
       I trust in him,
       I trust in him,
   to keep me in his care.

3. From fears and phantoms of the night,
   from foes about my way,
       I trust in him,
       I trust in him,
   by darkness as by day.

4. His holy angels keep my feet
   secure from every stone;
       I trust in him,
       I trust in him,
   and unafraid go on.

5. Strong in the everlasting name,
   and in my Father's care,
       I trust in him,
       I trust in him,
   who hears and answers prayer.

6. Safe in the shadow of the Lord,
   possessed by love divine,
       I trust in him,
       I trust in him,
   and meet his love with mine.

SONGS

517 © 1995 Darlene Zschech/Hillsongs Australia/
Kingsway's Thankyou Music

1. Father of life, draw me closer,
   Lord, my heart is set on you:
   let me run the race of time
   with your life enfolding mine,
   and let the peace of God –
   let it reign.

2. O Holy Spirit –
   Lord, my comfort;
   strengthen me, hold my head up high:
   and I'll stand upon your truth,
   bringing glory unto you,
   and let the peace of God –
   let it reign.

       O Lord, I hunger for more of you –
       rise up within me,
           let me know your truth:
       O Holy Spirit, saturate my soul
       and let the life of God fill me now;
       let your healing power
       bring life and make me whole,
       and let the peace of God –
       let it reign.

518 Graham Kendrick and Steve Thompson
© 1991 Make Way Music

1. How can I be free from sin –
    lead me to the cross of Jesus,
    from the guilt, the power, the pain?
        Lead me to the cross of Jesus.
    There's no other way,
    no price that I could pay;
    simply to the cross I cling.
    This is all I need,
    this is all I plead,
    that his blood was shed for me.

2. How can I know peace within?
        Lead me to the cross of Jesus,
    Sing a song of joy again!
        Lead me to the cross of Jesus.
    Flowing from above,
    all-forgiving love
    from the Father's heart to me!
    What a gift of grace
    his own righteousness
    clothing me in purity!

3. How can I live day by day –
        Lead me to the cross of Jesus,
    following his narrow way?
        Lead me to the cross of Jesus.

519 © 1990 Chris Falson Music/Maranatha! Music
Administered by CopyCare

I walk by faith,
each step by faith;
to live by faith
I put my trust in you.

Every step I take is a step of faith –
no weapon formed against me shall prosper;
and every prayer I make
    is a prayer of faith –
and if my God is for me
then who can be against me?

520 Samuel Sebastian Wesley

Lead me, Lord,
lead me in your righteousness,
make your way plain before my face.
Lead me, Lord . . .

For it is you, Lord,
you, Lord, only
    that makes me to dwell in safety.

521 From KOREA. From Matthew 6:23-34, John L. Bell
© 1991 WGRG, Iona Community

1. Look and learn from the birds of the air,
    flying high above worry and fear;
    neither sowing nor harvesting seed,
    yet they're given whatever they need.
    If the God of earth and heaven
    cares for birds as much as this,
    won't he care much more for you,
    if you put your trust in him?

2. Look and learn
        from the flowers of the field,
    bringing beauty and colour to life;
    neither sewing nor tailoring cloth,
    yet they're dressed in the finest attire.
    If the God of earth and heaven
    cares for flowers as much as this,
    won't he care much more for you
    if you put your trust in him?

3. What God wants should be our will;
    where God calls should be our goal.
    When we seek the Kingdom first,
    all we've lost is ours again.
    Let's be done with anxious thoughts,
    set aside tomorrow's cares,
    live each day that God provides
    putting all our trust in him.

522 Stuart Townend
© 1994 Kingsway's Thankyou Music

1. Say the word, I will be healed;
    you are the great Physician,
    you meet every need.
    Say the word, I will be free;
    where chains have held me captive,
    come sing your songs to me,
    say the word.

2. Say the word, I will be filled;
    my hands reach out to heaven,
    where striving is stilled,
    Say the word, I will be changed;
    where I am dry and thirsty,
    send cool, refreshing rain,
    say the word.

    His tears have fallen
        like rain on my life;
    each drop a fresh revelation.
    I will return to the place of the cross,
    where grace and mercy
    pour from heaven's throne.

3. Say the word, I will be poor,
    that I might know the riches
    that you have in store.
    Say the word, I will be weak;
    your strength will be the power
    that satisfies the meek,
    say the word.

    The Lord will see
        the travail of his soul,
    and he and I will be satisfied;
    complete the work you
        have started in me:
    O, come Lord Jesus,
        shake my life again.
    Say the word, say the word.

523 Noel Richards
© 1991 Kingsway's Thankyou Music

To be in your presence,
to sit at your feet,
where your love surrounds me,
and makes me complete:
    This is my desire, O Lord,
    this is my desire;
    this is my desire, O Lord,
    this is my desire.

To rest in your presence,
not rushing away,
to cherish each moment –
here I would stay:
    This is my desire . . .

524 John L. Bell
© 1995 WGRG, Iona Community, from *Come all you people* (Wild Goose Publications, 1987)

Take, O take me as I am,
yours and yours alone to be:
set your seal upon my heart,
    and live in me.

For other items on this theme, see

RESPONDING TO GOD:
IN HOPE AND CONFIDENCE

HYMNS

525 <small>Based on the German of Joachim Neander, Robert Bridges</small>

1. All my hope on God is founded,
   he doth still my trust renew;
   me through change
      and chance he guideth,
   only good and only true:
   God unknown,
   he alone,
   calls my heart to be his own.

2. Pride of man and earthly glory,
   sword and crown betray his trust;
   what with care and toil he buildeth,
   tower and temple, fall to dust;
   but God's power,
   hour by hour,
   is my temple and my tower.

3. God's great goodness aye endureth,
   deep his wisdom, passing thought:
   splendour, light and life attend him,
   beauty springeth out of naught;
   evermore
   from his store
   new-born worlds rise and adore.

4. Daily doth the almighty giver
   bounteous gifts on us bestow;
   his desire our soul delighteth,
   pleasure leads us where we go.
   Love doth stand
   at his hand,
   joy doth wait on his command.

5. Still from man to God eternal
   sacrifice of praise be done;
   high above all praises praising
   for the gift of Christ his Son:
   Christ doth call
   one and all –
   ye who follow shall not fall.

526 <small>© Jocelyn Marshall</small>

1. As Jesus walked the Emmaus Road
   beside his friends, their faces showed
      uncertainty, confusion.
   With loving care he shared their grief;
   his voice brought calm, his words belief
      transforming disillusion.

2. In days of sorrow, nights of pain
   Christ treads with us that road again,
      untiring, comprehending,
   he's at our side to heal and bless;
   his presence comforts our distress,
      with faithfulness unending.

3. And even though we dimly see
   this stranger, Man of Galilee,
      unrecognised, compelling,
   his words remind us with their power
   that he is with us hour by hour,
      his peace within us dwelling.

4. When for assurance still we yearn,
   do not our hearts within us burn
      all doubts and fears diminished.
   Then, faith renewed and hope restored
   we travel with our risen Lord
      until our work is finished.

5. Christ, you the lonely path have trod
   in showing us the way to God,
      abandoning us never.
   May we your followers walk with you
   the Emmaus road, our journey through,
      your Spirit with us ever.

527 Thomas Binney
© in this version Jubilate Hymns

1. Eternal light, eternal light!
   how pure the soul must be
   when, placed
       within your searching sight,
   it does not fear, but with delight
   can face such majesty.

2. The spirits who surround your throne
   may bear that burning bliss;
   but that is surely theirs alone,
   since they have never, never known
   a fallen world like this.

3. O how shall I, whose dwelling here
   is dark, whose mind is dim,
   before a holy God appear
   and on my naked spirit bear
   the uncreated beam?

4. There is a way for us to rise
   to that sublime abode:
   an offering and a sacrifice,
   a Holy Spirit's energies,
   an advocate with God.

5. Such grace prepares us for the sight
   of holiness above;
   the child of ignorance and night
   may dwell in the eternal light
   through the eternal love.

528 Shirley Erena Murray. © 1992 Hope Publishing Co
Administered by CopyCare

1. From the apple in the garden
   to the manger and the star,
   from the rainbow and the promise
   to the moment where we are,
       you are our hope, loving God.

2. From the manna in the desert
   to the breaking of the bread,
   from the hunger of the ages
   to our hunger to be fed,
       you are our hope, loving God.

3. From the prisons of the prophets
   to the growing light of day,
   from the death within the darkness
   to the stone that rolls away,
       you are our hope, loving God.

4. From the curse of Eve and Adam
   to the blessing of the Christ,
   from the spirits of division
   to your Spirit in our midst,
       still be our hope, loving God!

529 © Jocelyn Marshall

1. God comes to us as one unheard
       in silences profound,
   or marvels of a symphony,
       sublimity of sound.

2. God comes to us as one unseen
       in beauties of the earth;
   a sea-gull's flight, a sunset sky,
       the miracle of birth.

3. God comes to us as one unknown
       to share our joys, our pain;
   that presence felt, the gift of grace
       our peace and hope sustain.

4. God comes to us at every hour
       when strength and faith are weak;
   the smiles of friends, encircling arms,
       of reassurance speak.

5. God comes in unexpected ways
       surprising us with joy,
   reminding that the light of love
       no darkness can destroy.

6. Teach us, O God, to recognise
       your Spirit everywhere;
   make us aware, responsive, keen
       your love for all to share.

530 Brian Wren
© 1999 Stainer & Bell

1. Hidden Christ, alive for ever.
   Saviour, Servant, Friend and Lord,
   year by year, unseen, you offer,
   life undying, love outpoured.
   Day by day, you walk among us,
   known and honoured, yet concealed,
   freeing, chiding, leading, guiding,
   till your glory is revealed.

2. Endless orbits by our planet
   spinning round its speeding star
   cannot trace creation's secret:
   why we live, and whose we are.
   Jesus, you alone uncover
   nature's rhythm, reason, rhyme,
   so your birthday is our centre:
   hinge of history and time.

3. Still your life and way of living,
   God-revealing, Spirit-blown,
   teaching, healing, sins forgiving,
   measure and inspire our own,
   loving earth's despised, rejected,
   till with them you hang in pain,
   broken, buried, resurrected,
   life laid down, our life to gain.

4. Who can tell, through earthly eons,
   all your loving power has done,
   changing hearts and shaping nations,
   seeking all, rejecting none?
   Speeches fail, but songs soar higher,
   tracing how, in every place,
   twice ten hundred years have numbered
   countless works of boundless grace!

5. Christ our hope, alive among us,
   take our love, our work, our prayer.
   We will trust and tell your purpose,
   braving evil and despair,
   in your name befriending, mending,
   making peace and setting free,
   showing, giving and acclaiming
   signs of joy and jubilee.

531 Margaret Clarkson. © 1962 Hope Publishing Co.
Administered by CopyCare

1. I do not know tomorrow's way,
      if dark or bright its hours may be;
   but I know Christ, and come what may,
      I know that he abides with me.

2. I do not know what may befall
      of grief or gladness, peace or pain;
   but I know Christ, and through it all
      I know his presence will sustain.

3. I do not know when evening falls,
      if soon or late earth's day grows dim;
   but I know Christ, and when he calls,
      I know he'll call me home to him.

532 Isaac Watts
© in this version Jubilate Hymns

1. I'm not ashamed to name my Lord,
   or to defend his cause,
   maintain the honour of his word,
   the glory of his cross.

2. Jesus, my God! – I know his name,
   his name is all my trust;
   he will not put my soul to shame
   nor let my hope be lost.

3. Firm as his throne his promise stands,
   and he can well secure
   what he entrusted to my hands
   until that final hour.

4. Then he'll make known my guilty name
   before his Father's face,
   and in the new Jerusalem
   appoint to me a place.

533 © David Mowbray/Jubilate Hymns

1. In Christ shall all be made alive, we sing!
   in him God's children
       into life shall spring:
   though seed of Adam,
       creatures of the dust,
   we rise again through Christ
       in whom we trust.

2. This Christ shall reign,
       and sin and death defeat,
   beside the Father he will take his seat;
   then shall God's children
       share that victory
   and stand, new-clothed with immortality.

3. Yet here and now this faith
       is far from vain
   for in God's Son
       a forward glimpse we gain;
   in life's distress,
       with no fresh strength to draw,
   we rise, through him,
       to heights undreamed before.

4. In Christ shall all be made alive, we sing!
   with him God's faithful servants
       he will bring;
   gathered with joy before
       the Father's throne,
   there we shall know,
       as we ourselves are known.

534 Latin (12th Century), translated by Edward Caswall
© in this version Jubilate Hymns

1. Jesus, the very thought of you
   makes every moment blessed;
   but better still your face to view
   and in your presence rest.

2. No ear can hear, no voice proclaim,
   nor can the heart recall
   a sweeter sound than Jesus' name,
   the Saviour of us all.

3. Hope of each contrite, humble mind,
   joy of the poor and meek;
   to those who falter, O how kind,
   how good to those who seek!

4. But what to those who find? Ah, this
   nor tongue nor pen can show!
   The love of Jesus – what it is
   none but his loved ones know.

5. Jesus, be all our joy below,
   as you our prize will be ;
   Jesus, be all our glory now
   and through eternity.

535 After Johann Franck, Catherine Winkworth
© in this version Jubilate Hymns

1. Jesus, priceless treasure,
   source of purest pleasure,
   friend most sure and true:
   long my heart was burning,
   fainting much and yearning,
   thirsting, Lord, for you:
   yours I am, O spotless Lamb,
   so will I let nothing hide you,
   seek no joy beside you!

2. Let your arms surround me:
   those who try to wound me
   cannot reach me here;
   though the world is shaking,
   earth and nations quaking,
   Jesus calms my fear:
   Satan's force must run its course
   and his bitter storms assail me;
   Jesus will not fail me.

3. Banish thoughts of sadness
   for the Lord of gladness,
   Jesus, enters in;
   though the clouds may gather,
   those who love the saviour
   still have peace within:
   though I bear much sorrow here
   still in you lies purest pleasure,
   Jesus, priceless treasure!

536 © David Mowbray/Jubilate Hymns

1. Lord of our growing years,
   with us from infancy,
   laughter and quick-dried tears,
   freshness and energy:
       your grace surrounds us all our days –
       for all your gifts we bring our praise.

2. Lord of our strongest years,
   stretching our youthful powers,
   lovers and pioneers
   when all the world seems ours:
       your grace surrounds us . . .

3. Lord of our middle years,
   giver of steadfastness,
   courage that perseveres
   when there is small success:
       your grace surrounds us . . .

4. Lord of our older years,
   steep though the road may be,
   rid us of foolish fears,
   bring us serenity:
       your grace surrounds us . . .

5. Lord of our closing years,
   always your promise stands;
   hold us when death appears,
   safely within your hands:
       your grace surrounds us . . .

537 Edward Mote
© in this version Jubilate Hymns

1. My hope is built on nothing less
   than Jesus' blood and righteousness;
   no merit of my own I claim,
   but wholly trust in Jesus' name.
       On Christ, the solid rock, I stand –
       all other ground is sinking sand.

2. When weary in this earthly race,
   I rest on his unchanging grace;
   in every wild and stormy gale
   my anchor holds and will not fail.
       On Christ, the solid rock . . .

3. His vow, his covenant and blood
   are my defence against the flood;
   when earthly hopes are swept away
   he will uphold me on that day.
       On Christ, the solid rock . . .

4. When the last trumpet's voice
       shall sound,
   O may I then in him be found!
   clothed in his righteousness alone,
   faultless to stand before his throne.
       On Christ the solid rock . . .

538 © Hilary Jolly/Jubilate Hymns

1. Through the darkness of the ages,
   through the sorrows of the days,
   strength of weary generations,
   lifting hearts in hope and praise,
   light in darkness, joy in sorrow,
   presence to allay all fears,
   Jesus, you have kept your promise,
   faithful through two thousand years.

2. Bounty of two thousand harvests,
   beauty of two thousand springs;
   he who framed the times and seasons
   has vouchsafed us greater things.
   Word of God who spoke creation
   speaks forgiveness, speaks to save,
   gathers still his ransomed people
   in the life he freely gave.

3. Countless flowers have bloomed
       and withered,
   countless noons are sealed in night,
   shattered thrones and fallen empires,
   realms and riches lost from sight.
   Christ, your kingdom still increases
   as the centuries unfold.
   Grain that fell to earth and perished
   has brought forth ten thousandfold.

4. Master, we shall sing your praises,
   Man of sorrows, God of power,
   for the measured march of seasons
   shall at last bring in the hour
   when, as lightning leaps the heavens,
   you return to lead us home.
   You have promised, 'I am coming.'
   Swiftly, our Lord Jesus, come.

539 © Randle Manwaring

1. We shall see him in the morning
      when the mists of life have cleared,
   with his arms outstretched to greet us
      from a journey we have feared.

2. Those who toiled all night and struggled
      till the earthly fight was won
   will awaken to the music
      of his welcoming 'Well done!'

3. We shall recognise the Master
      with his wounded hands and side
   as we worship him, the glorious,
      the ascended Crucified.

4. Though the shore now seems so distant
      we await the morning light
   and the breakfast celebration
      when our faith gives way to sight.

540 Martin E. Leckebusch © Kevin Mayhew

1. When circumstances make my life
   too hard to understand,
   no doubt or fear, no pain or strife,
   can snatch me from God's hand.

2. In valleys where the path is steep,
   with shadows dark and long,
   I know the Shepherd leads his sheep –
   his grace will keep me strong.

3. Though sorrow and perplexity
   are often what I feel,
   Gethsemane and Calvary
   affirm God's love is real.

4. It is enough for me to know
   his promise and his care:
   wherever on life's path I go
   my Saviour will be there.

PSALMS

541 From Psalm 18 © Christopher Idle/Jubilate Hymns

1. I love you, O Lord, you alone,
   my refuge on whom I depend;
   my maker, my saviour, my own,
   my hope and my trust without end.
   The Lord is my strength and my song,
   defender and guide of my ways;
   my Master to whom I belong,
   my God who shall have all my praise.

2. The dangers of death gathered round,
   the waves of destruction came near;
   but in my despairing I found
   the Lord who released me from fear.
   I called for his help in my pain,
   to God my salvation I cried;
   he brought me his comfort again,
   I live by the strength he supplied.

3. The earth and the elements shake
   with thunder and lightning and hail;
   the cliffs and the mountain-tops break
   and mortals are feeble and pale.
   God's justice is full and complete,
   his mercy to us has no end;
   the clouds are a path for his feet,
   he comes on the wings of the wind.

4. My hope is the promise he gives,
   my life is secure in his hand;
   I shall not be lost, for he lives!
   He comes to my aid – I shall stand!
   Lord God, you are powerful to save,
   your Spirit will spur me to pray;
   your Son has defeated the grave:
   I trust and I praise you today!

542 From Psalm 90, Isaac Watts

1. O, God, our help in ages past,
   our hope for years to come,
   our shelter from the stormy blast,
   and our eternal home:

2. Beneath the shadow of your throne
   your people lived secure;
   sufficient is your arm alone,
   and our defence is sure.

3. Before the hills in order stood,
   or earth from darkness came,
   from everlasting you are God,
   to endless years the same.

4. A thousand ages in your sight
   are like an evening gone;
   short is the watch that ends the night,
   before the rising sun.

5. Time, like an ever-rolling stream,
   will bear us all away;
   we pass forgotten, as a dream
   dies with the dawning day.

6. O God, our help in ages past,
   our hope for years to come:
   be our defence while life shall last,
   and our eternal home!

543 From Psalm 16. Chorus © 1985 Paul Inwood Published by OCP Publications Verses © The Grail/A. P. Watt

O Lord, you are the centre of my life –
I will always praise you,
I will always serve you,
I will always keep you in my sight.

1. Keep me safe, O God;
   I take refuge in you!
   I say to the Lord, 'You are my God;
   my happiness lies in you alone,
   my happiness lies in you alone.
   O Lord . . .

2. I will bless the Lord
   who gives me counsel,
   who even at night directs my heart.
   I keep the Lord ever in my sight;
   since he is at my right hand,
   I shall stand firm.
   O Lord . . .

3. So my heart rejoices, my soul is glad,
   even in safety shall my body rest;
   for you will not leave my soul
   among the dead;
   not let your belovèd know decay.
   O Lord . . .

4. You will show me the path of life,
   the fullness of joy in your presence,
   at your right hand,
   at your right hand happiness for ever.
   O Lord . . .

544 From Psalm 89. After Bernhardt Ingemann, Sabine Baring-Gould © in this version Jubilate Hymns

1. Through the night of doubt and sorrow
   onward goes the pilgrim band,
   singing songs of expectation,
   marching to the promised land.

2. One the hymn a thousand voices
   sing as from the heart of one;
   one the conflict, one the danger,
   one the march in God begun:

3. One the object of our journey,
   one the faith that never tires,
   one the urgent looking forward,
   one the hope our God inspires:

4. Courage, therefore, Christian pilgrims;
   with the cross before your eyes,
   bear its shame, and fight its battle –
   die with Christ, with Christ arise!

5. Soon shall come the great awakening,
   soon the bursting of the tomb;
   then the scattering of all shadows
   and the end of tears and gloom.

545 From Psalm 25, Graham Kendrick
© 1997 Make Way Music

1. To you, O Lord
   I lift up my soul,
   in you I trust, O my God.
   Do not let me be put to shame,
   nor let my enemies triumph over me.
       No-one whose hope is in you
       will ever be put to shame;
       that's why my eyes are on you,
       O Lord.
       Surround me, defend me,
       O how I need you.
       To you I lift up my soul,
       to you I lift up my soul.

2. Show me your ways
         and teach me your paths,
   guide me in truth, lead me on;
   for you're my God, you are my Saviour,
   my hope is in you
         each moment of the day.
       No-one whose hope . . .

3. Remember, Lord, your mercy and love
   that ever flow from of old.
   Remember not the sins of my youth
   or my rebellious ways.
   According to your love, remember me,
   according to your love,
   for you are good, O Lord.
       No-one whose hope . . .

SONGS

546 From Isaiah 55, Michael Perry
© 1993 Mrs B. Perry/Jubilate Hymns

1. All who are thirsty, come to the Lord,
   all who are hungry, feed on his word;
   buy without paying, food without price,
   eat with thanksgiving God's sacrifice.

2. Why spend your money,
       yet have no bread;
   why work for nothing?
       Trust God instead!
   He will provide you richest of food:
   come to the waters, drink what is good.

3. Call on God's mercy while he is near,
   turn from your evil, come without fear;
   ask him for pardon – grace will abound!
   This is the moment he can be found.

4. Where once were briers,
       flowers will grow,
   where lives were barren, rivers will flow:
   praise to our Saviour; grace and renown –
   ours is the blessing, his be the crown!

547 Brian Doerksen © 1989 Mercy/Vineyard Publishing
Administered by CopyCare

Faithful One, so unchanging;
ageless One, you're my rock of peace.
Lord of all, I depend on you,
   I call out to you again and again.
   I call out to you again and again;
You are my rock in times of trouble,
you lift me up when I fall down;
all through the storm
       your love is the anchor –
my hope is in you alone.

548 Stuart Garrard. © 1995 Curious? Music UK/
Kingsway's Thankyou Music Worldwide (excl. USA)

   Have you heard the good news,
   have you heard the good news?
   We can live in hope
       because of what the Lord has done.
   Have you heard . . .

1. There is a way
       when there seems no other way,
   there is a light in the darkness;
   there is a hope, an everlasting hope,
   there is a God who can help us.
       Have you heard . . .

2. A hope for justice and a hope for peace,
   a hope for those in desperation;
   we have a future if only we believe
   he works in every situation.
       Have you heard . . .

549 Geoff Bullock. © 1997 Watershed Productions/ Kingsway's Thankyou Music. For UK only

1. I will rest in Christ
   like the calm within the storm;
   I can find security in him
      who leads me on;
   I will put my faith,
      my trust and every hope,
   for the peace of God will touch my soul,
   in him I will be whole.

2. I am not dismayed, I am not cast down;
   I will never be alone, I need never fear;
   I can always hope, I can always love;
   for the love of God
      has touched my heart,
   in him I am secure.

      I will rest in Christ;
      I will hope in him.
      I will find a place of comfort,
      I can find a place of rest,
      held in love, loved in him,
      safe, I am secure,
      as I rest in Christ,
      as I hope in him.

3. I will trust in Christ
      like a rock in stormy seas;
   I have found a shelter in his life
      and peace in me.
   I have found the way,
   the truth, this perfect life;
   and the hope in me is found in him,
   the lover of my soul.
      I will rest in Christ . . .

550 David Fellingham
© 1994 Kingsway's Thankyou Music

In every circumstance of life
you are with me, glorious Father,
and I have put my trust in you,
that I may know the glorious hope
to which I'm called;
and by the power that works in me,
you've raised me up and set me free;
and now in every circumstance
I'll prove your love without a doubt –
your joy shall be my strength,
your joy shall be my strength.

551 From SOUTH AFRICA, collected and edited by Anders
Nyberg, English vs 2 & 3 Andrew Maries/Sovereign
Music UK © 1990 Wild Goose Publications/Iona
Community

1. We are marching in the light of God,
   we are marching in the light of God,
   we are marching in the light of God,
   we are marching in the light of God
      (the light of God)
   We are marching (marching,
      we are marching, marching,) – Oh,
   we are marching in the light of God:
      (the light of God)!
   We are marching (marching,
      we are marching, marching) – Oh,
   we are marching in the light of God!

Optional Further Verses:

2. We are living in the love of God . . .

3. We are moving in the power of God . . .

      Siyahamb' ekukhanyeni 'kwenkhos,
      siyahamb' ekukhanyeni 'kwenkhos,
      siyahamb' ekukhanyeni 'kwenkhos,
      siyahamb' ekukhanyeni 'kwenkhos,
         (khanyeni 'kwenkhos).
      siyahamba (hamba;
         siyahamba, hamba) – Oo,
      siyahamb' ekukhanyeni 'kwenkhos,
         (khanyeni 'kwenkhos).
      Siyahamba (hamba;
         siyahamba, hamba) – Oo,
      siyahamb' ekukhanyeni 'kwenkhos.

552 Tricia Allen and Martin J. Nystrom
© 1992 Integrity's Hosanna! Music. Administered
by Kingsway's Thankyou Music. For UK only.

We will run and not grow weary,
we will walk and will not faint,
for the Lord will go before us
and his joy will be our strength.

Mounting up with wings as eagles,
as our spirits start to soar;
when we come into his presence,
and we wait upon the Lord.

We will wait upon the Lord
for his presence is fullness of joy;
and our strength will be restored,
as we wait upon the Lord.

For other items on this theme, see

HYMNS
23 All creatures of our God and king
397 All shall be well!
168 And can it be that I should gain
169 Before the throne of God above
32 Christ is alive! Let Christians sing
35 Glorious things of you are spoken
637 God is our fortress and our rock
667 Happy are those
173 He lives in us, the Christ of God
488 Heal me, hands of Jesus
455 Here from all nations, all tongues
505 His eyes will guide my footsteps
41 How good is the God we adore!
437 I cannot tell why he whom angels worship
201 Jesus, lover of my soul
177 Jesus, your blood and righteousness
49 Let us love and sing and wonder
604 Lord, your church on earth is seeking
53 O God beyond all praising
183 Oh the deep, deep love of Jesus!
66 The God of Abraham praise
293 Today I awake
309 Walk the hills and you will find him
649 Your hand, O God, has guided

PSALMS
84 I'll praise my maker while I've breath
88 Not to us be glory given
516 Safe in the shadow of the Lord
205 The king of love my shepherd is

SONGS
102 Almighty God, my Redeemer
21 Come, light of the world
657 For the joys and for the sorrows
377 He walked where I walk
120 He's given me a garment of praise
212 I am standing beneath your wings
521 Look and learn
125 Lord, I come before your throne of grace
425 My Redeemer Lives
659 Nothing can trouble
660 The Lord is my light
136 The name of the Lord
138 We are on the Lord's road
445 When the stars in their flight
249 Word of justice

RESPONDING TO GOD: IN LOVE AND DEVOTION

HYMNS

553 © Timothy Dudley-Smith

1. As water to the thirsty
   as beauty to the eyes,
   as strength that follows weakness,
   as truth instead of lies,
   as songtime and springtime
   and summertime to be,
      so is my Lord,
      my living Lord,
   so is my Lord to me.

2. Like calm in place of clamour,
   like peace that follows pain,
   like meeting after parting,
   like sunshine after rain,
   like moonlight and starlight
   and sunlight on the sea,
      so is my Lord,
      my living Lord,
   so is my Lord to me.

3. As sleep that follows fever,
   as gold instead of grey,
   as freedom after bondage,
   as sunrise to the day;
   as home to the traveller
   and all we long to see,
      so is my Lord,
      my living Lord,
   so is my Lord to me.

554 Edwin Hatch. © in this version Jubilate Hymns

1. Breathe on me, breath of God:
   fill me with life anew,
   that I may love as you have loved
   and do as you would do.

2. Breathe on me, breath of God,
   until my heart is pure,
   until my will is one with yours
   to do and to endure.

3. Breathe on me, breath of God;
   fulfil my heart's desire,
   until this earthly part of me
   glows with your heavenly fire.

4. Breathe on me, breath of God;
   so shall I never die,
   but live with you the perfect life
   of your eternity.

555 After Rabanus Maurus, John Cosin

1. Come, Holy Ghost, our souls inspire,
   and lighten with celestial fire:
   thou the anointing Spirit art,
   who dost thy sevenfold gifts impart.

2. Thy blessèd unction from above
   is comfort, life, and fire of love:
   enable with perpetual light
   the dullness of our blinded sight.

3. Anoint and cheer our soilèd face
   with the abundance of thy grace:
   keep far our foes, give peace at home –
   where thou art guide no ill can come.

4. Teach us to know the Father, Son,
   and thee of both to be but One:
   that, through the ages all along,
   this may be our endless song:
      'Praise to thy eternal merit,
      Father, Son, and Holy Spirit.' Amen.

556 From 1 Corinthians 13, Christopher Wordsworth
© in this version Jubilate Hymns

1. Holy Spirit, gracious guest,
   hear and grant our heart's request
   for that gift supreme and best:
   holy heavenly love.

2. Faith that mountains could remove,
   tongues of earth or heaven above,
   knowledge, all things, empty prove
   if I have no love.

3. Though I as a martyr bleed,
   give my goods the poor to feed,
   all is vain if love I need:
   therefore give me love.

4. Love is kind and suffers long,
   love is pure and thinks no wrong,
   love than death itself more strong:
   therefore give us love.

5. Prophecy will fade away,
   melting in the light of day;
   love will ever with us stay;
   therefore give us love.

6. Faith and hope and love we see
   joining hand in hand agree –
   but the greatest of the three,
   and the best, is love.

557 William Walsham How. © in this version Jubilate Hymns

1. It is a thing most wonderful –
   almost too wonderful to be –
   that God's own Son
     should come from heaven
   and die to save a child like me.

2. And yet I know that it is true:
   he came to this poor world below,
   and wept and toiled,
     and mourned and died,
   only because he loved us so.

3. I cannot tell how he could love
   a child so weak and full of sin;
   his love must be most wonderful
   if he could die my love to win.

4. I sometimes think about the cross,
   and shut my eyes, and try to see
   the cruel nails, and crown of thorns,
   and Jesus crucified for me.

5. But, even could I see him die,
   I could but see a little part
   of that great love which, like a fire,
   is always burning in his heart.

6. How wonderful it is to see
   my love for him so faint and poor,
   but yet more wonderful to know
   his love for me so free and sure.

7. And yet I want to love you, Lord:
   O teach me how to grow in grace,
   that I may love you more and more
   until I see you face to face.

558 © Michael Saward/Jubilate Hymns

1. Lord of the cross of shame,
   set my cold heart aflame
   with love for you,
     my saviour and my master;
   who on that lonely day
   bore all my sins away,
   and saved me from the judgement
     and disaster.

2. Lord of the empty tomb,
   born of a virgin's womb,
   triumphant over death,
     its power defeated;
   how gladly now I sing
   your praise, my risen king,
   and worship you,
     in heaven's splendour seated.

3. Lord of my life today,
   teach me to live and pray
   as one who knows
     the joy of sins forgiven;
   so may I ever be,
   now and eternally,
   one with my fellow-citizens in heaven.

559
Matthew Bridges
© in this version Jubilate Hymns

1. My God, accept my heart this day
   and make it yours alone;
   no longer let my footsteps stray
   from your belovèd Son.

2. Before the cross of him who died
   in awe and shame I fall:
   let every sin be crucified
   and Christ be all in all.

3. Anoint me with your heavenly grace
   and seal me as your own,
   that I may see your glorious face
   and worship at your throne.

4. Let every thought and work and word
   to you be ever given;
   then life shall be your service, Lord,
   and death the gate of heaven.

5. All glory to the Father be,
   the Spirit and the Son;
   all love and praise eternally
   to God the Three-in-One.

560 Charles Wesley

1. O thou who camest from above
   the pure celestial fire to impart,
   kindle a flame of sacred love
   on the mean altar of my heart!

2. There let it for thy glory burn
   with inextinguishable blaze;
   and trembling to its source return,
   in humble prayer and fervent praise.

3. Jesus, confirm my heart's desire
   to work and speak and think for thee;
   still let me guard the holy fire,
   and still stir up thy gift in me:

4. Ready for all thy perfect will,
   my acts of faith and love repeat,
   till death thy endless mercies seal
   and make my sacrifice complete.

PSALM

561
From Psalm 5, Brian Foley. From *The New Catholic Hymnal.* © 1971 By permission of the Publishers, Faber Music

1. Lord, as I wake I turn to you,
   yourself the first thought of my day;
   my king, my God, whose help is sure,
   yourself the help for which I pray.

2. There is no blessing, Lord, from you
   for those who make their will their way,
   no praise for those who will not praise,
   no peace for those who will not pray.

3. Your loving gifts of grace to me,
   those favours I could never earn,
   call for my thanks in praise and prayer,
   call me to love you in return.

4. Lord, make my life a life of love,
   keep me from sin in all I do;
   Lord, make your law my only law,
   your will my will, for love of you.

SONGS

562
From Philippians 3, Graham Kendrick
© 1993 Make Way Music

1. All I once held dear,
   built my life upon,
   all this world reveres and wars to own;
   all I once thought gain
       I have counted loss –
   spent and worthless now,
       compared to this.
   Knowing you, Jesus,
   knowing you,
       there is no greater thing;
   you're my all, you're the best,
   you're my joy, my righteousness;
   and I love you, Lord.

2. Now my heart's desire
       is to know you more,
   to be found in you and known as yours;
   to possess by faith
       what I could not earn –
   all-surpassing gift of righteousness.
   Knowing you . . .

3. Oh to know the power of your risen life,
and to know you in your sufferings;
to become like you
in your death, my Lord,
so with you to live and never die!
Knowing you, Jesus,
knowing you,
there is no greater thing;
you're my all, you're the best,
you're my joy, my righteousness;
and I love you, Lord.

563 Brian Doerkson. © 1994 Mercy/Vineyard Publishing
Administered by CopyCare

Don't let my love grow cold,
I'm calling out,
'light the fire again.'
Don't let my vision die,
I'm calling out,
'light the fire again.'

You know my heart, my deeds,
I'm calling out,
'light the fire again.'
I need your discipline,
I'm calling out,
'light the fire again.'

I am here to buy gold,
refined in the fire;
naked and poor,
wretched and blind, I come.
Clothe me in white,
so I won't be ashamed:
'Lord, light the fire again!'

Don't let my love . . .

564 The words of Jesus from Revelation 3, John L. Bell
© 1988 WGRG, Iona Community, from *Enemy of
apathy* (Wild Goose Publications, 1988)

'Here I stand at the door
and knock, and knock:
I will come and dine
with those who ask me in.'

565 Matt Redman
© 1994 Kingsway's Thankyou Music

I will offer up my life
in spirit and truth,
pouring out the oil of love
as my worship to you.
In surrender I must give
my every part:
Lord, receive the sacrifice
of a broken heart.
Jesus, what can I give,
what can I bring
to so faithful a friend,
to so loving a king?
Saviour, what can be said,
what can be sung
as a praise of your name
for the things you have done?
Oh, my words could not tell,
not even in part,
of the debt of love that is owed
by this thankful heart.

You deserve my every breath,
for you've paid the great cost –
giving up your life to death,
even death on a cross.
You took all my shame away,
there defeated my sin,
opened up the gates of heaven
and have beckoned me in.
Jesus, what can I give . . .
What can I give, what can I bring,
what can I sing as an offering, Lord?
What can I give . . .

566 © 1992 John Ezzy, Daniel Grul, Stephen McPherson/
Hillsongs Australia. Administered by Kingsway's
Thankyou Music

Jesus, lover of my soul,
Jesus, I will never let you go;
you've taken me from the miry clay,
you've set my feet upon the rock,
and now I know:
I love you, I need you,
though my world will fall,
I'll never let you go.
My Saviour, my closest friend,
I will worship you until the very end.

567
From THE PHILIPPINES, Teresita Valeriano. © Asian School for Music, Worship and the Arts.
English Words: © 1995 Word & Music/Jubilate Hymns

1. Let me tell you how I need you;
   take my love, I give it to you:
   for you have died to bring me life –
   O Lord Jesus Christ,
       you're my heart's desire!
   Jesus, I want to know you,
   Jesus, I want to serve you;
   Jesus, I want to love you –
   love you more, to love your more.

2. In your mercy, Lord, forgive me,
   by your grace come, cleanse, renew me:
   for you alone can change my life –
   O Lord Jesus Christ,
       you're the living fire.
   Jesus, I want . . .

1. *Kunin Mo ang aking puso;*
   kusang ibinibigay ito.
   Hesus ang 'Yong pagmamahal ang
   mananahan sa pusong pagal.
       Dahil Ikaw ang buhay
       at ang katotohanan,
       aking isinusuko buhay na
       mula sa'Yo.

2. *Kunin Mo ang aking buhay;*
   sa 'Yo aking inaalay.
   Hesus sa 'Yong kalakasan ay
   nais kitang mapaglingkuran.
       Dahil Ikaw ang buhay . . .

And like a child I will dance
in your presence,
O, let the joy of heaven
pour down on me;
I still remember the first day
    I met you,
and I don't ever want to lose that fire,
my first love.

2. My first love is a rushing river,
   a waterfall that will never cease;
   and in the torrent of tears and laughter,
   I feel a healing power released;
   and I will draw
       from your well of life, my love,
   and in your grace
       I'll be satisfied, my love.
   And like a child . . .

3. Restore the years
       of the church's slumber,
   revive the fire that has grown so dim;
   renew the love of those first encounters,
   that we may come alive again;
   and we will rise like the dawn
   throughout the earth,
   until the trumpet announces your return.
       And like a child . . .

568
Stuart Townend
© 1996 Kingsway's Thankyou Music

1. My first love is a blazing fire,
   I feel his powerful love in me;
   for he has kindled a flame of passion,
   and I will let it grow in me;
   and in the night
       I will sing your praise, my love,
   and in the morning
       I'll seek your face, my love.

569
Graham Kendrick
© 1986 Kingsway's Thankyou Music

O Lord, your tenderness –
melting all my bitterness!
    O Lord, I receive your love.
O Lord, your loveliness,
changing all my ugliness,
    O Lord, I receive your love;
    O Lord, I receive your love;
    O Lord, I receive your love.

For other items on this theme, see

HYMNS
378 Ah, holy Jesus, how have you offended
661 All for Jesus, all for Jesus
372 Blessed are the pure in heart
346 Brightest and best of the sons of the morning
145 Forgive our sins as we forgive
353 In the bleak mid-winter
534 Jesus, the very thought of you
626 Light of the minds that know him
627 Lord Christ, we praise your sacrifice
202 My God, how wonderful you are
374 O changeless Christ, for ever new
149 O for a heart to praise my God
204 O worship the Lord in the beauty of holiness
678 Take my life and let it be
151 Teach us how grave a thing it is
186 The love of God comes close
388 There is a green hill far away

PSALMS
512 Be now our guardian and our guide
541 I love you, O Lord, you alone
206 The Lord's my shepherd

SONGS
686 All that I am
242 Be still
210 Holy, holy, holy
688 I'll follow my Lord
215 Jesus, Jesus, holy and anointed one
129 My Jesus, my Saviour
274 Restore, O Lord

RESPONDING TO GOD:
IN UNITY AND GROWTH

HYMNS

570
From 1 Thessalonians 5
© Christopher Idle/Jubilate Hymns

1. As sons of the day
    and daughters of light,
   no longer we sleep
    like creatures of night:
   for Jesus has died
    that with him we may live;
   by all he has given
    we learn how to give.

2. One body in Christ,
    let all play their part:
   the lazy be warned, the timid take heart;
   let those who are hurt
    never pay back with wrong,
   but serve one another:
    together be strong!

3. Be constant in prayer,
    at all times rejoice,
   in all things give thanks –
    let God hear your voice!
   Alive to his Spirit, alert to his word,
   test all things,
    and hold to what pleases the Lord.

4. May God who first called,
    gave peace and made whole,
   preserve us from fault in body and soul:
   our Lord Jesus Christ
    keep us firm in his grace
   until at his coming we meet face to face.

571
Martin E. Leckebusch
© Kevin Mayhew

1. By the sacrifice of Jesus –
   body broken, blood outpoured –
   we are made for ever holy,
   free to stand before the Lord:
    Christ as Saviour we confess –
   he is all our righteousness.

2. Though we once were godless sinners,
   gone are all our guilt and shame;
   we are chosen, cleansed, acquitted,
   justified in Jesus' name:
    held within his constant care
    in his kingdom now we share.

3. Called to be a royal priesthood
   praising God in life and song,
   built into a living temple,
   to each other we belong;
    so together now we bring
    thankful worship to our King.

572
From the Latin, John Neale
© in this version Jubilate Hymns

1. Christ is made the sure foundation,
   Christ the head and corner-stone
   chosen of the Lord and precious,
   binding all the Church in one;
   holy Zion's help for ever,
   and her confidence alone.

2. All within that holy city
   dearly loved of God on high,
   in exultant jubilation
   sing, in perfect harmony;
   God the One-in-Three adoring
   in glad hymns eternally.

3. We as living stones implore you:
   Come among us, Lord, today!
   with your gracious loving-kindness
   hear your children as we pray;
   and the fullness of your blessing
   in our fellowship display.

4. Here entrust to all your servants
   what we long from you to gain –
   that on earth and in the heavens
   we one people shall remain,
   till united in your glory
   evermore with you we reign.

5. Praise and honour to the Father,
   praise and honour to the Son,
   praise and honour to the Spirit,
   ever Three and ever One:
   one in power and one in glory
   while eternal ages run.

573 Patrick Appleford
© Josef Weinberger

1. Christ our King in glory reigning,
   all our strength from you proceeds;
   born of Mary, not disdaining
   work or pain to share our needs;
   you have conquered sin's infection,
   guiltless victim for us killed;
   by your mighty resurrection,
   Christ in us your church rebuild.

2. Lord, look down in your compassion,
   free your people from their sin;
   only by your Cross and passion
   may we rise renewed within;
   make us honest in our living,
   with your grace may we be filled;
   by your love and free forgiving,
   Christ in us your church rebuild.

3. Lord, to everyone supplying
   different gifts for all to use;
   give us strength, on you relying,
   all our selfishness to lose;
   may we each in our vocation
   with your Spirit be instilled;
   by your humble incarnation,
   Christ in us your Church rebuild.

4. Lord, you call us all to witness
   by our worship and our love;
   Lord, look not on our unfitness,
   send your Spirit from above;
   may he lead us to inherit
   life with you as you have willed;
   by the sending of your Spirit,
   Christ in us your church rebuild.

574 Harry Emerson Fosdick
© Elinor F. Downs

1. God of grace and God of glory,
   come among us in your power;
   crown your ancient church's story,
   bring her bud to glorious flower.
     Grant us wisdom,
     grant us courage
   for the facing of this hour.

2. See the hosts of evil round us
   scorn your Christ, attack his ways!
   Fears and doubts too long
     have bound us –
   free our hearts to work and praise.
     Grant us wisdom,
     grant us courage
   for the living of these days.

3. Save us from weak resignation
   to the evils we deplore;
   let the search for your salvation
   be our glory evermore.
     Grant us wisdom,
     grant us courage
   serving you whom we adore.

4. Heal your children's warring madness,
   bend our pride to your control;
   shame our wanton, selfish gladness,
   rich in things and poor in soul.
     Grant us wisdom,
     grant us courage
   lest we miss your kingdom's goal.

575 From a line by William Dunkerley, Michael Perry
© Mrs B. Perry/Jubilate Hymns

1. In Christ there is no east or west,
   in him no pride of birth;
   the chosen family God has blessed
   now spans the whole wide earth.

2. For God in Christ has made us one
   from every land and race;
   has reconciled us through his Son
   and met us all with grace.

3. It is by grace we are assured
   that we belong to him:
   the love we share in Christ our Lord,
   the Spirit's work within.

4. So brothers, sisters, praise his name
   who died to set us free
   from sin, division, hate and shame,
   from spite and enmity!

5. In Christ there is no east or west –
   he breaks all barriers down;
   by Christ redeemed,
      by Christ possessed,
   in Christ we live as one.

576
Fred Pratt Green
© 1971 Stainer & Bell

1. Let every Christian pray,
   this day, and every day,
      Come, Holy Spirit, come!
   Was not the Church we love
   commissioned from above?
      Come, Holy Spirit, come!

2. The Spirit brought to birth
   the church of Christ on earth
      to seek and save the lost:
   never has he withdrawn,
   since that tremendous dawn,
      his gifts at Pentecost.

3. Age after age, he strove
   to teach her how to love:
      Come, Holy Spirit, come!
   Age after age, anew
   she proved the gospel true:
      Come, Holy Spirit, come!

4. Only the Spirit's power
   can fit us for this hour:
      Come, Holy Spirit, come!
   Instruct, inspire, unite;
   and make us see the light:
      Come, Holy Spirit, come!

577
© Timothy Dudley-Smith

1. Lord of the church,
      we pray for our renewing:
   Christ over all, our undivided aim.
   Fire of the Spirit, burn for our enduing,
   wind of the Spirit, fan the living flame!
   We turn to Christ
      amid our fear and failing,
   the will that lacks the courage
      to be free,
   the weary labours, all but unavailing,
   to bring us nearer
      what a church should be.

2. Lord of the church,
      we seek a Father's blessing,
   a true repentance and a faith restored,
   a swift obedience and a new possessing,
   filled with the Holy Spirit of the Lord!
   We turn to Christ
      from all our restless striving,
   unnumbered voices with a single prayer:
   the living water for our souls' reviving,
   in Christ to live,
      and love and serve and care.

3. Lord of the church,
      we long for our uniting,
   true to one calling, by one vision stirred;
   one cross proclaiming
      and one creed reciting,
   one in the truth of Jesus and his word!
   So lead us on;
      till toil and trouble ended,
   one church triumphant
      one new song shall sing,
   to praise his glory, risen and ascended,
   Christ over all, the everlasting king!

578
Charles Wesley
© in this version Jubilate Hymns

1. Let saints on earth together sing
   with those whose work is done;
   for all the servants of our king
   in earth and heaven, are one.

2. One family, we live in him,
   one church above, beneath,
   though now divided by the stream,
   the narrow stream of death.

3. One army of the living God,
   to his command we bow;
   part of his host have crossed the flood
   and part are crossing now.

4. But all unite in Christ their head,
   and love to sing his praise:
   Lord of the living and the dead,
   direct our earthly ways!

5. So we shall join our friends above
   who have obtained the prize;
   and on the eagle wings of love
   to joys celestial rise.

579 John Newton

1. May the grace of Christ our saviour
   and the Father's boundless love,
   with the Holy Spirit's favour,
   rest upon us from above.

2. So may we remain in union
   with each other and the Lord,
   and possess, in sweet communion,
   joys which earth cannot afford.

580 Brian Wren
© 1992 Stainer & Bell

1. Sing together on our journey!
   Sing with joy, Alleluia!
   Share, as we proceed,
   canticle and creed,
   and with faith and fervour strong
   spin our stories into song:
   sing with joy, Alleluia!

2. Pray together on our journey!
   Pray in love, Alleluia!
   Say the Name you praise
   not in hurtful ways
   as a hammer or a sword,
   but as life for all outpoured;
   pray in love, Alleluia!

3. Seek together on our journey!
   Seek the truth, Alleluia!
   In the Spirit grow,
   trusting we will know,
   where to look and when to leap,
   reaching high, and digging deep;
   seek the truth, Alleluia!

4. Walk together on our journey!
   Walk in peace, Alleluia!
   With the Crucified
   risen at our side,
   let us listen and befriend,
   quick to mediate and mend;
   walk in peace, Alleluia!

5. Dance together on our journey!
   Dance with hope, Alleluia!
   Follow with your feet
   freedom's thrilling beat,
   with endurance ample shod,
   doing justice, knowing God:
   dance with hope, Alleluia!

6. Sing together on our journey!
   Sing with joy, Alleluia!
   Stewards of the earth,
   given second birth,
   to our Maker we belong,
   praise the Source of every song,
   sing with joy, Alleluia!

581 Samuel Stone
© in this version Jubilate Hymns

1. The church's one foundation
   is Jesus Christ her Lord;
   she is his new creation
   by water and the word:
   from heaven he came and sought her
   to be his holy bride;
   with his own blood he bought her
   and for her life he died.

2. Called out from every nation,
   yet one through all the earth;
   her charter of salvation
   one Lord, one faith, one birth;
   one holy name she blesses,
   and shares one holy food;
   as to one hope she presses
   with every grace endued.

3. We see her long divided
   by heresy and sect;
   yet she by God is guided –
   one people, one elect:
   her vigil she is keeping,
   her cry goes up, 'How long?'
   and soon the night of weeping
   shall be the dawn of song.

4. In toil and tribulation,
   and tumult of her war,
   she waits the consummation
   of peace for evermore:
   till with the vision glorious
   her longing eyes are blessed;
   at last the church victorious
   shall be the church at rest!

5. Yet she on earth has union
   with God the Three-in-One;
   and mystic, sweet communion
   with those whose rest is won:
   O happy ones and holy!
   Lord, grant to us your grace,
   with them the meek and lowly,
   in heaven to see your face.

582 Thomas Troeger. By permission of Oxford University Press Inc., New York USA

1. We need each other's voice to sing
   the songs our hearts would raise,
   to set the whole world echoing
   with one great hymn of praise.
   We blend our voices to complete
   the melody that starts
   with God who sets and keeps the beat
   that life and love imparts.
       We give our alleluias
       to the church's common chord:
       Alleluia! Alleluia!
       Praise, O praise, O praise the Lord!

2. We need each other's strength to lift
   the cross we're called to bear.
   Each other's presence is a gift
   of God's incarnate care.
   When acts of love and tender speech
   convey the Saviour's voice,
   then praise exceeds
       what words can reach
   and we with song rejoice:
       We give our alleluias . . .

3. We need each other's views to see
   the limits of the mind,
   that God in fact turns out to be
   far more than we've defined,
   that God's one image shines in all,
   in every class and race,
   and every group receives the call
   to sing with faith and grace:
       We give our alleluias . . .

4. We need each other's voice to sing,
   each other's strength to love,
   each other's views to help us bring
   our hearts to God above.
   Our lives like coals placed side by side
   to feed each other's flame,
   shall with the Spirit's breath provide
   a blaze of faith to claim:
       We give our alleluias . . .

583 © Michael Baughen/Jubilate Hymns

1. We worship God in harmony
   with hearts in full accord;
   we share one Spirit, hope and faith,
   one Father and one Lord:
       In Jesus Christ our Lord and king,
       In Jesus Christ our Lord,
       the Spirit makes us all as one
       In Jesus Christ our Lord.

2. We're children now of God by grace –
   our new life has begun,
   where male and female, Greek and Jew,
   both bound and free are one.
       In Jesus Christ . . .

3. We live as those whom Christ has called
   to love with Christ-like mind
   that looks towards each other's needs,
   forbearing, patient, kind.
       In Jesus Christ . . .

4. One day we'll see him face to face,
   to him we'll bow the knee;
   we'll never say goodbye again –
   the best is yet to be!
       In Jesus Christ . . .

584
Fred Pratt Green
© 1975 Stainer & Bell

1. What shall our greeting be?
   Jesus is Lord!
   Sign of our unity –
   Jesus is Lord!
   may we no more defend
   barriers he died to end:
   give me your hand, my friend:
   one Church, one Lord.

2. What is our mission here?
   one world, one Lord!
   He makes his purpose clear:
   one world, one Lord!
   Spirit of truth descend,
   all our confusions end:
   give me your hand, my friend:
   Jesus is Lord!

3. He comes to save us now,
   Jesus, our Lord!
   To serve him is to know
   life's true reward.
   May he our lives amend,
   all our betrayals end:
   give me your hand, my friend:
   Jesus is Lord!

PSALM

585
From Psalm 133, James Seddon
© Mrs M. Seddon/Jubilate Hymns

1. How good a thing it is,
   how pleasant to behold,
   when all God's people live at one,
   the law of love uphold!

2. As perfume, by its scent,
   breathes fragrance all around,
   so life itself will sweeter be
   where unity is found.

3. And like refreshing dew
   that falls upon the hills,
   true union sheds its gentle grace,
   and deeper love instils.

4. God grants his choicest gifts
   to those who live in peace;
   to them his blessings shall abound
   and evermore increase.

SONGS

586
From KOREA, paraphrased by Marion Pope; altered.
© 1991 Geonyong Lee

1. Come now, O Prince of peace,
   make us one body,
   come, O Lord Jesus,
   reconcile your people.

2. Come now, O God of love,
   make us one body,
   come, O Lord Jesus,
   reconcile your people.

3. Come now and set us free,
   O God, our Saviour,
   come, O Lord Jesus,
   reconcile all nations.

4. Come, Hope of unity,
   make us one body,
   come, O Lord Jesus,
   reconcile all nations.

587
Graham Kendrick
© 1995 Make Way Music

1. How good and how pleasant it is
   when we all live in unity –
   refreshing as dew at the dawn,
   like rare anointing oil upon the head.
     It's so good, so good
     when we live together
     in peace and harmony;
     it's so good, so good
     when we live together in his love.

2. How deep are the rivers that run
   when we are one in Jesus,
   and share, with the Father and Son,
   the blessings of his everlasting life.
     It's so good . . .

588
From BOLIVIA
© 1991 Zoilo Yanapa/Copyright Control

1. Men and women, let us walk,
   and let's walk together;
   men and women, let us walk,
   and let's walk together.
   Brothers, sisters, children and youth,
   let's all move together;
   brothers, sisters, children and youth,
   let's all move together.

2. Let the Church be one strong body,
   walking together;
   let the Church be one strong body,
   walking together.
   Every member touched by each other,
   keeping together;
   every member touched by each other,
   keeping together.

1. *Tatanaca, mamanaca, Sarantañani!*
   Tatanaca, mamanaca, Sarantañani!
   Waynanaka, tawaconaka, sayt' asiñani,
   Waynanaka, tawaconaka, sayt' asiñani.

2. *Take Iglesia nacasaja mayaghasiñani,*
   take Iglesia nacasaja mayaghasiñani,
   Mayaqui, takeni, Sarantañani.
   Mayaqui, takeni, Sarantañani.

589
Graham Kendrick
© 1996 Make Way Music

Turn our hearts, turn our hearts.

1. Turn our hearts to one another,
   let your kindness show:
   where our words or deeds
        have wounded,
   let forgiveness flow.
        Turn our hearts, turn our hearts.

2. Turn our hearts from pride and anger
   to your ways of peace,
   for you died and shed your blood
   that enmity may cease.
        Turn our hearts, turn our hearts.

3. Turn the hearts of generations
   that we may be one:
   make us partners in the kingdom
   till your work is done.
        Turn our hearts, turn our hearts.

4. As we all have been forgiven,
   so must we forgive;
   as we all have found acceptance,
   so let us receive.
        Turn our hearts,
        change our hearts,
        turn our hearts.

For other items on this theme, see

HYMNS
31 Christ is the king! O friends rejoice
591 Christ is the world's Light, he and none other
432 Christ is the world's true light
592 Church of God, elect and glorious
15 Come with the sound of trumpet
453 Dear Christ, uplifted from the earth
593 Filled with the Spirit's power
594 Forth in the peace of Christ we go
528 From the apple in the garden
35 Glorious things of you are spoken
4 Here in this place
506 Here on the threshold
469 I come with joy, a child of God
17 Like the murmur of the dove's song
180 Love is his word, love is his way
671 May the mind of Christ my saviour
476 O Christ, at your first eucharist
480 'Peace be with you all,' we sing
60 Rejoice in God! Let trumpets sound
629 The saints in Christ are one in every place
450 The Spirit came as promised
679 To him we come
649 Your hand, O God, has guided

SONGS
105 Bless the Lord my soul
280 One is the body
12 We have come as the family of God

RESPONDING TO GOD: IN MISSION

HYMNS

590 © Brian Hoare/Jubilate Hymns

1. All authority is yours,
   Son of Man, enthroned in might.
   Powers and presidents and kings
   are but shadows in your light.

2. As we go, through all the world,
   we would heed your last command:
   make disciples, teach your truth,
   place the nations in your hand.

3. Help us to obey your will;
   share our faith by word and deed;
   in the triune name baptise
   all who will your gospel heed.

4. You are with us evermore,
   risen, ascended, reigning Lord.
   Long as space and time shall be,
   we will trust your parting word.

5. Then at last, all things made new,
   every tribe and tongue shall sing:
   'Worthy, worthy, worthy Lord!
   Glory to the King of kings!'

591 Fred Pratt Green
© 1969 Stainer & Bell

1. Christ is the world's Light,
   he and none other;
   born in our darkness,
   he became our Brother.
   If we have seen him,
   we have seen the Father:
   Glory to God on high!

2. Christ is the world's Peace,
   he and none other;
   no man can serve him
   and despise his brother
   who else unites us,
   one in God the Father?
   Glory to God on high!

3. Christ is the world's Life,
   he and none other;
   sold once for silver,
   murdered here, our Brother –
   he, who redeems us,
   reigns with God the Father:
   Glory to God on high!

4. Give God the glory,
   God and none other;
   give God the glory,
   Spirit, Son and Father;
   give God the glory,
   God in Man my brother:
   Glory to God on high!

592 From 1 Peter 2, James Seddon
© Mrs M. Seddon/Jubilate Hymns

1. Church of God, elect and glorious,
   holy nation, chosen race;
   called as God's own special people,
   royal priests and heirs of grace:
   know the purpose of your calling,
   show to all his mighty deeds;
   tell of love which knows no limits,
   grace which meets all human needs.

2. God has called you out of darkness
   into his most marvellous light;
   brought his truth to life within you,
   turned your blindness into sight.
   Let your light so shine around you
   that God's name is glorified;
   and all find fresh hope and purpose
   in Christ Jesus crucified.

3. Once you were an alien people,
   strangers to God's heart of love;
   but he brought you home in mercy,
   citizens of heaven above.
   Let his love flow out to others,
   let them feel a Father's care;
   that they too may know his welcome
   and his countless blessings share.

4. Church of God, elect and holy,
   be the people he intends;
   strong in faith and swift to answer
   each command your master sends:
   royal priests, fulfil your calling
   through your sacrifice and prayer;
   give your lives in joyful service –
   sing his praise, his love declare.

593
John Peacey
© M. J. Hancock

1. Filled with the Spirit's power,
     with one accord
   the infant church confessed
     its risen Lord:
   O Holy Spirit, in the church today
   no less your power of fellowship display.

2. Now with the mind of Christ
     set us on fire,
   that unity may be our great desire;
   give joy and peace,
     give faith to hear your call,
   and readiness in each to work for all.

3. Widen our love, good Spirit, to embrace
   the people of all lands and every race;
   like wind and fire
     with life among us move,
   till we are known as Christ's,
     and Christians prove.

594
© James Quinn S.J. reprinted by permission of
Cassell & Co.

1. Forth in the peace of Christ we go;
   Christ to the world with joy we bring:
   Christ in our minds, Christ on our lips,
   Christ in our hearts,
     the world's true king.

2. King of our hearts,
     Christ makes us kings;
   kingship with him his servants gain:
   with Christ, the Servant-Lord of all,
   Christ's world we serve
     to share Christ's reign.

3. Priests of the world,
     Christ sends us forth
   the world of time to consecrate,
   our world of sin by grace to heal,
   Christ's world in Christ to re-create.

4. Prophets of Christ, we hear his word:
   he claims our minds, to search his ways,
   he claims our lips, to speak his truth,
   he claims our hearts, to sing his praise.

5. We are his church; he makes us one:
   here is one hearth for all to find,
   here is one flock, one Shepherd-King,
   here is one faith, one heart, one mind.

595
© Christopher Idle/Jubilate Hymns

1. Glory to God,
     the source of all our mission!
   Jesus be praised, the Saviour,
     Lord and Son!
   Praise to the Spirit
     who confirms the vision:
   in all the world the will of God be done!

2. Proud in our wealth,
     or destitute and broken,
   we cannot live by earthly bread alone
   but by the word
     that God himself has spoken;
   we are set free
     to make our Master known.

3. Eastward or westward,
     northward, southward moving,
   finding new fields,
     new patterns and new role,
   Christ's fellow-workers,
     all his goodness proving,
   see how our God
     is making people whole!

4. Linked by the cross
   at which we are forgiven,
joined by the love
   that came to find and save,
one in the hope of God's new earth
   and heaven,
we love and give
   since he first loved and gave.

5. Send us, Lord Christ,
   to serve at your direction,
dying and living, yours in loss and gain,
true to the gospel of your resurrection,
working and praying
   till you come to reign.

596 James Seddon
© Mrs M. Seddon/Jubilate Hymns

1. Go forth and tell!
   O church of God, awake!
God's saving news
   to all the nations take;
proclaim Christ Jesus, saviour,
   Lord, and king,
that all the world
   his worthy praise may sing.

2. Go forth and tell!
   God's love embraces all;
he will in grace respond to all who call:
how shall they call
   if they have never heard
the gracious invitation of his word?

3. Go forth and tell
   where still the darkness lies;
in wealth or want, the sinner surely dies:
give us, O Lord,
   concern of heart and mind,
a love like yours
   which cares for all mankind.

4. Go forth and tell!
   The doors are open wide:
share God's good gifts –
   let no one be denied;
live out your life
   as Christ your Lord shall choose,
your ransomed powers
   for his sole glory use.

5. Go forth and tell!
   O church of God, arise!
go in the strength
   which Christ your Lord supplies;
go till all nations his great name adore
and serve him,
   Lord and king for evermore.

597 John Marriott

1. God, whose almighty word
   chaos and darkness heard,
   and took their flight:
   hear us, we humbly pray,
   and where the gospel-day
   sheds not its glorious ray,
   let there be light!

2. Saviour, who came to bring
   on your redeeming wing
   healing and sight,
   health to the sick in mind,
   sight to the inly blind:
   O now to all mankind
   let there be light!

3. Spirit of truth and love,
   life-giving, holy Dove,
   speed on your flight!
   move on the water's face
   bearing the lamp of grace
   and, in earth's darkest place,
   let there be light!

4. Gracious and holy Three,
   glorious Trinity,
   wisdom, love, might:
   boundless as ocean's tide
   rolling in fullest pride
   through the world far and wide,
   let there be light!

598 © Timothy Dudley-Smith

1. 'How shall they hear,'
   who have not heard
   news of a Lord who loved and came,
   nor known his reconciling word,
   nor learned to trust a Saviour's name?

2. 'To all the world,' to every place,
   neighbours and friends
     and far-off lands,
   preach the good news of saving grace;
   go while the great commission stands.

3. 'Whom shall I send?' Who hears the call,
   constant in prayer, through toil and pain,
   telling of one who died for all,
   to bring a lost world home again?

4. 'Lord, here am I:' Your fire impart
   to this poor cold self-centred soul;
   touch but my lips, my hands, my heart,
   and make a world for Christ my goal.

5. Spirit of love, within us move:
   Spirit of truth, in power come down!
   So shall they hear and find and prove
   Christ is their life, their joy, their crown.

599 From Romans 10, Michael Perry
© Mrs B. Perry/Jubilate Hymns

1. How shall they hear the word of God
   unless his truth is told?
   How shall the sinful be set free,
   the sorrowful consoled?
     To all who speak the truth today
     impart your Spirit, Lord, we pray.

2. How shall they call to God for help
   unless they have believed?
   How shall the poor be given hope,
   the prisoners reprieved?
     To those who help the blind to see
     give light and love and clarity.

3. How shall the gospel be proclaimed
   that sinners may repent?
   How shall the world find peace at last
   if heralds are not sent?
     So send us, Lord, for we rejoice
     to speak of Christ with life and voice!

600 Henry Scott Holland
© in this version Jubilate Hymns

1. Judge eternal, throned in splendour,
   Lord of lords and King of kings,
   with your living fire of judgement
   purge this realm of bitter things;
   comfort all its wide dominion
   with the healing of your wings.

2. Weary people still are longing
   for the hour that brings release,
   and the city's crowded clamour
   cries aloud for sin to cease;
   and the countryside and woodlands
   plead in silence for their peace.

3. Crown, O Lord, your own endeavour,
   cleave our darkness with your sword,
   cheer the faint and feed the hungry
   with the richness of your word;
   cleanse the body of this nation
   through the glory of the Lord.

601 George Kitchin and Michael Newbolt
© Hymns Ancient & Modern and in this version
Jubilate Hymns

Lift high the cross,
  the love of Christ proclaim
till all the world
  adores his sacred name!

1. Come, Christians,
     follow where the captain trod,
   the king victorious,
     Christ the Son of God:
   Lift high the cross . . .

2. Each new-born soldier of the crucified
   signed with the cross,
     the seal of him who died:
   Lift high the cross . . .

3. This is the sign that Satan's armies fear
   and angels veil their faces to revere:
   Lift high the cross,
   the love of Christ proclaim
   till all the world
   adores his sacred name!

4. Saved by the cross
       on which their Lord was slain,
   see Adam's children
       their lost home regain:
   Lift high the cross . . .

5. From north and south,
       from east and west they raise
   in growing unison their songs of praise:
   Lift high the cross . . .

6. Let every race and every language tell
   of him who saves our souls
       from death and hell!
   Lift high the cross . . .

7. O Lord, once lifted on the tree of pain,
   draw all the world
       to seek you once again:
   Lift high the cross . . .

8. Set up your throne,
       that earth's despair may cease
   beneath the shadow
       of its healing peace:
   Lift high the cross . . .

602 © Timothy Dudley-Smith

1. Lord, for the years your love
       has kept and guided,
   urged and inspired us,
       cheered us on our way,
   sought us and saved us,
       pardoned and provided,
   Lord of the years,
       we bring our thanks today.

2. Lord, for that word,
       the word of life which fires us,
   speaks to our hearts
       and sets our souls ablaze,
   teaches and trains,
       rebukes us and inspires us,
   Lord of the word,
       receive your people's praise.

3. Lord, for our land, in this our generation,
   spirits oppressed by pleasure,
       wealth and care;
   for young and old,
       for commonwealth and nation,
   Lord of our land,
       be pleased to hear our prayer.

4. Lord, for our world;
       when we disown and doubt him,
   loveless in strength,
       and comfortless in pain;
   hungry and helpless,
       lost indeed without him,
   Lord of the world,
       we pray that Christ may reign.

5. Lord for ourselves;
       in living power remake us,
   self on the cross
       and Christ upon the throne;
   past put behind us,
       for the future take us,
   Lord of our lives, to live for Christ alone.

603 © Michael Saward/Jubilate Hymns

1. Lord of glory, in our darkness
   shine upon us with your light
   as, when walking to Damascus,
   Saul beheld the vision bright:
   filled with fear he learned your gospel,
   then proclaimed it with delight.

2. He who served you in the Spirit,
   preached to Roman, Greek, and Jew,
   and with burning love and passion
   lived a message that was true;
   Paul, apostle to the nations,
   held the whole wide world in view.

3. Now, rejoicing at his memory,
   in this consecrated place;
   we recall the truths he taught us
   and the hope of saving grace.
   So, we worship you, Lord Jesus,
   reigning King of time and space.

Hugh Sherlock and Michael Saward
© Methodist Publishing House and Michael Saward/
Jubilee Hymns

604

1. Lord, your church on earth is seeking
   power and wisdom from above:
   teach us all the art of speaking
   with the accents of your love.
   We will heed your great commission
   sending us to every place –
   'Go, baptize, fulfil my mission;
   serve with love and share my grace!'

2. You release us from our bondage,
   lift the burdens caused by sin;
   give new hope, new strength
       and courage,
   grant release from fears within.
   Light for darkness, joy for sorrow,
   love for hatred, peace for strife –
   these and countless blessings follow
   as the Spirit gives new life.

3. In the streets of every city
   where the bruised and lonely live,
   we will show the saviour's pity
   and his longing to forgive.
   In all lands and with all races
   we will serve, and seek to bring
   all the world to render praises
   Christ, to you, redeemer king.

After James R. Lowell
© Richard Bewes/Jubilee Hymns

605

1. Once to every generation
   comes the moment to decide;
   in the clash of truth with falsehood,
   all must choose and all must side.
   On the rock of Christ's salvation
   stands or falls each mortal soul;
   and the choice goes by forever,
   sealed in God's eternal scroll.

2. Truth in every generation,
   fragile as a mountain flower,
   looks afresh for faithful guardians;
   who will speak in danger's hour?
   When the enemy advances,
   flooding in with lies outpoured,
   in the breach we'll fight together –
   raise a standard for the Lord!

3. Saints in every generation
   kept the flame of truth alive;
   in the face of death, defying
   thrones they knew would not survive.
   Heroes of the cross of Jesus
   win with him in this our day,
   by his blood and by their witness –
   come and follow in his way!

4. Christ in every generation
   greatest name the world has known;
   teachers, thinkers, faiths and cultures
   find their goal in him alone.
   His the truth and his the kingdom,
   at his cross our paths divide;
   once to every generation
   comes the moment to decide!

606 James Montgomery

1. O Spirit of the living God,
   in all the fullness of your grace,
   wherever human feet have trod,
   descend upon our fallen race:

2. Give tongues of fire and hearts of love
   to preach the reconciling word;
   anoint with power from heaven above
   whenever gospel truth is heard:

3. Let darkness turn to radiant light,
   confusion vanish from your path;
   those who are weak inspire with might:
   let mercy triumph over wrath!

4. O Spirit of our God, prepare
   the whole wide world the Lord to meet;
   breathe out new life, like morning air,
   till hearts of stone begin to beat:

5. Baptize the nations; far and near
   the triumphs of the cross record;
   till Christ in glory shall appear
   and all the earth declare him Lord!
   (Amen)

607 Martin E. Leckebusch
© Kevin Mayhew

1. We are called to stand together
   with the saints of ages past,
   with the patriarchs and prophets
   in the faith they once held fast;
   promises and hopes they treasured
   now we find fulfilled at last!

2. Those whom Jesus called apostles
   journeyed with him side by side,
   heard his teaching, felt his power,
   saw the way he lived and died;
   then the news of resurrection
   they delivered far and wide.

3. Through the intervening ages
   round the world the gospel spread:
   faithful heralds took the message,
   guided where the Spirit led;
   so the body grew in stature,
   serving Christ, its living Head.

4. Now in many tongues and cultures
   songs of celebration ring;
   millions who confess our Saviour
   honour him as Lord and King
   and, for courage, grace and guidance
   every day their prayers they bring.

5. To each coming generation
   tell the truth, persuade, explain,
   till the time when time is ended,
   till the Saviour comes again –
   till the saints are all united
   under Christ's eternal reign!

608 James Seddon
© Mrs M. Seddon/Jubilate Hymns

1. Tell all the world of Jesus,
   our saviour, Lord and king;
   and let the whole creation
   of his salvation sing:
   proclaim his glorious greatness
   in nature and in grace;
   creator and redeemer,
   the Lord of time and space.

2. Tell all the world of Jesus,
   that everyone may find
   the joy of his forgiveness –
   true peace of heart and mind:
   proclaim his perfect goodness,
   his deep, unfailing care;
   his love so rich in mercy,
   a love beyond compare.

3. Tell all the world of Jesus,
   that everyone may know
   of his almighty triumph
   defeating every foe:
   proclaim his coming glory,
   when sin is overthrown,
   and he shall reign in splendour –
   the King upon his throne!

SONGS

609 © Steve James/Jubilate Hymns

1. Come see a vision for all human kind –
   whose hearts were so cold,
       whose eyes were so blind –
   now joining the ransomed,
       restored and refined:
   sing to the Lord of our lives,
       it's a glorious love!

2. Come see the King in his glory arrayed –
   majestic in power,
       his name shall be praised –
   who stoops from the heavens
       to save those he made:
   sing to the Lord of our lives,
       it's a glorious love!

For over the nations
  our Jesus shall reign,
he rules through his cross
  as the Lamb who was slain;
there's pardon and peace
  if you bow to his name:
sing to the Lord of our lives,
  it's a glorious love!

3. Come see the life
    that restores and remakes,
  the hope of the world
    that breaks through the grave
  for the judge of the earth
    is the Jesus who saves:
  sings to the Lord of our lives,
    it's a glorious love!
    For over the nations . . .

610 Graham Kendrick
© 1996 Make Way Music

1. Far and near hear the call,
   worship him, Lord of all;
   families of nations come
   celebrate what God has done.

2. Deep and wide is the love
   heaven sent from above;
   God's own Son, for sinners died,
   rose again – he is alive.
     Say it loud, say it strong,
     tell the world what God has done;
     say it loud, praise his name,
     let the earth rejoice –
     for the Lord reigns.

3. At his name, let praise begin –
   oceans roar, nature sing;
   for he comes to judge the earth
   in righteousness and in his truth.
     Say it loud . . .

611 From SPAIN © Josep Laporta & Ethel Lopez. English
Words © 1995 Word & Music/Jubilate Hymns

1. Go in Jesus' name
   to spread the news of joy and peace:
   the harvest fields are ready now –
   it's time to start to reap.
   Go – his love proclaim:
   his promises will be fulfilled,
   and when you are called
     to speak for him
   he'll give you the words to say.
     Let all the world believe him,
     let all the world receive him!
     In Christ there is peace,
     in Christ there is power;
     Christ is the hope of all the world.

2. Go in Jesus' name –
   yes, go to set the prisoners free,
   to preach the good news to the poor,
   to comfort those who weep.
   Go to heal the lame,
   bind up the weary, broken hearts;
   for where you are called to work for him
   he'll give you his strength each day.
     Let all the world . . .

612 © 1980 Bernadette Farrell. Published by OCP
Publications

1. God has chosen me, God has chosen me
     to bring good news to the poor;
   God has chosen me, God has chosen me
     to bring new sight
     to those searching for light:
   God has chosen me, chosen me.
     And to tell the world
       that God's kingdom is near,
     to remove oppression
       and break down fear,
     yes, God's time is near,
       God's time is near,
     God's time is near, God's time is near.

2. God has chosen me, God has chosen me
   to set alight a new fire;
   God has chosen me, God has chosen me
   to bring to birth
   a new kingdom on earth;
   God has chosen me, chosen me.
   And to tell the world
   that God's kingdom is near,
   to remove oppression
   and break down fear,
   yes, God's time is near,
   God's time is near,
   God's time is near, God's time is near.

3. God is calling me, God is calling me
   in all whose cry is unheard;
   God is calling me, God is calling me
   to raise up the voice
   with no power or choice,
   God is calling me, calling me.
   And to tell the world . . .

613 © Chris Rolinson/Jubilate Hymns

1. How do we start
   to touch the broken hearts,
   the barren lives,
   the lonely and bereaved?
   Lord, in your name we shall go forth:
   your healing power for ever is the same!
   That the world may believe
   that the world may believe
   that the world may believe in you!

2. We shall proclaim
   the love of Jesus Christ –
   a man of sorrows, yet a man divine;
   his worthiness, his loveliness,
   his faithfulness for ever we will sing!
   That the world . . .

3. And so we go into a lonely world
   where fear reigns
   and sorrow fills the air;
   yet, as we go your Spirit comes –
   your cleansing power
   you give to us to share!
   That the world . . .

614 Graham Kendrick
© 1987 Make Way Music

1. Lord the light of your love is shining,
   in the midst of the darkness, shining:
   Jesus, light of the world, shine upon us;
   set us free by the truth
   you now bring us –
   shine on me, shine on me.
   Shine, Jesus, shine,
   fill this land with the Father's glory;
   blaze, Spirit, blaze,
   set our hearts on fire.
   Flow, river, flow,
   flood the nations with grace
   and mercy:
   send forth your word, Lord,
   and let there be light.

2. Lord, I come to your awesome presence,
   from the shadows into your radiance;
   by the Blood I may enter
   your brightness;
   search me, try me,
   consume all my darkness –
   shine on me, shine on me.
   Shine, Jesus, shine . . .

3. As we gaze on your kingly brightness
   so our faces display your likeness,
   ever changing from glory to glory:
   mirrored here,
   may our lives tell your story –
   shine on me, shine on me.
   Shine, Jesus, shine . . .

615 Martin Smith. © 1995 Curious? Music UK
Administered by Kingsway's Thankyou
Music. Worldwide (Excluding USA)

1. Men of faith, rise up and sing
   of the great and glorious King:
   you are strong when you feel weak,
   in your brokenness complete.
   Shout to the north and the south,
   sing to the east and the west:
   'Jesus is saviour to all,
   Lord of heaven and earth.'

2. Rise up, women of the truth,
   stand and sing to broken hearts:
   who can know the healing power
   of our glorious King of love?
      Shout to the north . . .

We've been through fire,
      we've been through rain;
we've been refined
      by the power of his name.
We've fallen deeper in love with you –
you've burned the truth on our lips.
      Shout to the north . . .

3. Rise up, church with broken wings,
   fill this place with songs, again,
   of our God who reigns on high:
   by his grace, again we'll fly.
      Shout to the north . . .
      . . . Lord of heaven and earth,
   Lord of heaven and earth,
   Lord of heaven and earth.

616 From NICARAGUA, from the oral tradition
Translation © 1991 Jorge Maldonado

Sent by the Lord am I;
my hands are ready now
to make the earth the place
in which the kingdom comes.
Sent by the Lord am I;
my hands are ready now
to make the earth the place
in which the kingdom comes.

The angels cannot change
a world of hurt and pain
into a world of love,
of justice and of peace.
The task is mine to do,
to set it really free.
Oh, help me to obey;
help me to do your will.

617 Graham Kendrick
© 1989 Make Way Music

1. We'll walk the land with hearts on fire;
   and every step will be a prayer.
   Hope is rising, new day dawning:
   sound of singing fills the air.

2. Two thousand years, and still the flame
   is burning bright across the land.
   Hearts are waiting, longing, aching,
   for awakening once again.
      Let the flame burn brighter
   in the heart of the darkness,
   turning night to glorious day,
   let the song grow louder,
   as our love grows stronger;
   let it shine! Let it shine!

3. We'll walk for truth, speak out for love;
   in Jesus' name we shall be strong,
   to lift the fallen, to save the children,
   to fill the nation with your song.
      Let the flame . . .

For other items on this theme, see

HYMNS
24 All hail the power of Jesus' name
461 As we gather at your table
28 Born in song
573 Christ our king in glory reigning
400 Christ the Lord is risen again
620 Christ who called disciples to him
295 Creation sings!
453 Dear Christ, uplifted from the earth
451 God is working his purpose out
504 God of gods, we sound his praises
574 God of grace and God of glory
226 Help us, O Lord, to learn
532 I'm not ashamed to name my Lord
45 Jesus shall reign where'er the sun
323 Jesus! the name high all over
475 Now let from this table rise
55 O for a thousand tongues to sing
291 O Trinity, O Trinity
308 Praise God for the harvest
60 Rejoice in God! Let trumpets sound
62 Tell out, my soul
629 The saints in Christ are one in every place
69 There's a spirit in the air
679 To him we come
310 To you, O Lord, our hearts we raise
331 We have a gospel to proclaim
75 You servants of God, your master proclaim

SONGS
264 Great is the darkness
633 I, the Lord of sea and sky
694 Send me, Lord
444 There is a louder shout to come
257 Who can sound the depths of sorrow

RESPONDING TO GOD: IN SERVING OTHERS

HYMNS

618
Thomas Ken
© in this version Jubilate Hymns

PART 1

1. Awake, my soul, and with the sun
   your daily stage of duty run;
   shake off your sleep, and joyful rise
   to make your morning sacrifice.

2. Redeem your mis-spent time that's past
   and live this day as if your last;
   improve your talent with due care,
   for God's great Day yourself prepare.

3. Let all your speaking be sincere,
   your conscience as the noonday clear;
   think how all-seeing God surveys
   your secret thoughts and all your ways.

PART 2

4. Give praise to God, who safely kept
   and well refreshed me while I slept:
   grant, Lord, that when
       from death I wake
   I may of endless life partake.

5. To you my vows I here renew:
   disperse my sins as morning dew;
   guard my first springs of thought
       and will
   and with yourself my spirit fill.

6. Direct, control, suggest this day
   all I desire or do or say;
   that all my powers with all their might
   for your sole glory may unite.

DOXOLOGY

7. Praise God,
       from whom all blessings flow
   in heaven above and earth below;
   one God, three persons, we adore –
   to him be praise for evermore!

619
Richard Gillard. © 1977 Scripture in Song, a division of Integrity Music. Administered by Kingsway's Thankyou Music. For UK only.

1. Brother, sister, let me serve you,
   let me be as Christ to you;
   pray that I may have the grace to
   let you be my servant too.

2. We are brothers on a journey,
   we are sisters on the road;
   we are here to help each other
   walk the mile and bear the load.

3. I will hold the Christ light for you
   in the night time of your fear;
   I will hold my hand out to you.
   speak the peace you long to hear.

4. I will weep when you are weeping;
   when you laugh I'll laugh with you
   I will share your joy and sorrow
   till we've seen this journey through.

5. When we sing to God in heaven
   we shall find such harmony
   born of all we've known together
   of Christ's love and agony.

6. Brother, sister, let me serve you,
   let me be as Christ to you;
   pray that I may have the grace to
   let you be my servant too.

620
© Timothy Dudley-Smith

1. Christ who called disciples to him
       from their nets beside the sea,
   taught and trained the twelve
       who knew him
       by the shores of Galilee,
   still he calls us to his service,
   saying 'Come and follow me'.

2. Christ whose touch was life and healing,
    sight to blind and strength to lame,
deed and word alike revealing
    mercy evermore the same,
    still he calls us to his service,
strong in faith to bear his Name.

3. Christ, in whom for our salvation
    God's unchanging love is shown,
risen now in exaltation,
    reigning from the Father's throne,
    still he calls us to his service,
and to make his gospel known.

4. Christ whose calling knows no ending,
    no reserve and no delays,
by his Spirit's power defending
    those who follow in his ways,
    we are come to be his servants,
faithful now and all our days.

621 David Mowbray. © 1979 Stainer & Bell and the
Trustees for Methodist Church Purposes

1. Come to us, creative Spirit,
    in our Father's house;
every human talent hallow,
    hidden skills arouse,
that within your earthly temple,
    wise and simple,
    may rejoice.

2. Poet, painter, music-maker
    all your treasures bring;
craftsman, actor, graceful dancer,
    make your offering:
join your hands in celebration!
    let creation
    shout and sing!

3. Word from God eternal springing
    fill our minds, we pray;
and in all artistic vision
    give integrity.
May the flame within us burning
    kindle yearning
    day by day.

4. In all places and forever
    glory be expressed
to the Son, with God the Father
    and the Spirit blessed:
in our worship and our living
    keep us striving
    for the best.

622 From *The Song of Christ's Glory*, Philippians 2
© Gavin Reid

1. Empty he came
    as a man to our race,
equal with God
    yet forsaking his place –
    humbly he served in our world,
    humbly he served in our world.

2. Lowlier still,
    he was willing to die
nailed to a cross
    as the people passed by –
    bravely he died in our world,
    bravely he died in our world.

3. Raised by our God
    for us all to revere,
given a name
    that shall stand without peer –
    honoured as Lord in our world,
    honoured as Lord in our world.

4. Give us that mind
    that refuses to claim
even our rights,
    make our outlook the same –
    humbly to serve in our world,
    humbly to serve in our world.

623 Charles Wesley
© in this version Jubilate Hymns

1. Forth in your name, O Lord, I go
    my daily labour to pursue;
you, Lord, alone I long to know
    in all I think or speak or do.

2. The task your wisdom has assigned
    here let me cheerfully fulfil;
in all my work your presence find
    and prove your good and perfect will.

3. You I would set at my right hand
   whose eyes my inmost secrets view;
   and labour on at your command
   and offer all my work to you.

4. Help me to bear your easy yoke
   and every moment watch and pray;
   and still to things eternal look
   and hasten to that glorious day.

5. Gladly for you may I employ
   all that your generous grace has given;
   and run my earthly course with joy,
   and closely walk with you to heaven.

624 © 1988, 1997 WGRG, Iona Community

1. Jesus Christ is waiting,
   waiting in the streets;
   no one is his neighbour,
   all alone he eats.
   Listen, Lord Jesus,
   I am lonely too:
   Make me, friend or stranger,
   fit to wait on you.

2. Jesus Christ is raging,
   raging in the streets,
   where injustice spirals
   and real hope retreats.
   Listen, Lord Jesus,
   I am angry too:
   in the kingdom's causes
   let me rage with you.

3. Jesus Christ is healing,
   healing in the streets,
   curing those who suffer,
   touching those he greets.
   Listen, Lord Jesus,
   I have pity too:
   let my care be active,
   healing just like you.

4. Jesus Christ is dancing,
   dancing in the streets,
   where each sign of hatred
   he, with love, defeats.
   Listen, Lord Jesus,
   I should triumph too;
   where good conquers evil
   let me dance with you.

5. Jesus Christ is calling,
   calling in the streets,
   'Who will join my journey?
   I will guide their feet.'
   Listen, Lord Jesus,
   let my fears be few:
   walk one step before me;
   I will follow you.

625 Catherine Cameron. © 1967 Hope Publishing Co.
Administered by CopyCare

1. God, who stretched
      the spangled heavens
   infinite in time and place,
   flung the suns in burning radiance
   through the silent fields of space;
   we, your children, in your likeness,
   share inventive powers with you;
   great Creator, still creating,
   show us what we yet may do.

2. Proudly rise our modern cities,
   stately buildings row on row;
   yet their windows, blank, unfeeling,
   stare on canyoned streets below,
   where the lonely drift unnoticed
   in the city's ebb and flow,
   lost to purpose and to meaning
   scarcely caring where they go.

3. We have conquered
      worlds undreamed of
   since the childhood of our race;
   known the ecstasy of winging
   through unchartered realms of space;
   probed the secrets of the atom,
   yielding unimagined power,
   facing us with life's destruction
   or our most triumphant hour.

4. As each far horizon beckons,
   may it challenge us anew,
   children of creative purpose,
   serving others, honouring you.
   May our dreams prove rich
     with promise,
   each endeavour, well begun,
   great Creator, give us guidance
   till our goals and yours are one.

626 After Augustine
© Timothy Dudley-Smith

1. Light of the minds that know him,
     may Christ be light to mine!
   my sun in risen splendour,
     my light of truth divine;
   my guide in doubt and darkness,
     my true and living way,
   my clear light ever shining,
     my dawn of heaven's day.

2. Life of the souls that love him,
     may Christ be ours indeed!
   the living bread from heaven
     on whom our spirits feed;
   who died for love of sinners
     to bear our guilty load,
   and make of life's brief journey
     a new Emmaus road.

3. Strength of the wills that serve him,
     may Christ be strength to me,
   who stilled the storm and tempest,
     who calmed the tossing sea;
   his Spirit's power to move me,
     his will to master mine,
   his cross to carry daily
     and conquer in his sign.

4. May it be ours to know him
     that we may truly love,
   and loving, fully serve him
     as serve the saints above;
   till in that home of glory
     with fadeless splendour bright,
   we serve in perfect freedom
     our strength, our life, our light.

627 Alan Gaunt
© 1991 Stainer & Bell

1. Lord Christ, we praise your sacrifice,
   your life in love so freely given.
   For those who took your life away
   you prayed: that they might be forgiven;
   and there, in helplessness arrayed,
   God's power was perfectly displayed.

2. Once helpless in your mother's arms,
   dependent on her mercy then;
   at last by choice, in other hands,
   you were as helpless once again;
   and, at their mercy crucified,
   you claimed your victory and died.

3. Though helpless and rejected then
   you're now as risen Lord acclaimed;
   for ever, by your sacrifice,
   is God's eternal love proclaimed –
   the love which dying brings to birth,
   new life and hope for all on earth.

4. So, living Lord, prepare us now
   your willing helplessness to share;
   to give our selves in sacrifice
   to overcome the world's despair;
   in love to give our selves away
   and claim your victory today.

628 © Christopher Idle/Jubilate Hymns

1. My Lord, you wore no royal crown;
   you did not wield the powers of state,
   nor did you need a scholar's gown
   or priestly robe, to make you great.

2. You never used a killer's sword
   to end an unjust tyranny;
   your only weapon was your word,
   for truth alone could set us free.

3. You did not live a world away
   in hermit's cell or desert cave,
   but felt our pain and shared each day
   with those you came to seek and save.

4. You made no mean or cunning move,
   chose no unworthy compromise,
   but carved a track of burning love
   through tangles of deceit and lies.

5. You came unequalled, undeserved,
   to be what we were meant to be;
   to serve, instead of being served,
   to pay for our perversity.

6. So when I stumble, set me right;
   command my life as you require;
   let all your gifts be my delight
   and you, my Lord, my one desire.

629 © Christopher Idle/Jubilate Hymns

1. The saints in Christ
       are one in every place
   to serve the gospel of his costly grace;
   from those first days to this,
       our hope the same:
   the love of Christ,
       one Lord, one saving name.

2. In chains for Christ!
       his prisoners love to sing,
   for slaves and free rejoice
       to praise our King;
   what though the church
       on earth still suffers wrong?
   The cross of Christ
       remains our pilgrim song.

3. To live is Christ, for us, to die is gain;
   where then shall be our hunger,
       danger, pain?
   Our joy to preach good news
       to rich and poor,
   then be with Christ, to live for evermore.

4. Lord Jesus Christ!
       Heaven's praise let earth repeat;
   the work that you began,
       you will complete:
   your enemies by grace
       become your friends;
   the day of Christ shall dawn,
       and never ends.

630 © Paul Wigmore/Jubilate Hymns

1. Waterfall and ocean,
   canyon, cliff and shore;
   valley, hill and mountain,
   river, rock and moor,
   wonders God created,
   treasures to defend!
   We should love them,
       work to save them,
   strength and spirit spend.
       Thank God for this world of wonders,
       priceless treasure stored;
       go in peace and daring,
       love and serve the Lord.

2. Rainbow on a stormcloud,
   snow in winter's eye;
   rising green of springtime,
   summer sapphire sky;
   blaze of gold in autumn,
   crimson sunset glow;
   out in space more wonders waiting,
   more than we can know:
       Thank God for this world of wonders . . .

3. Earth and sky and water
   all God's creatures share;
   living things may perish
   if we do not care.
   God on earth has shown us
   we must play our part,
   love creation, love each other,
   thinking with our heart:
       Thank God for this world of wonders . . .

631 Fred Pratt Green
© 1969 Stainer & Bell

1. When the church of Jesus
       shuts its outer door,
   lest the roar of traffic
       drown the voice of prayer:
   may our prayers, Lord,
       make us ten times more aware
   that the world we banish
       is our Christian care.

2. If our hearts are lifted
    where devotion soars
    high above this hungry,
        suffering world of ours:
    lest our hymns should drug us
        to forget its needs,
    forge our Christian worship
        into Christian deeds.

3. Lest the gifts we offer,
        money, talents, time,
    serve to salve our conscience,
        to our secret shame:
    Lord, reprove,
        inspire us by the way you give;
    teach us, dying Saviour,
        how true Christians live.

SONGS

632 Graham Kendrick
© 1983 Kingsway's Thankyou Music

1. From heaven you came, helpless babe –
    entered our world your glory veiled,
    not to be served but to serve,
    and give your life that we might live.
        This is our God – the servant king,
        he calls us now to follow him,
        to bring our lives as a daily offering
        of worship to the servant king.

2. There in the garden of tears
    my heavy load he chose to bear;
    his heart with sorrow was torn,
    'Yet not my will but yours,' he said.
        This is our God . . .

3. Come see his hands and his feet,
    the scars that speak of sacrifice,
    hands that flung stars into space
    to cruel nails surrendered.
        This is our God . . .

4. So let us learn how to serve
    and in our lives enthrone him,
    each other's needs to prefer –
    for it is Christ we are serving.
        This is our God . . .

633 From Isaiah 6
© 1981 Daniel L. Schutte/New Dawn Music

1. I, the Lord of sea and sky,
    I have heard my people cry:
    all who dwell in dark and sin
    my hand will save.
    I who made the stars of night,
    I will make their darkness bright.
    Who will bear my light to them?
    Whom shall I send?
        Here I am, Lord,
        Is it I, Lord?
        I have heard you calling in the night.
        I will go, Lord,
        if you lead me;
        I will hold your people in my heart.

2. I, the Lord of snow and rain,
    I have borne my people's pain;
    I have wept for love of them –
    they turn away.
    I will break their hearts of stone,
    give them hearts for love alone;
    I will speak my word to them.
    Whom shall I send?
        Here I am, Lord . . .

3. I, the Lord of wind and flame,
    I will tend the poor and lame,
    I will set a feast for them –
    my hand will save.
    Finest bread I will provide
    till their hearts are satisfied;
    I will give my life to them.
    Whom shall I send?
        Here I am, Lord . . .

634 John L. Bell and Graham Maule
© 1987 WGRG, Iona Community, from *Heaven shall not Wait* (Wild Goose Publications 1987

1. Will you come and follow me
    if I but call your name;
    will you go where you don't know
    and never be the same?
    Will you let my love be shown,
    will you let my name be known,
    will you let my life be grown
    in you, and you in me?

2. Will you leave yourself behind
    if I but call your name;
    will you care for cruel and kind
    and never be the same?
    Will you risk the hostile stare –
    should your life attract or scare?
    Will you let me answer prayer
    in you, and you in me?

3. Will you let the blinded see
    if I but call your name;
    will you set the prisoners free
    and never be the same?
    Will you kiss the leper clean,
    and do such as this unseen,
    and admit to what I mean
    in you, and you in me?

4. Will you love the 'you' you hide
    if I but call your name;
    will you quell the fear inside
    and never be the same?
    Will you use the faith you've found
    to reshape the world around
    through my sight and touch and sound
    in you, and you in me?

5. Lord, your summons echoes true
    when you but call my name:
    let me turn and follow you
    and never be the same.
    In your company I'll go
    where your love and footsteps show;
    thus I'll move and live and grow
    in you, and you in me.

For other items on this theme, see

HYMNS
661 All for Jesus, all for Jesus
461 As we gather at your table
453 Dear Christ, uplifted from the earth
593 Filled with the Spirit's power
299 For the fruits of his creation
594 Forth in the peace of Christ we go
529 God comes to us as one unheard
300 God in his love for us
469 I come with joy, a child of God
 46 Join all the glorious names
602 Lord, for the years
670 Lord Jesus Christ, you have come to us
604 Lord, your church on earth is seeking
179 Love divine, all loves excelling
180 Love is his word, love is his way
473 Make strong for service, Lord
559 My God, accept my heart this day
384 My song is love unknown
 53 O God beyond all praising
676 O Jesus, I have promised
385 O sacred head surrounded
560 O thou who camest from above
251 Our cities cry to you, O God
479 Put peace into each other's hands
 64 Thanks be to God for his saints
450 The Spirit came as promised
679 To him we come
310 To you, O Lord, our hearts we raise
582 We need each other's voice to sing
681 Wind of God, dynamic Spirit

PSALMS
  6 I rejoiced to hear them say
543 O Lord, you are the centre of my life
654 Through all the changing scenes of life

SONGS
242 Be still
263 Beauty for brokenness (God of the poor)
252 Christ's the world in which we move
214 I will worship you, almighty God
567 Let me tell you how I need you
125 Lord, I come before your throne of grace
280 One is the body
616 Sent by the Lord am I
257 Who can sound the depths of sorrow

RESPONDING TO GOD:
IN CONFLICT AND ENDURANCE

HYMNS

635 John Monsell

1. Fight the good fight with all your might,
   Christ is your strength,
     and Christ your right;
   lay hold on life, and it shall be
   your joy and crown eternally.

2. Run the straight race
     through God's good grace,
   lift up your eyes and seek his face:
   life with its way before you lies,
   Christ is the path and Christ the prize.

3. Cast care aside, lean on your guide,
   his boundless mercy will provide;
   trust, and your trusting soul shall prove
   Christ is its life, and Christ its love.

4. Faint not, nor fear, his arms are near;
   he does not change, and you are dear;
   only believe and Christ shall be
   your all-in-all eternally.

636 William Walsham How
© in this version Jubilate Hymns

1. For all the saints,
     who from their labours rest;
   who to the world by faith
     their Lord confessed,
   your name, O Jesus, be for ever blessed:
     Alleluia, alleluia!

2. You were their rock,
     their fortress, and their might;
   you, Lord, their captain
     in the well-fought fight,
   and in the darkness their unfailing light.
     Alleluia, alleluia!

3. So may your soldiers,
     faithful, true and bold,
   fight as the saints
     who nobly fought of old
   and win with them
     the victor's crown of gold.
     Alleluia, alleluia!

4. One holy people, fellowship divine!
   we feebly struggle, they in glory shine –
   in earth and heaven
     the saints in praise combine:
     Alleluia, alleluia!

5. And when the fight is fierce,
     the warfare long,
   faintly we hear the distant triumph-song;
   and hearts are brave again,
     and arms are strong.
     Alleluia, alleluia!

6. The golden evening
     brightens in the west;
   soon, soon to faithful warriors
     comes their rest,
   the peaceful calm of paradise
     the blessed.
     Alleluia, alleluia!

7. But look! –
     there breaks a yet more glorious day;
   saints all-triumphant rise in bright array –
   the king of glory passes on his way!
     Alleluia, alleluia!

8. From earth's wide bounds,
     from ocean's farthest shore,
   through gates of pearl,
     ascending, they adore,
   the Father, Son and Spirit evermore:
     Alleluia, alleluia!

637 After Martin Luther, Michael Perry
© Mrs B. Perry/Jubilate Hymns

1. God is our fortress and our rock,
   our mighty help in danger;
   who shields us from the battle's shock
   and thwarts the devil's anger:
     for still the prince of night
     prolongs his evil fight;
     he uses every skill
     to work his wicked will –
     no earthly force is like him.

2. Our hope is fixed on Christ alone,
   the Man, of God's own choosing;
   without him nothing can be won
   and fighting must be losing:
     so let the powers accursed
     come on and do their worst,
     the Son of God shall ride
     to battle at our side,
     and he shall have the victory.

3. The word of God will not be slow
   while demon hordes surround us,
   though evil strike its cruellest blow
   and death and hell confound us:
     for even if distress
     should take all we possess,
     and those who mean us ill
     should ravage, wreck, or kill,
     God's kingdom is immortal!

638 After William Williams, Peter Williams and others

1. Guide me, O my great Redeemer,
   pilgrim through this barren land:
   I am weak, but you are mighty,
   hold me with your powerful hand:
     Bread of heaven, bread of heaven,
     feed me now and evermore!

2. Open now the crystal fountain
   where the healing waters flow;
   let the fiery, cloudy pillar
   lead me all my journey through:
     Strong Deliverer, strong Deliverer,
     ever be my strength and shield.

3. When I tread the verge of Jordan
   bid my anxious fears subside;
   Death of death, and hell's Destruction,
   land me safe on Canaan's side:
     songs of praises, songs of praises,
     I will ever sing to you.

639 From *The English Hymnal*. After John Bunyan, Percy
Dearmer. By permission of Oxford University Press

1. He who would valiant be
     'gainst all disaster,
   let him in constancy
     follow the Master:
   there's no discouragement
     shall make him once relent
   his first avowed intent
     to be a pilgrim.

2. Who so beset him round
     with dismal stories
   do but themselves confound –
     his strength the more is:
   no foes shall stay his might,
     though he with giants fight;
   he will make good his right
     to be a pilgrim.

3. Since, Lord, thou dost defend
     us with thy Spirit,
   we know we at the end
     shall life inherit:
   then, fancies, flee away!
     I'll fear not what men say,
   I'll labour night and day
     to be a pilgrim.

For alternative version see no. 647

640 James Edmeston
© in this version Jubilate Hymns

1. Lead us, heavenly Father, lead us
   through this world's tempestuous sea;
   guard us, guide us, keep us, feed us,
   for your help is full and free;
   here possessing every blessing
   if our God our Father be.

2. Saviour, by your grace restore us –
   all our weaknesses are plain;
   you have lived on earth before us,
   you have felt our grief and pain:
   tempted, taunted, yet undaunted,
   from the depths you rose again.

3. Spirit of our God, descending,
   fill our hearts with holy peace;
   love with every passion blending,
   pleasure that can never cease:
   thus provided, pardoned, guided,
   ever shall our joys increase.

641 Fred Pratt Green
© 1989 Stainer & Bell

1. Lord, in our lonely hours,
      and when our spirit faints,
   we are encouraged by your life,
      and by your saints.

2. If we've no breath for praise,
      no thoughts to frame a prayer,
   we know you need no words of ours
      to prompt your care.

3. If in excess of pain,
      or grief, we stammer WHY?
   It comforts us that on your cross
      this was your cry.

4. Yet, in serenest faith,
      transforming Calvary,
   you trusted in the Father's love –
      and so must we.

642 Michael Perry
© Mrs B. Perry/Jubilate Hymns

1. O Christ of all the ages, come!
   We fear to journey on or own;
   without you near we cannot face
   the future months, the years unknown.

2. Afflicted, tempted, tried like us,
   you match our moments of despair;
   with us you watch the desert hours,
   and in our sorrows you are there.

3. O Saviour, fastened to a cross
   by tearing nails – our selfish ways;
   the grieving, caring Lord of love,
   you bear the sins of all our days.

4. Triumphant from the grave you rise –
   the morning breaks upon our sight;
   and with its dawning, future years
   will shine with your unending light.

5. O Christ of all the ages, come!
   The days and months and years go by:
   accept our praise, redeem our lives –
   our strength for all eternity! (Amen.)

643 Charles Wesley

1. Soldiers of Christ, arise
   and put your armour on;
   strong in the strength
      which God supplies
   through his eternal Son.

2. Strong in the Lord of hosts,
   and in his mighty power;
   who in the strength of Jesus trusts
   is more than conqueror.

3. Stand then in his great might,
   with all his strength endued
   and take, to arm you for the fight,
   the weapons of our God.

4. To keep your armour bright
   attend with constant care,
   still walking in your captain's sight
   and keeping watch with prayer.

5. From strength to strength go on:
   wrestle and fight and pray;
   tread all the powers of darkness down
   and win the well-fought day:

6. Till, having all things done
   and all your conflicts past,
   you overcome through Christ alone
   and stand complete at last.

644
George Duffield
© in this version Jubilate Hymns

1. Stand up, stand up for Jesus,
   you soldiers of the cross!
   lift high his royal banner,
   it must not suffer loss:
   from victory on to victory
   his army he shall lead
   till evil is defeated
   and Christ is Lord indeed.

2. Stand up, stand up for Jesus!
   the trumpet-call obey;
   then join the mighty conflict
   in this his glorious day;
   be strong in faith and serve him
   against unnumbered foes;
   let courage rise with danger,
   and strength to strength oppose.

3. Stand up, stand up for Jesus
   stand in his power alone,
   for human might will fail you –
   you dare not trust your own:
   put on the gospel armour,
   keep watch with constant prayer;
   where duty calls or danger
   be never failing there.

4. Stand up, stand up for Jesus!
   the fight will not be long;
   this day the noise of battle,
   the next the victor's song:
   to everyone who conquers,
   a crown of life shall be;
   we, with the king of glory,
   shall reign eternally.

645
Charles Everest

1. 'Take up your cross,' the Saviour said,
   'if you would my disciple be;
   deny yourself, forsake the world,
   and humbly follow after me.'

2. Take up your cross – let not its weight
   fill your weak soul with vain alarm;
   his strength shall bear your spirit up,
   and brace your heart,
        and nerve your arm.

3. Take up your cross, nor heed the shame
   nor let your foolish pride rebel;
   the Lord for you endured the cross
   to save your soul from death and hell.

4. Take up your cross, then, in his strength,
   and calmly every danger brave;
   he guides us to a better home,
   and leads to conquest of the grave.

5. Take up your cross and follow Christ,
   nor think till death to lay it down;
   for only they who bear the cross
   may hope to win the glorious crown.

646
John Scriven

1. What a friend we have in Jesus,
   all our sins and griefs to bear;
   what a privilege to carry
   everything to God in prayer!
   Oh, what peace we often forfeit,
   Oh, what needless pain we bear,
   all because we do not carry
   everything to God in prayer.

2. Have we trials and temptations,
   is there trouble anywhere?
   We should never be discouraged:
   take it to the Lord in prayer.
   Can we find a friend so faithful
   who will all our sorrows share?
   Jesus knows our every weakness –
   take it to the Lord in prayer.

3. Are we weak and heavy-laden,
   burdened with a load of care?
   Jesus is our mighty saviour:
   he will listen to our prayer.
   Do your friends despise, forsake you?
   take it to the Lord in prayer;
   in his arms he will enfold you
   and his love will shield you there.

647 After John Bunyan
© Michael Saward/Jubilate Hymns

1. Who honours courage here,
    who fights the devil?
   who boldly faces fear,
    who conquers evil?
   We're not afraid to fight!
    we'll scorn the devil's spite:
   Christ gives to us the right
    to be his pilgrims.

2. Some may be terrified
    by Satan's testing,
   but faith is verified
    when we're resisting.
   There's no discouragement
    shall cause us to relent
   our firm declared intent
    to be his pilgrims.

3. Though evil powers intend
    to break our spirit,
   we know we at the end
    shall life inherit.
   So, fantasies, away!
    why fear what others say?
   We'll labour night and day
    to be his pilgrims.

For traditional version see no. 639

648 Martin E. Leckebusch
© Kevin Mayhew

1. Within the busy rush of life
    I find a resting-place;
   when I submit to Christ my Lord
    and let him set my pace
   he shows the way that I should take
    whatever trials I face.

2. Amid the choices I must make
    and duties that increase
   he comes to calm my anxious thoughts,
    to make the turmoil cease;
   as in his presence I remain
    he guides me into peace.

3. The timeless, all-sufficient God
    my every longing knows
   and daily he refreshes me
    with joy which overflows;
   anointed by tranquility
    my strength to serve him grows.

4. My Saviour bids me walk with him
    and follow all his ways –
   his plan for me is fruitfulness
    throughout my earthly days,
   since now and evermore I live
    beneath his loving gaze.

649 Edward Plumptre

1. Your hand, O God, has guided
   your flock, from age to age;
   your faithfulness is written
   on history's every page.
   They knew your perfect goodness,
   whose deeds we now record;
   and both to this bear witness:
    one church, one faith, one Lord.

2. Your heralds brought the gospel
   to greatest as to least;
   they summoned us to hasten
   and share the great king's feast.
   And this was all their teaching
   in every deed and word;
   to all alike proclaiming:
    one church, one faith, one Lord.

3. Through many days of darkness,
   through many scenes of strife,
   the faithful few fought bravely
   to guard the nation's life.
   Their gospel of redemption –
   sin pardoned, hope restored –
   was all in this enfolded:
    one church, one faith, one Lord.

4. And we, shall we be faithless?
   shall hearts fail, hands hang down?
   shall we evade the conflict
   and throw away the crown?
   Not so! In God's deep counsels
   some better thing is stored;
   we will maintain, unflinching,
       one church, one faith, one Lord.

5. Your mercy will not fail us
   nor leave your work undone;
   with your right hand to help us,
   the victory shall be won.
   And then by earth and heaven
   your name shall be adored;
   and this shall be their anthem;
       one church, one faith, one Lord.

PSALMS

650 From Psalm 46
© Richard Bewes/Jubilate Hymns

1. God is our strength and refuge,
   our present help in trouble;
   and we therefore will not fear,
   though the earth should change!
   Though mountains shake and tremble,
   though swirling waters are raging,
   God the Lord of hosts
       is with us evermore!

2. There is a flowing river,
   within God's holy city;
   God is in the midst of her –
   she shall not be moved!
   God's help is swiftly given,
   thrones vanish at his presence –
   God the Lord of hosts
       is with us evermore!

3. Come, see the works of our maker,
   learn of his deeds all-powerful:
   wars will cease across the world
   when he shatters the spear!
   Be still and know your creator,
   uplift him in the nations –
   God the Lord of hosts
       is with us evermore!

651 From Psalm 13
© Barbara Woollett/Jubilate Hymns

1. How long, O Lord,
   will you forget
   an answer to my prayer?
   No tokens of your love I see,
   your face is turned away from me:
       I wrestle with despair.

2. How long, O Lord,
   will you forsake
   and leave me in this way?
   When will you come to my relief?
   My heart is overwhelmed with grief,
       by evil night and day.

3. How long, O Lord –
   but you forgive,
   with mercy from above.
   I find that all your ways are just,
   I learn to praise you and to trust
       in your unfailing love.

652 From Psalm 61, James Seddon
© Mrs M. Seddon/Jubilate Hymns

1. Listen to my prayer, Lord,
   hear my humble cry;
   when my heart is fainting,
   to your throne I fly.

2. In earth's farthest corner
   you will hear my voice:
   set me on your rock, Lord,
   then I shall rejoice.

3. You have been my shelter
   when the foe was near,
   as a tower of refuge
   shielding me from fear.

4. I will rest for ever
   in your care and love,
   guarded and protected
   as by wings above.

5. All that I have promised,
   help me to fulfil;
   and in all who love you
   work your perfect will.

6. May your truth and mercy
   keep me all my days;
   let my words and actions
   be my songs of praise!

653 From Psalm 27, Michael Perry
© Mrs. B. Perry/Jubilate Hymns

1. Safe in the hands of God who made me,
   what can there be that I should fear?
   God is my light and my salvation,
   strong is his help when foes are near.

2. This have I prayed and will seek after,
   that I may walk with God each day;
   then will he give me his protection,
   no trouble shall my heart dismay.

3. God of my life, my Lord, my master,
   father and mother now to me:
   come, shield me from the threat of evil,
   open your hands and set me free!

4. Teach me your way
       and lead me onwards,
   save me from those who do me wrong;
   give me the grace to wait with patience,
   help me to trust, hold firm, be strong.

654 From Psalm 34, Nahum Tate and Nicholas Brady
© in this version Jubilate Hymns

1. Through all the changing scenes of life,
   in trouble and in joy,
   the praises of my God shall still
   my heart and tongue employ.

2. O magnify the Lord with me,
   with me exalt his name!
   when in distress, to him I called –
   he to my rescue came.

3. The hosts of God encamp around
   the dwellings of the just;
   his saving help he gives to all
   who in his mercy trust.

4. O taste his goodness, prove his love!
   experience will decide
   how blessed they are, and only they,
   who in his truth confide.

5. Fear him, you saints, and you will then
   have nothing else to fear;
   his service shall be your delight,
   your needs shall be his care.

6. To Father, Son and Spirit, praise!
   to God whom we adore
   be worship, glory, power and love,
   both now and evermore!

SONGS

655 From Psalm 137
© Ewald Bash/Copyright Control

1. By the Babylonian rivers
   we sat down in grief and wept;
   hung our harps upon a willow,
   mourned for Zion while we slept.

2. There our captors, in derision,
   did require of us a song;
   so we sat with staring vision
   and the days were hard and long.

3. How shall we sing the Lord's song
   in a strange and bitter land;
   can our voices veil the sorrow?
   Lord God, hear your lonely band.

4. Let your cross be benediction
   for all bound in tyranny;
   by the power of resurrection
   loose them from captivity.

656 © Ateliers et Presses de Taizé

In the Lord I'll be ever thankful,
in the Lord I will rejoice!
Look to God,
    do not be afraid:
lift up your voices,
the Lord is near,
lift up your voices,
the Lord is near!

657 Graham Kendrick
© 1994 Make Way Music

1. For the joys and for the sorrows –
      the best and worst of times,
   for this moment, for tomorrow,
      for all that lies behind:
   fears that crowd around me,
      for the failure of my plans,
   for the dreams of all I hope to be,
      the truth of what I am:
      for this I have Jesus,
      for this I have Jesus,
      for this I have Jesus,
      I have Jesus.

2. For the tears that flow in secret,
      in the broken times,
   for the moments of elation,
      or the troubled mind:
   for all the disappointments,
      or the sting of old regrets –
   all my prayers and longings,
      that seem unanswered yet:
      for this I have Jesus . . .

3. For the weakness of my body,
      the burdens of each day,
   for the nights of doubt and worry
      when sleep has fled away;
   needing reassurance
      and the will to start again –
   a steely-eyed endurance,
      the strength to fight and win;
      for this I have Jesus . . .

658 John L. Bell and Graham Maule
©1987 WGRG, Iona Community, from 'Heaven Shall
not Wait' (Wild Goose Publications, 1987)

Kindle a flame
to lighten the dark
and take all fear away.

659 St Teresa d'Avila
© Ateliers et Presses de Taizé

Nothing can trouble,
nothing can frighten –
those who seek God
shall never go wanting.

Nothing can trouble,
nothing can frighten –
God alone fills us.

Nada te turbe,
nada te espante.
Quien a Dios tiene
nada le falta.

Nada te turbe,
nada te espante,
Solo Dios basta.

660 From Czechoslovakia, from Psalm 27, paraphrased
John L. Bell. © 1990 WGRG, Iona Community

The Lord is my light,
my light and my salvation.
With God protecting me from every danger,
whom shall I fear?

Should evil powers advance,
should armies try to kill,
let them surround me
      and let them attack me,
I'll still trust God.

One thing I ask the Lord.
This only I desire:
always in worship
      to gaze at God's goodness
and seek his aid.

Preserved by God from harm,
secure in him alone,
I will rejoice in the face of affliction
and sing God's song.

For other items on this theme, see

HYMNS
495 Abide with me
  23 All creatures of our God and king
  26 Amazing grace
  30 By every nation, race and tongue
200 Father in heaven, grant to your children
381 Forty days and forty nights
529 God comes to us as one unheard
574 God of grace and God of glory
531 I do not know tomorrow's way
  43 I will sing the wondrous story
535 Jesus, priceless treasure
  46 Join all the glorious names
507 Just as I am, without one plea
  49 Let us love and sing and wonder
181 No weight of gold or silver
674 O dearest Lord, thy sacred head
  53 O God beyond all praising
676 O Jesus, I have promised
  58 Praise to the Holiest in the height
  61 Sing of the Lord's goodness
376 Songs of thankfulness and praise
581 The church's one foundation
  66 The God of Abraham praise
186 The love of God comes close
  69 There's a spirit in the air
679 To him we come
510 We trust in you, our shield and our defender
  73 When all your mercies, O my God
540 When circumstances make my life

PSALMS
512 Be now our guardian and our guide
513 Because the Lord is my shepherd
172 Happy are those beyond all measure blessed
491 O Lord my God
516 Safe in the shadow of the Lord
544 Through the night of doubt and sorrow
268 When the waters cover me

SONGS
562 All I once held dear
101 Alleluia, alleluia, alleluia, alleluia (Celtic Alleluia)
242 Be still
  18 Be still and know that I am God
273 Come to be our hope, Lord Jesus
547 Faithful One
377 He walked where I walk
633 I, the Lord of sea and sky
549 I will rest in Christ
125 Lord, I come before your throne of grace
425 My Redeemer Lives
342 Prepare the way
274 Restore, O Lord
616 Sent by the Lord am I
217 There is a longing

551 We are marching
552 We will run and not grow weary
140 Where there once was only hurt
249 Word of justice

RESPONDING TO GOD:
IN COMMITMENT AND CHARACTER

HYMNS

661 © William J. Sparrow-Simpson and in this version Jubilate Hymns. Amended text Novello and Co.

1. All for Jesus, all for Jesus!
   this our song shall ever be:
   you our only hope, our saviour,
   yours the love that sets us free!

2. All for Jesus: you will give us
   strength to serve you hour by hour:
   none can move us from your presence
   while we trust your grace and power.

3. All for Jesus – you have loved us,
   all for Jesus – you have died,
   all for Jesus – you are with us;
   all for Jesus crucified.

4. All for Jesus, all for Jesus,
   all our talents and our powers,
   all our thoughts and words and actions,
   all our passing days and hours.

5. All for Jesus, all for Jesus!
   this the church's song shall be
   till at last her children gather,
   one in him eternally.

662 © Michael Saward/Jubilate Hymns

1. All-creating heavenly giver,
   bringing light and life to birth
   all-sustaining heavenly Father
   of the families of earth:
   We, your children, lift our voices
   singing gladly of your love:
   never-ending are the praises
   rising to your throne above.

2. Ever-living Lord and Saviour,
   breaking chains of sin and shame;
   ever-loving intercessor,
   prayers are answered in your name:
   We, your servants, liberated
   at a fearful ransom-price,
   in your kingdom are united
   by that mighty sacrifice.

3. Life-conceiving wind of heaven,
   breathing gifts upon us all;
   life-enhancing Spirit, given
   to enrich us, great and small:
   We, whose talents widely differ,
   now restore to you your own,
   and in true thanksgiving offer
   all we are before the throne.

4. Father, Son and Holy Spirit,
   blessing all within your hand:
   full the cup that we inherit,
   firm the ground on which we stand:
   We, your people, undeserving
   of the grace you freely give,
   now and ever, in thanksgiving
   to your praise and glory live.

663 After Bianco da Siena, Richard Littledale © in this version Jubilate Hymns

1. Come down, O Love divine!
   seek out this soul of mine
   and visit it with
       your own ardour glowing;
   O Comforter, draw near,
   within my heart appear,
   and kindle it, your holy flame bestowing.

2. There let it freely burn
   till earthly passions turn
   to dust and ashes in its heat consuming;
   and let your glorious light
   shine ever on my sight,
   and make my pathway clear,
       by your illuming.

3. Let holy charity
my outward vesture be,
and lowliness become my inner clothing;
true lowliness of heart
which takes the humbler part,
and for its own shortcomings
    weeps with loathing.

4. And so the yearning strong
with which the soul will long
shall far surpass the power
    of human telling;
for none can guess its grace
till we become the place
in which the Holy Spirit
    makes his dwelling.

4. May bitter hearts fresh mercy feel
and thieving hands no longer steal;
none damn their neighbour with a lie,
nor stoke the fires of jealousy:
    Give us Christ's love . . .

5. Father of all, whose laws have stood
as signposts for our earthly good;
whose Son has come
    with truth and grace,
your likeness shining in his face:
    Give us Christ's love . . .

665 Horatius Bonar

1. Fill now my life, O Lord my God,
in every part with praise;
that my whole being may proclaim
your being and your ways.

2. Not for the lip of praise alone,
nor yet the praising heart,
I ask, but for a life made up
of praise in every part.

3. Praise in the common things of life,
its goings out and in;
praise in each duty and each deed,
exalted or unseen.

664 © David Mowbray/Jubilate Hymns

1. Father of all, whose laws have stood
as signposts for our earthly good;
whose Son has come
    with truth and grace,
your likeness shining in his face:
    Give us Christ's love,
        its depth and length,
    its heart and soul
        and mind and strength.

2. The first and finest day is yours
to consecrate all other hours;
all other lords may we disown
and worship bring to you alone:
    Give us Christ's love . . .

3. Surround our homes with joy and peace,
with loyalty and cheerfulness;
let partners live without pretence
and children grow in confidence:
    Give us Christ's love . . .

4. Fill every part of me with praise;
let all my being speak
of you and of your love, O Lord,
poor though I be and weak.

5. Then, Lord, from me you shall receive
the praise and glory due;
and so shall I begin on earth
the song for ever new.

6. So shall no part of day or night
from sacredness be free;
but all my life, with you my God,
in fellowship shall be.

666 After R. Pynson

1. God be in my head
   and in my understanding.

2. God be in my eyes
   and in my looking.

3. God be in my mouth
   and in my speaking.

4. God be in my heart
   and in my thinking.

5. God be at my end
   and at my departing.

667 © Michael Saward/Jubilate Hymns

1. Happy are those
       who acknowledge their need,
   theirs is the kingdom of heaven.
   Happy are those
       who know sadness today,
   for God shall uphold them for ever.
       Laugh and rejoice!
       Sing and be glad!
       Yours is the kingdom of heaven.
       Laugh and rejoice!
       Sing and be glad!
       You shall be with him for ever.

2. Happy are those
       who are gentle and kind,
   happy are those who show mercy,
   happy the hungry and thirsty of soul,
   for God shall delight them for ever.
       Laugh and rejoice . . .

3. Happy are those
       who make peace in the world,
   happy though scorned and insulted.
   Happy, because
       they are pure in their hearts,
   for God shall reward them for ever.
       Laugh and rejoice . . .

668 Cecil Alexander

1. Jesus calls us! – in the tumult
   of our life's wild restless sea;
   day by day his voice is sounding
   saying, 'Christian, follow me!'

2. As of old, apostles heard it
   by the Galilean lake,
   turned from home and toil and kindred,
   leaving all for his dear sake.

3. Jesus calls us – from the worship
   of the vain world's golden store,
   from each rival that would claim us,
   saying, 'Christian, love me more!'

4. In our joys and in our sorrows,
   days of toil and hours of ease,
   still he calls, in cares and pleasures,
   'Christian, love me more than these!'

5. Jesus calls us! – by your mercies,
   Saviour, make us hear your call,
   give to you our heart's obedience,
   serve and love you best of all.

From the Irish, Mary Byrne and Eleanor Hull and in
this version Jubilate Hymns © The Estate of Eleanor
Hull, from *The Source* selected and edited by E. Hull.

669 Published by Chatto & Windus

1. Lord, be my vision,
       supreme in my heart,
   bid every rival give way and depart:
   you my best thought
       in the day or the night,
   waking or sleeping,
       your presence my light.

2. Lord, be my wisdom
       and be my true word,
   I ever with you and you with me, Lord:
   you my great father
       and I your true child,
   once far away, but by love reconciled.

3. Lord, be my breastplate,
      my sword for the fight:
   be my strong armour,
      for you are my might;
   you are my shelter
      and you my high tower –
   raise me to heaven,
      O Power of my power.

4. I need no riches,
      nor earth's empty praise:
   you my inheritance through all my days;
   all of your treasure to me you impart,
   high King of heaven,
      the first in my heart.

5. High King of heaven,
      when battle is done,
   grant heaven's joy to me,
      bright heaven's sun;
   Christ of my own heart, whatever befall,
   still be my vision, O Ruler of all.

670 Patrick Appleford
© 1960 Josef Weinberger

1. Lord Jesus Christ, you have come to us,
   you are one with us, Mary's son;
   cleansing our souls from all their sin,
   pouring your love and goodness in:
   Jesus, our love for you we sing –
      living Lord!

2. Lord Jesus Christ, you have come to us,
   born as one of us, Mary's son;
   led out to die on Calvary,
   risen from death to set us free:
   living Lord Jesus, help us see
      you are Lord!

This verse may be sung at Communion:

3. Lord Jesus Christ, now and every day
   teach us how to pray, Son of God;
   you have commanded us to do
   this in remembrance, Lord, of you:
   into our lives your power
      breaks through –
      living Lord!

4. Lord Jesus Christ, I would come to you,
   live my life for you, Son of God;
   all your commands I know are true,
   your many gifts will make me new:
   into my life your power breaks through –
      living Lord!

671 Katie Wilkinson
© in this version Jubilate Hymns

1. May the mind of Christ my saviour
   live in me from day to day,
   by his love and power controlling
   all I do and say.

2. May the word of God enrich me
   with his truth, from hour to hour,
   so that all may see I triumph
   only through his power.

3. May the peace of God my Father
   in my life for ever reign,
   that I may be calm to comfort
   those in grief and pain.

4. May the love of Jesus fill me
   as the waters fill the sea,
   him exalting, self abasing –
   this is victory!

5. May his beauty rest upon me
   as I seek to make him known;
   so that all may look to Jesus,
   seeing him alone.

672 © Paul Wigmore/Jubilate Hymns

1. May we, O Holy Spirit, bear your fruit –
   your joy and peace
      pervade each word we say;
   may love become of life the very root,
   and grow more deep and strong
      with every day.

2. May patience stem the harmful word
      and deed,
   and kindness seek the good
      among the wrong;
   may goodness far beyond
      our lips proceed,
   as manifest in action as in song.

3. May faithfulness endure, yet as we grow
may gentleness
    lend courage to the weak;
and in our self-restraint help us to know
the grace
    that made the King of Heaven meek.

673 After Hal Pink
© David Mowbray/Jubilate Hymns

1. O Christ, the Master Carpenter,
high on a cross you died;
a wooden cross, with iron nails,
a spear thrust in your side.

2. O Christ, upon that Friday cross
your work on earth was done;
yet, truly, in my life today
your work has just begun.

3. O Christ, take up your workman's tools
and shape my life anew,
that I who now appear rough-hewn
may be restored by you.

4. O Christ, the Master Carpenter,
let beauty gently shine
within the workshop of my life –
the praise be yours, not mine.

674 Henry Hardy
© Cassell & Co.

1. O dearest Lord, thy sacred head
with thorns was pierced for me;
O pour thy blessing on my head
that I may think for thee.

2. O dearest Lord, thy sacred hands
with nails were pierced for me;
O shed thy blessing on my hands
that they may work for thee.

3. O dearest Lord, thy sacred feet
with nails were pierced for me;
O pour thy blessing on my feet
that they may follow thee.

4. O dearest Lord, thy sacred heart
with spear was pierced for me;
O pour thy Spirit in my heart
that I may live for thee.

675 Fred Pratt Green
© 1973, 1980 Stainer & Bell

1. Rejoice in God's saints,
    today and all days!
A world without saints
    forgets how to praise.
Their faith in acquiring
    the habit of prayer,
their depth of adoring,
    Lord, help us to share.

2. Some march with events
    to turn them God's way;
some need to withdraw,
    the better to pray.
Some carry the gospel
    through fire and through flood:
our world is their parish:
    their purpose is God.

3. Rejoice in those saints,
    unpraised and unknown,
who bear someone's cross,
    or shoulder their own.
They shame our complaining,
    our comforts, our cares:
what patience in caring,
    what courage, is theirs!

4. Rejoice in God's saints,
    today and all days!
A world without saints
    forgets how to praise.
In loving, in living,
    they prove it is true:
the way of self giving,
    Lord, leads us to you.

676 John Bode

1. O Jesus, I have promised
   to serve you to the end –
   be now and ever near me,
   my Master and my Friend:
   I shall not fear the battle
   if you are by my side,
   nor wander from the pathway
   if you will be my guide.

2. O let me feel you near me,
   the world is ever near;
   I see the sights that dazzle,
   the tempting sounds I hear;
   my foes are ever near me,
   around me and within;
   but Jesus, draw still nearer
   and shield my soul from sin!

3. O let me hear you speaking
   in accents clear and still;
   above the storms of passion,
   the murmurs of self-will:
   O speak to reassure me,
   to hasten or control;
   and speak to make me listen,
   O Guardian of my soul.

4. O Jesus, you have promised,
   to all who follow you,
   that where you are in glory
   your servant shall be too;
   And Jesus, I have promised
   to serve you to the end,
   O give me grace to follow,
   my Master and my friend.

5. O let me see your footmarks
   and in them place my own;
   my hope to follow truly
   is in your strength alone:
   O guide me, call me, draw me,
   uphold me to the end;
   and then in heaven receive me,
   my Saviour and my Friend.

677 © Timothy Dudley-Smith

1. Spirit of God within me,
   possess my human frame;
   fan the dull embers of my heart,
   stir up the living flame.
   Strive till that image Adam lost,
   new minted and restored,
   in shining splendour brightly bears
   the likeness of the Lord.

2. Spirit of truth within me,
   possess my thought and mind;
   lighten anew the inward eye
   by Satan rendered blind;
   shine on the words that wisdom speaks
   and grant me power to see
   the truth made known to all in Christ,
   and in that truth be free.

3. Spirit of love within me,
   possess my hands and heart;
   break through the bonds of self-concern
   that seeks to stand apart:
   grant me the love that suffers long,
   that hopes, believes and bears,
   the love fulfilled in sacrifice,
   that cares as Jesus cares.

4. Spirit of life within me,
   possess this life of mine;
   come as the wind of heaven's breath,
   come as the fire divine!
   Spirit of Christ, the living Lord,
   reign in this house of clay,
   till from its dust with Christ I rise
   to everlasting day.

678 Frances Havergal
© in this version Jubilate Hymns

1. Take my life and let it be
   all you purpose, Lord, for me;
   consecrate my passing days,
   let them flow in ceaseless praise.

2. Take my hands, and let them move
   at the impulse of your love;
   take my feet, and let them run
   with the news of victory won.

3. Take my voice, and let me sing
   always, only, for my King;
   take my lips, let them proclaim
   all the beauty of your name.

4. Take my wealth – all I possess,
   make me rich in faithfulness;
   take my mind that I may use
   every power as you shall choose.

5. Take my motives and my will,
   all your purpose to fulfil;
   take my heart – it is your own,
   it shall be your royal throne.

6. Take my love – my Lord, I pour
   at your feet its treasure-store;
   take myself, and I will be
   yours for all eternity.

679 James Seddon
© Mrs M. Seddon/Jubilate Hymns

1. To him we come –
   Jesus Christ our Lord,
   God's own living Word,
   his dear Son:
   in him there is no east and west,
   in him all nations shall be blessed;
   to all he offers peace and rest –
      loving Lord!

2. In him we live –
   Christ our strength and stay,
   life and truth and way,
   friend divine:
   his power can break the chains of sin,
   still all life's storms without, within,
   help us the daily fight to win –
      living Lord!

3. For him we go –
   soldiers of the cross,
   counting all things loss
   him to know;
   going to every land and race,
   preaching to all redeeming grace,
   building his church in every place –
      conquering Lord!

4. With him we serve –
   his the work we share
   with saints everywhere,
   near and far;
   one in the task which faith requires,
   one in the zeal which never tires,
   one in the hope his love inspires –
      coming Lord!

5. Onward we go –
   faithful, bold, and true,
   called his will to do
   day by day
   till, at the last, with joy we'll see
   Jesus, in glorious majesty;
   live with him through eternity –
      reigning Lord!

680 Isaac Watts

1. When I survey the wondrous cross
   on which the prince of glory died,
   my richest gain I count as loss,
   and pour contempt on all my pride.

2. Forbid it, Lord, that I should boast
   save in the cross of Christ my God;
   the very things that charm me most –
   I sacrifice them to his blood.

3. See from his head, his hands, his feet,
   sorrow and love flow mingled down;
   when did such love and sorrow meet,
   or thorns compose so rich a crown?

4. Were the whole realm of nature mine,
   that were an offering far too small;
   love so amazing, so divine,
   demands my soul, my life, my all!

681 © Michael Saward/Jubilate Hymns

1. Wind of God, dynamic Spirit,
   breathe upon our hearts today;
   that we may your power inherit
   hear us, Spirit, as we pray:
   fill the vacuum that enslaves us –
   emptiness of heart and soul;
   and, through Jesus Christ who saves us,
   give us life and make us whole.

2. Voice of God, prophetic Spirit,
   speak to every heart today
   to encourage or prohibit,
   urging action or delay:
   clear the vagueness which impedes us –
   come, enlighten mind and soul;
   and, through Jesus Christ who leads us,
   teach the truth that makes us whole.

3. Fire of God, volcanic Spirit,
   burn within our hearts today;
   cleanse our sin – may we exhibit
   holiness in every way:
   purge the squalidness that shames us,
   soils the body, taints the soul;
   and, through Jesus Christ who claims us,
   purify us, make us whole.

PSALMS

682 From Psalm 51, Andrew Snedden
© 1987 Sovereign Music UK

1. Create in us clean hearts, O God,
   our stumbling faith renew,
   that in all our ways
      we may worship you.

2. Create in us sound minds, O God,
   lead us in knowledge true,
   that in all our ways,
   through living praise,
   we may honour you.

You are our rock,
you are our shield,
our promise of salvation;
alone, you are Lord,
alone, you are holy –
we exalt your name in all creation.

3. Strengthen in us your image, Lord,
   shatter our stubborn wills
   that we rejoice to seek your voice,
   and see your love fulfilled.

683 From Psalm 139
© Christopher Idle/Jubilate Hymns

1. Lord all-knowing, you have found me;
   every secret thought and word,
   all my actions, all my longings
   you have seen and you have heard.

2. Lord almighty, you have made me,
   fashioned me to keep your laws;
   your design and your creation,
   every part of me is yours.

3. Lord all-holy, you have judged me
   by a standard true and right;
   all the best I have to offer
   withers in your burning light.

4. Lord all-loving, you have saved me
   in supreme and mighty grace;
   by your Son's triumphant mercy,
   suffering, dying in my place.

5. Lord all-glorious, you will take me
   where your ransomed servants sing;
   you have spoken, rescued, conquered –
   Christ, our prophet, priest, and king!

684 From Psalm 15
© Paul Wigmore/Jubilate Hymns

1. Lord, who may dwell within your house
   and on your holy hill?
   All those who walk a blameless way,
   who love the right, who win the day
   with truthful words and, come what may,
   will speak no word of ill:

2. All those who love their neighbour well,
   who hate the way of sin,
   who honour all that fear the Lord,
   whose promise is a binding cord,
   who help, and seek no rich reward –
   these, Lord, you welcome in.

1. Lord, be the strength
      within my weakness,
   be the supply in every need
   that I may prove your promises to me,
   faithful and true in word and deed.
      All that I am . . .

2. Into your hands I place the future;
   the past is nailed to Calvary
   that I may live in resurrection power –
   no longer I but Christ in me.
      All that I am . . .

SONGS

685 © Steve James/Jubilate Hymns

1. All my ways, all our hearts,
   the Maker's hand reflected in each part;
   but broken lives have shattered
   all of you that we can see.
   Restore, O Lord, your face in me.
      Through you, through you,
      you make all things new through you;
      this King on a cross has died
      and I'm reconciled:
      you make all things new through you.

2. The Spirit's work, obedience won,
   you will not rest till we reflect the Son.
   His broken life restores us
   in forgiveness to your side;
   his cross-work done – the victory won.
      Through you . . .

686 James Wright
© 1994 Kingsway's Thankyou Music

   All that I am, I lay before you;
   all I possess, Lord, I confess,
   is nothing without you.
   Saviour and King.
   I now enthrone you;
   take my life, my living sacrifice to you.

687 © 1993 Bernadette Farrell
Published by OCP Publications

   ALL: Alleluia, alleluia,
      alleluia, alleluia.
      Alleluia, alleluia,
      alleluia, alleluia.

1. CHOIR/GROUP
   Word of God, Jesus Christ,
   live within our hearts:
   open our eyes,
   open our minds to you today.
      ALL: Alleluia . . .

2. CHOIR/GROUP
   Word of God, Jesus Christ,
   show us how to live:
   challenge your church,
   call us to rise with you today.
      ALL: Alleluia . . .

3. CHOIR/GROUP
   Word of God, Jesus Christ,
   sharper than a sword:
   enter our lives,
   strike through our comfort
   and our fear.
      ALL: Alleluia . . .

688 From The Philippines. Words © Tagalog Copyright Control. English words © 1993 in this version Word & Music/Jubilate Hymns

I'll follow my Lord,
I'll follow my Lord,
I'll follow my Lord – to Jesus I cling;
I'll follow my Lord,
I'll follow my Lord,
I'll follow my Lord – my love I will bring!

Kay Yahweh ako, kay Yahweh ako
Kay Yahweh ako manananagan
Kay Yahweh ako, kay Yahweh ako,
Kay Yahweh ako mananagan.

689 Geoff Bullock. © 1992 Word/Maranatha! Music Administered by CopyCare

1. Lord, I come to you
   let my heart be changed, renewed
   flowing from the grace
       that I found in you
   and, Lord, I've come to know
   the weaknesses I see in me
   will be stripped away
   by the power of your love.
       Hold me close,
       let your love surround me,
       bring me near, draw me to your side;
       and as I wait, I'll rise up like the eagle,
       and I will soar with you;
       your Spirit leads me on
       in the power of your love.

2. Lord unveil my eyes,
   let me see you face to face,
   the knowledge of your love
   as you live in me;
   Lord, renew my mind
   as your will unfolds in my life,
   in living every day
       in the power of your love.
       Hold me close . . .

690 © 1993 Geoff Twigg/Jubilate Hymns

1. Lord, help me to know your presence
   in all I do today,
   Lord, help me declare your praises
   in everything I say;
       live in my heart,
       and fill every part
   with your Holy Spirit's flame –
   O let the world see Jesus in me,
   and glorify your name!

2. Lord, may I become like Jesus
   in everything I do:
   then, if any action pleases,
   glory will come to you.
       Lord, may my mind
       and will be refined
   by your Holy Spirit's flame –
   O let the world see Jesus in me
   and glorify your name!

691 From the traditional prayer, Sebastian Temple, dedicated to Mrs. Frances Tracy. © 1967 OCP Publications

1. Make me a channel of your peace:
   where there is hatred
       let me bring your love,
   where there is injury, your pardon, Lord,
   and where there's doubt,
       true faith in you:
   O Master, grant
   that I may never seek
   so much to be consoled
   as to console;
   to be understood
   as to understand,
   to be loved,
   as to love with all my soul!

2. Make me a channel of your peace:
   where there's despair in life
       let me bring hope,
   where there is darkness, only light,
   and where there's sadness, ever joy:
       O Master, grant . . .

3. Make me a channel of your peace:
   it is in pardoning that we are pardoned,
   in giving of ourselves that we receive,
   and in dying
       that we're born to eternal life.

692 © Roger Mayor/Jubilate Hymns

1. Out of the world
       and into your presence,
   I come to you, I come to you,
   drawn by your love
       and your voice gently calling,
   I come to you, I come to you.

2. Out of the strain and stress I am living,
   I come to you, I come to you,
   all of my tears, all my joys
       and my sorrows,
   I bring to you, I bring to you.
       Draw me ever closer to you,
       draw me with your love;
       help me follow in your footsteps,
       draw me with your love.

3. Out of my sin
       and the times I have failed you,
   I come to you, I come to you,
   all of the guilt and the burdens I carry,
   I lay on you, I lay on you.

4. Into the joy of knowing your presence,
   I come to you, I come to you,
   I need your love to enfold
       and embrace me,
   I come to you, I come to you.
       Draw me ever closer to you . . .
       . . . draw me with your love.

693 Geoff Twigg
© 1994 Kingsway's Thankyou Music

   Send forth your light and your truth,
   let them guide me,
   let them bring me
       to your holy mountain,
   to the place where you dwell.
   Send forth . . .

1. Then I will come to the altar of God,
   my joy and my delight;
   then I will offer the whole of my life,
   a living sacrifice.
       Send forth . . .

2. Jesus, the Way
       and the Truth and the Life,
   my Saviour and my Lord,
   knowing your presence
       will be my delight,
   your glory my reward.
       Send forth . . .
       . . . O Lord.

694 From SOUTH AFRICA, African Origin, collected and edited by Anders Nyberg ©1991 Wild Goose Publications, Iona Community, from *Freedom is coming* (Wild Goose Publications, 1990)

LEADER: Send me, Lord:
ALL: Send me, Jesus,
           send me, Jesus,
           send me, Jesus,
           send me, Lord.

LEADER: Lead me, Lord:
ALL: Lead me, Jesus . . .

LEADER: Fill me, Lord:
ALL: Fill me, Jesus . . .

LEADER: *Thuma mina,*
ALL: *thuma mina*
           thuma mina
           thuma mina,
           somandla.

695 Geoff Bullock. © 1994 Word/Maranatha! Music
Administered by CopyCare

This love, this hope,
this peace of God, this righteousness,
this faith, this joy,
this life complete in me.

Now healed and whole,
and risen in his righteousness,
I live in him –
he lives in me,
and, filled with this hope in God,
reflecting his glory.

Now is the time to worship you,
now is the time to offer you
all of my thoughts, my dreams and plans;
I lay them down.
Now is the time to live for you,
now is the time I'm found in you,
now is the time your kingdom comes.

You know me, you formed me,
I'm alive in you, alive in you.
You know me, you formed me,
I'm alive in you, alive in you.

696 Mike Stanley
© 1995 CJM Music

1. You know me, you formed me,
   you gave me life;
   from darkness you called me,
   you changed my life;
   and even as the sun sinks down,
   I see your light shine through –
   for still the stars of heaven shine
   and I'm alive in you, alive in you.

2. You know me, you heal me,
   you set me free,
   you opened up your arms
   and gave your life for me;
   and though the skies were darkened
   and the heavens torn apart –
   for love your life had ended,
   that in truth my life may start,
      my life may start.

3. You know me reach out
   and take my emptiness,
   transform me
   and let me share your holiness;
   though clouds may gather round me
   when you seem so far away –
   mould me in your image
   as the potter moulds the clay,
      moulds the clay.

4. You know me, I know you,
   we are as one,
   the old life has ended, the new begun;
   for in the silent moments
   in the sunrise, in the fields –
   all creation sings in praise
   and so you are revealed,
      you are revealed.

For other items on this theme, see

HYMNS
317 At the name of Jesus
618 Awake, my soul, and with the sun
554 Breathe on me, breath of God
145 Forgive our sins as we forgive
594 Forth in the peace of Christ we go
623 Forth in your name, O Lord, I go
226 Help us, O Lord, to learn
624 Jesus Christ is waiting
558 Lord of the cross of shame
559 My God, accept my heart this day
149 O for a heart to praise my God
250 O God, we bear the imprint of your face
560 O thou who camest from above
291 O Trinity, O Trinity
448 Our blest Redeemer, as he breathed
151 Teach us how grave a thing it is
 69 There's a spirit in the air
583 We worship God in harmony

PSALMS
561 Lord, as I wake I turn to you
314 The stars declare his glory

SONGS
562 All I once held dear
157 Father, hear our prayer
565 I will offer up my life
520 Lead me, Lord
163 Purify my heart
522 Say the word
616 Sent by the Lord I am
524 Take, O take me as I am
277 Through our lives and by our prayers
222 When the music fades

SPECIAL OCCASIONS:
CHRISTINGLE SERVICES, WEDDINGS.

CHRISTINGLE SERVICES

697 © Timothy Dudley-Smith

1. God whose love is everywhere
       made our earth and all things fair,
   ever keeps them in his care;
       praise the God of love!
   He who hung the stars in space
   holds the spinning world in place;
       praise the God of love!

2. Come with thankful songs to sing
   of the gifts the seasons bring,
   summer, winter, autumn, spring;
       praise the God of love!
   He who gave us breath and birth
   gives us all the fruitful earth;
       praise the God of love!

3. Mark what love the Lord displayed,
   all our sins upon him laid,
   by his blood our ransom paid;
       praise the God of love!
   Circled by that scarlet band
   all the world is in his hand;
       praise the God of love!

4. See the sign of love appear,
   flame of glory, bright and clear,
   light for all the world is here;
       praise the God of love!
   Gloom and darkness, get you gone!
   Christ the Light of life has shone;
       praise the God of love!

WEDDINGS

698 John L. Bell
© 1989 WGRG, Iona Community

1. God, in the planning
       and purpose of life,
   hallowed the union
       of husband and wife;
   this we embody where love is displayed,
   rings are presented and promises made.

2. Jesus was found, at a similar feast,
   taking the roles
       of both waiter and priest,
   turning the worldly towards the divine,
   tears into laughter and water to wine.

3. Therefore we pray that his spirit preside
   over the wedding
       of bridegroom and bride,
   fulfilling all that they've hoped
       will come true,
   lighting with love
       all they dream of and do.

4. Praise then the Maker,
       the Spirit, the Son,
   source of the love through
       which two are made one,
   God's is the glory,
       the goodness and grace,
   seen in this marriage
       and known in this place.

ADDITIONAL THEMATIC INDEXES

491 O Lord my God
268 When the waters cover me
Songs
562 All I once held dear
252 Christ's is the world in which
we move
120 He's given me a garment of praise
218 There is none like you
249 Word of justice
167 You came to heal the broken
hearted

FUNERALS

See also section **'AFFIRMING OUR BELIEF IN HEAVEN'**
Hymns
495 Abide with me
238 Great shepherd of your
people, hear!
177 Jesus, your blood and
righteousness
150 Rock of ages, cleft for me
Psalms
513 Because the Lord is my shepherd
205 The king of love my shepherd is
207 The Lord's my shepherd, I'll
not want

MILLENNIUM

Hymns
506 Here on the threshold
530 Hidden Christ, alive for ever
304 It is God who holds the nations
602 Lord for the years
303 Lord of the changing year
642 O Christ of all the ages, come!
542 O God, our help in ages past
605 Once to every generation
 64 Thanks be to God for his saints
538 Through the darkness of the ages

EPIPHANY

Hymns
343 As with gladness men of old
346 Brightest and best of the sons
of the morning
204 O worship the Lord in the
beauty of holiness
365 We thank you, God almighty
368 Wise men of old came seeking
369 Wise men, they came to look
for wisdom

TRANSFIGURATION

Hymn
453 Dear Christ, uplifted from the earth

PALM SUNDAY

Hymns
380 All glory, praise and honour
384 My song is love unknown
386 Ride on, ride on
 70 This is the day the Lord has made
Songs
211 Holy holy holy Lord of power
and might
119 Hosanna, hosanna, hosanna in
the highest

MAUNDY THURSDAY

Hymns
462 At the supper, Christ the Lord

180 Love is his word, love is his way
389 This is the night, dear friends
Song
395 Meekness and Majesty

GOOD FRIDAY

See also section **'AFFIRMING OUR BELIEF IN JESUS, SUFFERING AND DYING FOR US'**
Hymns
641 Lord, in our lonely hours
385 O sacred head surrounded
384 Sing, my tongue, the glorious
battle
388 There is a green hill far away
391 What have we to show our saviour
680 When I survey the wonderous
cross
292 When you prayed beneath
the trees
187 With loving hands
Songs
518 How can I be free from sin
193 How deep the Father's love for us
194 My Lord, what love is this

HARVEST

See also section **'AFFIRMING OUR BELIEF IN GOD THE CREATOR'**
Hymns
294 All things bright and beautiful
 34 Come, you thankful people, come
299 For the fruits of his creation
300 God in his love for us
302 God whose farm is all creation
306 O Lord of heaven and earth
and sea
307 Praise God for harvest-time
308 Praise God for the harvest
310 To you, O Lord, our hearts
we raise
311 We plough the fields, and scatter
Psalms
 80 Fill your hearts with joy and
gladness
313 The earth is yours, O God

ALL SAINTS DAY

Hymns
636 For all the saints
 38 God we praise you! God we
bless you!
626 Light of the minds that know him
641 Lord, in our lonely hours
605 Once to every generation
675 Rejoice in God's saints
 64 Thanks be to God for his saints
629 The saints in Christ are one in
every place
 68 The victory of our God
607 We are called to stand together
 76 You holy angels bright

FAMILY LIFE

Hymns
664 Father of all, whose laws
have stood
298 For the beauty of the earth
475 Now let us from this table rise
 54 Now thank we all our God

WORK

Hymns
460 As we break the bread
618 Awake, my soul, and with
the sun
573 Christ our king in glory
reigning
621 Come to us, creative Spirit
623 Forth in your name, O Lord, I go
625 God, who stretched the
spangled heavens
509 Lord of all hopefulness
673 O Christ, the Master Carpenter
560 O thou who camest from above
308 Praise God for the harvest
292 Sing of a God in majestic
divinity
293 Today I awake
648 Within the busy rush of life

MORNING

Hymns
618 Awake, my soul, and with the sun
509 Lord of all hopefulness
 3 Thanks be to God
 70 This is the day the Lord has made
483 Welcome to another day!
 74 When morning gilds the skies
Psalms
561 Lord as I wake I turn to you
 97 Sweet is the work, my God,
my King
Songs
 85 Let everything that has breath
568 My first love

EVENING

Hymns
487 At evening, when the sun had set
502 Glory to you, my God, this night
531 I do not know tomorrow's way
 50 Light of gladness, Lord of glory
508 Lighten our darkness
509 Lord of all hopefulness
 3 Thanks be to God
 65 The day you gave us, Lord,
is ended
389 This the night, dear friends
Psalms
515 I lift my eyes
 97 Sweet is the work, my God,
my King
Songs
 85 Let everything that has breath
568 My first love

DOXOLOGY

Hymns
 57 Praise God from whom all
blessings flow
 82 From all who live beneath
the skies
Song
281 May the peace of God the
Father

COPYRIGHT ADDRESSES

Ascent Music Ltd	PO Box 263, Croydon, CR9 5AP, UK
Asian School of Music, Worship & The Arts	PO Box 10533, Quezon City 1112, The Philippines
Bridge, Basil	124 Linacre Avenue, Sprowston, Norwich, Norfolk NR7 8JS UK
Burns, Edward	Christchurch Vicarage, 6 Watling Street Road, Fulwood, Preston, Lancs. PR2 4DY, UK
Cassell & Co	Wellington House, 125 Strand, London WC2R 0BB, UK
Central Board of Finance of the Church of England	Church House, Great Smith Street, London SW1P 3NZ, UK
Chappell Music Ltd	IMP Ltd, Griffin House, 161 Hammersmith Road,, London N6 8BS, UK
Chatto & Windus Ltd	Random House, 20 Vauxhall Bridge Road, London SW1V 2SA, UK
Christian Conference of Asia	96 2nd District, Pak Tin Village, Mei Tin Road, Shatin, N.T. Hong Kong
CJM Music Ltd.	St Mary's House, Coventry Road, Coleshill, West Midlands, B46 3ED UK
CopyCare	PO Box 77, Hailsham, East Sussex BN27 3EF UK
Cosnett, Elizabeth	34 Meadway, Liverpool L13 7LZ, UK.
Dargie, Dave	PO Box 36, 5721 Hogsback, South Africa
Downs, Elinor	44-46 Allandale Street, #507, Boxton, MA 02130, USA
Duckworth, C. C.	1 Charlham Lane, Down Ampney, Cirencester, Gloucester, GL7 5RQ UK
Dudley-Smith, Timothy	9 Ashlands, Ford, Salisbury, Wiltshire SP4 6DY, UK
Faber Music Ltd	3 Queen Square, London WC1N 3AU UK
GIA Publications, Inc.	7404 S Mason Avenue, Chicago, IL 60638, USA
Hancock, M. J.	55 Huntspill Road, London SW17 0AA, UK
His Banner Publishing	Music Lifeline, PO Box 9863, Birmingham, AL 35220, USA
Hughes, Paul	4 Northmead, Prestbury, Cheshire SK10 4XD, UK
Hymns Ancient & Modern	St Mary's Works, St Mary's Plain, Norwich, Norfolk NR3 3BH, UK
Iona Community	WGRG, The Iona Community, Pearce Institute, 840 Govan Road, Glasgow G51 3UU, Scotland, UK
IQ Music	Orchard House, Tylers Green, Cuckfield, West Sussex RH17 5DZ, UK
John Ireland Trust	35 St Mary's Mansions, St Mary's Terrace, London W2 1SQ, UK
Jubilate Hymns	4 Thorne Park Road, Chelston, Torquay TQ2 6RX
Kay-Mouat, Jon	The Presbytery, Alderney, Channel Islands GY9 3TF, UK
Kingsway's ThankYou Music Ltd	PO Box 75, Eastbourne, East Sussex BN23 6NW, UK
Laporta, Josep	c/Francisco de Miranda, 26-C, 43850-Cambrils (Tarragona), Spain
Lee, Geonyong	Korean National Institute of Arts, 700 Seocho-Dong, Seocho-ku, Seoul, Korea
MakeWay Music Ltd	PO Box 263, Croydon, Surrey, CR9 5AP, UK
Maldonado, J	Centro Hispana de Estudios Teologicos, 6113, Clara Street, Bell Gardens, CA 90201, USA
Manwaring, Randle	Marbles Barn, High Street, Newick, Near Lewes, East Sussex BN8 4LG, UK
Maraschin, Jaci	Rua Leao XIII, 230 ap 11, 089735-220, Rudge Ramos, Sao Bernardo do Campo, SP, Brasil
Maries, Andrew	The Keynote Trust, Townhaven, Pound Square, Cullompton, Devon EX15 1DN, UK
Marshall, Jocelyn	45 Lake Domain Drive, Hamilton, New Zealand
Mayhew, Kevin	Buxhall, Stowmarket, IP14 3DJ, UK
McCrimmon Publishing Co Ltd	10-12 High Street, Great Wakering, Southend-on-Sea, Essex SS3 0EQ, UK
Methodist Publishing House	20 Ivatt Way, Peterborough PE3 7PG, UK
Mickelm, Caryl	Wells House, 11 Chapmangate, Pocklington, York YO42 2AY, UK
Morgan, Richard	The Rectory, Church Lane, Therfield, Nr Royston SG8 9QD, UK
Motyer, Alec	10 Littlefield, Bishopsteignton, Devon TQ14 9SG, UK
Motyer-Lowndes, Catherine	16 George's Road East, Poynton, Cheshire SK12 1NP, UK
Music Sales Ltd	8/9 Frith Street, London W1V 5TZ, UK
Mxadana, Gobingca George	Imilonji Kantu Choral Society, 6942 Malie Street, PO Orlando, Soweto 1804, Johannesburg, South Africa
New Dawn Music	5536 NE Hassalo, Portland, OR 97213 U.S.A
North Amercian Liturgy Resources (NALR)	5536 NE Hassalo, Portland, OR 97213 U.S.A
Novello & Co Ltd	9/9 Frith Street, London W1V 5TZ, UK
OCP Publications	OCP Publications, 5536 NE Hassalo, Portland, OR 97213 U.S.A
O'Driscoll, Herbert	1000 Jasmine Avenue, Victoria, BC, Canada, V8Z 2P4
OMF International (UK)	Station Approach, Borough Green, Sevenoaks, Kent TN15 8BG, UK

Oxford University Press	Great Clarendon Street, Oxford OX2 6DP UK
Reid, Gavin	Bishop's House, Pett Lane, Charing, Ashford, Kent TN27 0DL, UK
Samuel, E	11 Broadlands, Holland Road, Frinton-on-Sea, Essex CO13 9ES, UK
Scott, Alexander	4 Anthony Close, Colchester, Essex CO4 4LD, UK
Scripture Union, The	207-209 Queensway, Bletchley, Milton Keynes MK2 2EB, UK
Selah Publishing Co	58 Pearl Street, PO Box 3037, Kingston, NY 12401-0902 USA
Sovereign Lifestyle Music Ltd/ Sovereign Music UK/ Restoration Music Ltd	PO Box 356, Leighton Buzzard, Beds. LU7 8WP, UK
Stainer & Bell Ltd	PO Box 110, Victoria House, 23 Gruneisen Road, Finchley, London N3 1DZ, UK
Taizé, Ateliers et Presses de	Brother Donagh, F-71250 Taizé Communaute, France
Thompson, Colin	Creeper Cottage, High Street, Charlton-on-Otmoor, Oxon OX5 2UQ, UK
Tyrell, Mrs J	41 Minster Road, Godalming, Surrey GU7 1SR, UK
United Reformed Church	United Reformed Church, 86 Tavistock Place, London WC1H 9RX, UK
Vineyard Songs (UK/Eire)	37 Blagdon Road, New Malden, KT3 4AH, UK
Warner / Chappell Music Ltd.	IMP Ltd., Griffin House, 161 Hammersmith Road, London W6 8BS, UK
Watt, A. P. Ltd	20 John Street, London WC1N 2DR, UK
Weinberger, Josef, Ltd.,	12-14 Mortimer Street, London W1N 7RD, UK
Windswept Pacific Music Ltd	Hope House, 40 St Peter's Road, London W6 9BD, UK
World Library Publications	3825 N Willow Road, Schiller Park, IL 60 176-9936 USA

BIBLICAL INDEX

MAIN INDEX

SING **GLORY**